P9-CMF-869

UNIVERSAL CLASSICS LIBRARY

APPLETON PRENTISS CLARK GRIFFIN
LIBRARY OF CONGRESS
EDITORIAL DIRECTOR

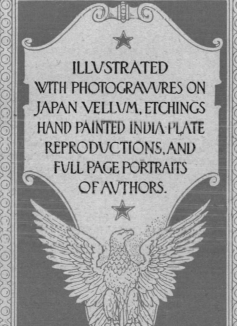

★

ILLUSTRATED
WITH PHOTOGRAVURES ON
JAPAN VELLUM, ETCHINGS
HAND PAINTED INDIA PLATE
REPRODUCTIONS, AND
FULL PAGE PORTRAITS
OF AUTHORS.

★

M. WALTER DUNNE, PUBLISHER

WASHINGTON & LONDON

Copyright, 1901,

by

M. Walter Dunne,

Publisher

MARIE STUART AND CHASTELARD

Hand-painted photogravure after the painting by Micquet.

MARIE STUART AND CHASTELARD

Hand-painted photogravure after the painting by Mignot

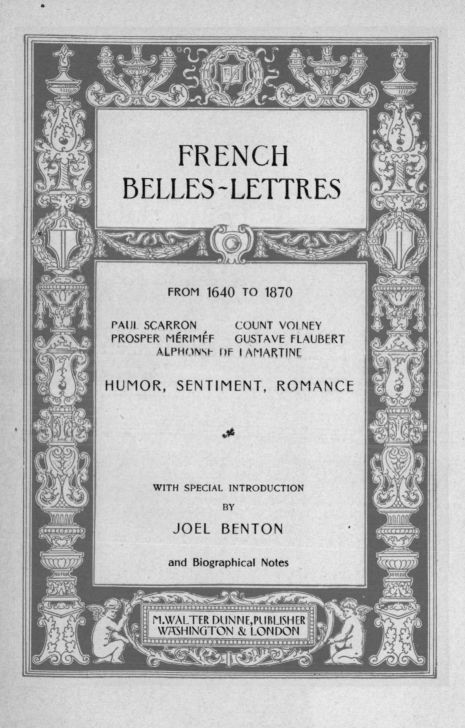

FRENCH BELLES-LETTRES

FROM 1640 TO 1870

PAUL SCARRON — COUNT VOLNEY
PROSPER MÉRIMÉE — GUSTAVE FLAUBERT
ALPHONSE DE LAMARTINE

HUMOR, SENTIMENT, ROMANCE

WITH SPECIAL INTRODUCTION

BY

JOEL BENTON

and Biographical Notes

M. WALTER DUNNE, PUBLISHER
WASHINGTON & LONDON

Copyright, 1901,

by

M. WALTER DUNNE,

publisher

ILLUSTRATIONS

d

SPECIAL INTRODUCTION

WHEN we pause to think of a particular nation, or literature, we see that it stands for, or typifies, certain qualities. In Greece, beauty and art were dominant; in Rome, dominion and written law. In France came very early a certain flowerage of culture, the direct product of intelligence and art, so that it has long had supremacy for the finest things that engage the human mind.

There are writers who say that when you go to Paris you feel at once its seductive atmosphere and thrill. You seem to be in an entrancing world where pleasure, gayety, wit and intelligence abound, and where art permeates and inspires everything. Only there could it be said of a conspirator against the life of the nation's ruler that his throwing of a bomb, execrable as it is, was a " beautiful gesture." This may be an extravagant illustration, but it will serve to show how beauty almost condones crime, and how it lifts up to honor all that is well shaped and well said with the people who use the flexible French language.

This tongue is a wonderful instrument, indeed, in the hands of its masters. Who would not give up his days and nights to attain the art of Flaubert and Maupassant rather than to spend them upon Addison — exemplar though Addison was for those of his generation in respect to style?

In the French feuilletonists even we see that style is the watchword. A recent writer remarks that the eighty daily papers of the French metropolis disseminate ideas rather than concrete news, and that their journalism is not a province outside of literature, but it is literature. And all this signifies much.

(ix)

The French writer of essays and poems may not invariably have much to say, but what constitutes his message he says well. He holds to verity rather than to mysticism. He deplores lumbering and awkward expression. Poetic and fruitful of thought as Richter, the German, and Carlyle, the Englishman, are, they are too nebulous to suit the French taste ; and in spite of Taine's acuteness as a critic, Carlyle remained an unsolved riddle to him. For lucidity and not obscurity is the French author's primary trait.

It has been said that "it is impossible to be at once correct and obscure in French." The language perhaps lends itself to clarity and proportion. Such critics as Scherer and St. Beuve rank among the very first in the world, for their keen perception, their balanced judgment, and their fluid, captivating style. Vivacity, or *esprit*, lightness of touch, and a fine aërial delicacy in the French essay or poem never fail to confront the reader, and lead him on.

Sometimes the flippant, staccato style of as great a writer as Victor Hugo may seem to the English mind too thin, too much a pose or an attitude to be nutrient, but with his best thoughts this form produces magical influence. If we cannot all credit the supremacy that Swinburne allots him, few there are who venture to deny his masterly literary force. A quatrain of Emerson's, to be sure, has a depth of thought enfolded in it that might furnish forth the substance for a long lyric in the Hugo manner. Yet the majority of readers in any country would most likely better enjoy the diluted lyric than the compressed quatrain.

It is noticeable that, with Villon and Verlaine, the aspiring translator stands baffled. Their delicacy of word-structure has no equivalent outside of the French tongue. Lamartine and Béranger deal with themes that are more cosmopolitan than these frailer and daintier writers, and, therefore, are better known to us through translations.

Of the poets which French literature has to show — Romantic, Parnassian, and Symbolist or Decadent — reams have been from time to time written. Lanson says, in a recent exhaustive essay on the latest French poets, that "when Victor Hugo took leave of the world in 1885 it seemed as if he had carried French poetry with him." But the work of Banville, Leconte de Lisle, Sully-Prudhomme, Coppée and others was left. There are indeed too many names to note and to put in fair perspective in a small space, for an opportunity here to consider well the wonderful body of French verse, early and late.

The Decadent school of which we have heard so much, with their whims of syntax and color, their dismissal of concrete fact for atmosphere and spirit, and their "polymorphous" forms, do not show now their "violent zeal." They were not to bring an end to French poetry. Lanson says they were merely to modify its development. Their first flavor perhaps will change, if it has not already done so, for better forms to follow.

But it must be said here that a great literature, so massive and multi-colored as the French, cannot be known thoroughly by any one (if I may borrow Professor Dowden's idea). Many great and minor authors must be left out of any brief synopsis of it. Of such varying names as Renan, De Musset, Gautier, Daudet, La Fontaine, and Joubert alone there is enough to be said for separate monographs. Saintsbury affirms that "of all European Literature the French is by general consent that which possesses the most uniformly fertile, brilliant, and unbroken history." It took nearly a thousand years to develop it, and, though of Latin origin, it has differentiated itself widely from that which is to be found in any one of the other Latin-born tongues. Indeed, its early dominance in Europe has overflowed to the equipment of authors not natives of France. Can it be doubted that Arnold and Pater of England, for instances easily recognized, would not have written as they have had they not been influenced by French models.

The French are said to write in jest what they feel in earnest. In Rivarol's phrase, the French language has a *probité attachet à son génie.* Along with these, and other traits, it cannot be said that the French have much to show that comes up to the altitude of Æschylus and Shakespeare, and their kind. But French writers are great in lesser fields than the epic or the tragedy. They are masters of mirth and lightness, and especially of the short story. They excel in opalescent grace, in charm of narrative; and, if authorship has for its purpose the delight of the reader through the spell of sorcery, by the magic mating of words to ideas, then there is no literature in the world which can make that of the French tongue seem subsident or secondary.

Joel Benton

CONTENTS

HUMOR

SCARRON

THE STROLLING PLAYERS

HUMOR

PAUL SCARRON

IN THE shadow of Madame de Maintenon's personality the literary brilliance of her first husband has been somewhat obscured. Paul Scarron was born in 1610, the son of a parliament man. He was put into the church but soon developed capacities better fitted to a secular career. As the consequence of reckless roistering he contracted a disease of a rheumatic nature with complications that baffled the doctors and made a distorted cripple of him for the last twenty years of his life. Like Heine, he existed in physical torment which left his brain undimmed, and, strangely enough, it was while in this state of pain and poverty that the Maintenon girl of sixteen became his faithful wife. For eight years she was the light of his life and shared the admiration of his crowd of friends who were regaled with their feasts of wit and philosophic art of making the best of bad luck.

He earned something as a ready writer for the booksellers and for a time he enjoyed pensions from the queen and Cardinal Mazarin. He lost them by rash radicalism. His lively plays, *Jodelet* and *Don Japhet d'Arménie*, are the best known of his dramatic works, and he is credited with having given direct inspiration to Molière. The poems and novels are to be judged in the light of the times. They abound in racy touches and pungent wit, each point having its aim and purpose.

The happiest legacy of Scarron's caustic pen is the *Roman Comique*. It tells the adventures of a troop of strolling players in the days when the drama was content to go a gipsying in wayside tents and its merriest performances were in the old tavern yards. As the tale unfolds it shows a fine perspective of unconventional life and manners. This comic romance illustrates French humor as well as national characteristics with a vivacity unrivaled up to its period. The extraordinary mixture of the romantic and tragic in his own career lends a peculiar interest to Paul Scarron and his work. He died at fifty.

THE STROLLING PLAYERS

A COMPANY OF STROLLERS COME TO THE TOWN OF MANS

B RIGHT Phœbus had already performed above half his career; and his chariot having passed the meridian, and got on the declivity of the sky, rolled on swifter than he desired. Had his horses been willing to have made use of the slopingness of the way, they might have finished the remainder of the day in less than half a quarter of an hour; but instead of pulling amain, they curveted about, snuffing a briny air, which set them a-neighing, and made them sensible that they were near the sea, where their father is said to take his rest every night. To speak more like a man, and in plainer terms, it was betwixt five and six of the clock, when a cart came into the market-place of Mans. This cart was drawn by two yoke of lean oxen, led by a breeding mare, who had a colt that skipped to and fro like a silly creature as he was. The cart was laden with trunks, portmanteaus, and great packs of painted clothes, that made a sort of pyramid, on the top of which sat a damsel, in a half-city, half-country dress. A young man, as poor in clothes as rich in mien, walked by the side of the cart: he had a great patch on his face (which covered one of his eyes and half of one cheek), and carried a long birding-piece on his shoulder, wherewith he had murdered several magpies, jays, and crows, which having strung together made him a sort of bandoleer; at the bottom of which hung a hen and goose, that looked as if they had been taken from the enemy by way of plunder. Instead of a hat he wore a nightcap, tied about his head with garters of several colors, and which was without doubt a kind of unfinished turban. His doublet was a griset-coat, girt about with a

(5)

leather thong, which served likewise to support a rapier so
very long, that it could not be used dexterously without the
help of a rest. He wore a pair of breeches tucked up to
above the middle of his thighs, like those that players have
when they represent an ancient hero. Instead of shoes he
wore tragic buskins, bespattered with dirt up to the ankles.
An old man, something more regular in his dress, though
in very ordinary habit, walked by his side. He carried a
bass viol on his shoulders; and because he stooped a little
as he went, one might have taken him at a distance for a
great tortoise walking upon his hind feet. Some critic or
other will perhaps find fault with the comparison, by reason of the disproportion between that creature and a man;
but I speak of those great tortoises that are to be found
in the Indies; and besides, I make bold to use the simile
upon my own authority. Let us return to our strolling
company. They passed by the tennis-court at the " Hind,"
before which were then assembled several of the chief
men of the town. The novelty of our strollers' equipage,
and the noise of the mob, who by this time had
gathered about the cart, drew the eyes of all those
honorable burgomasters upon our unknown travelers.
Among the rest, an under-sheriff, La Rappinière by
name, made up to them, and with the authority of a
magistrate, asked them who they were. The young
man, whom I described before, without offering to
pull off his turban (because with one hand he held his
gun, and with the other the hilt of his sword, lest it
should beat against his legs), answered him that they were
Frenchmen by birth, and players by profession : that his
stage name was Destiny ; his old comrade's Rancour ; and
the gentlewoman (who sat roosting like a hen on the top
of their baggage) Cave. This odd name set some of the
company a laughing ; whereupon the young stroller added
that the name of Cave ought not to seem more strange to
men of wit than those of La Montagne, Valley, Rose, or
Thorn. The conversation ended with the noise of blows,
cursing, and swearing, that was heard before the cart. The
squabble had been occasioned by the servant of the tennis-
court falling foul upon the carter, without saying why or

wherefore ; yet the reason was because his oxen and mare had been a little too free with a truss of hay that lay before the door. However, the combatants were at length parted ; and the mistress of the tennis-court, who loved to hear a play more than a sermon or vespers, out of unheard of generosity in a keeper of a tennis-court, bid the carter let his cattle eat their bellies full. He took her at her word ; and while the hungry beasts were feeding, the author rested a while, and bethought himself what he should say in the next chapter.

WHAT SORT OF MAN LA RAPPINIÈRE WAS

THE Sieur la Rappinière was at that time the droll or jester of Mans ; for you must know there is not a town in France, though never so small, but has such an animal belonging to it. The city of Paris has several in each ward, and I myself might have been the jester of mine, had I been willing to undertake it ; but everybody knows, it is a long time since I have forsaken all the vanities of this world. To return to Monsieur la Rappinière. He soon renewed the conversation which the squabble had interrupted, and asked the young player whether their company consisted only of Mrs. Cave, Monsieur Rancour, and himself. " Our company," answered he, " is as complete as that of the Prince of Orange or of his Grace the Duke of Epernon ; but through a misfortune that befell us at Tours, where our rattle-headed doorkeeper happened to kill one of the Fusiliers of the intendant of the province, we were forced to fly in a hurry, and in the sad pickle you see us." " Those Fusiliers of the inten- dants," said La Rappinière, " have been as troublesome to you strollers as La Flèche." " Ay, devil take them," said the mistress of the tennis-court, " if they could help it we should have no plays." " Nay," answered the old stroller, " had we but the keys of our trunks, we might entertain the town for four or five days, for all them, before we reach Alençon, where the rest of our company are to ren-

dezvous." This player's answer made everybody to prick
up their ears. La Rappinière offered an old gown of his
wife's to Cave, and the tennis woman two or three suits
of clothes, which had been left with her in pawn, to Destiny and Rancour. " But," added some of the standers-by,
" there are but three of you." " No matter for that," replied Rancour, " for I once acted a whole play myself, and
represented the king, queen, and the ambassador with my
single person. I made use of a false treble tone when I
personated the queen ; I spoke through the nose for the
ambassador, and addressed myself to the crown which I
placed upon a chair ; and as for the king, I resumed my
seat, crown, and gravity, and lowered the key of my voice
to a bass. Now to convince you of this, if you will satisfy
our carter, defray our charges in the inn, and lend us
what clothes you can spare, we will act still before night ;
otherwise we must beg leave to go to drink, or rest ourselves, for we are come a great way." The company liked
the proposal, but that devil La Rappinière, who was ever
hatching some mischief or other, said there was no occasion for any other clothes than those of two young men of
the town, who were then playing a set at tennis, and that
Mrs. Cave in her ordinary dress might pass for anything
in a play. No sooner said but done ; in less than half a
quarter of an hour the strollers drank three or four glasses
of wine apiece ; shifted themselves ; and the company, who
by this time had increased to a full audience, having taken
their places in an upper room, a dirty cloth, instead of a
painted curtain, was drawn up, which discovered Destiny
lying on a quilt, with a strawberry basket on his head in
the room of a crown, rubbing his eyes like one who had
waked out of his sleep, and mouthing in the tone of
Mondori the part of Herod, which begins thus : —

"Injurious phantom, that disturbs my rest."

The patch which almost covered one half of his face did
not hinder him from showing himself an excellent player.
Madam Cave acted to admiration the parts of Mariamne
and Salome ; Rancour pleased everybody with his action ;
and the play was carrying on to a happy conclusion, when

the devil, who never sleeps, interposed, and made the tragedy end, not with the death of Mariamne and Herod's despair, but with a thousand cuffs and boxes on the ears, as many kicks, numberless oaths, and, last of all, a verbal process and information, which was taken out by La Rappinière, the most skillful of all men in those matters.

WHAT DEPLORABLE SUCCESS THE PLAY HAD

IN ALL the inferior towns of the kingdom, there is generally a tennis-court, whither all the idle people are used to resort, some to play, others only to look on. It is in those places where cursing and swearing passes for a rhetorical flourish, and where the absent are murdered with the tongues of backbiters and bullies; no man escapes scot-free; there all live in open defiance, and everybody is admitted to rail according to his talent. It was in one of these tennis-courts, if my memory fails me not, that I left three comical persons reciting Mariamne before an honorable company, at which presided Monsieur la Rappinière. Now while Herod and Mariamne were telling each other their faults, the two young men, whose clothes they had so freely borrowed, came into the room in their drawers, each of them with his racket in his hand, having neglected to get themselves rubbed, that they might come and hear the play. They were not long in the room before they perceived that Herod and Pherores had their clothes on; when the most passionate of the two, addressing himself to the waiter of the tennis-court: "Thou son of a dog," said he to him; "why didst thou give my clothes to that mountebank?" The innocent waiter, who knew him to be a brutish sort of a man, told him with great humility that he had no hand in it. "Who, then, scoundrel?" added he. The poor fellow durst not accuse La Rappinière in his presence; but he himself, the most insolent of all men, rising from his seat, told him, "It was I; what have you to say to it?" "That you are a rascal," replied the other; and at the same time gave him a plaguy blow over the pate with his racket. La Rap-

pinière was so surprised to be struck first, whereas he used
to be beforehand with all men, that he stood motionless,
either through amazement, or because he was not yet angry
enough, and that it was not a small provocation that could
make him resolve to fight, though it were but at fisticuffs.
Nay, perhaps the quarrel had gone no farther, had not his
man, who was more choleric than he, fallen foul upon the
aggressor, and dealt him a sound cuff on the chops, and
in the middle of his face, and afterward in a great many
other places where he could find room to imprint his fury.
La Rappinière charged him behind, and worked on him like
one that had received the first provocation : a relation of
his adversaries invested La Rappinière after the same manner.   This relation was attacked by one of La Rappinière's
friends, in order to make a diversion : this combatant was
assaulted by another, and this last again by another.   In
short, the whole audience divided into parties ; some cursed
and swore ; others called names ; all beat one another.   The
tennis woman, who saw her goods broken to pieces, rent the
air with doleful cries.   In all probability they had murdered
one another with stools, kicks, and cuffs, had not some of the
magistrates of the town (who happened at that time to be
walking in the piazza of the market-place, with Des Essars,
seneschal of Mayne) ran with all speed to the squabble.
Some proposed to throw two or three pails full of water on
the combatants ; which perhaps might have been successful :
however, they at length gave over fighting through weariness.   Beside two Capuchins, who out of charity flung
themselves into the field of battle, procured, though not a
firm peace betwixt the contending parties, yet a sort of
truce ; during which a negotiation was set on foot, without
derogating from the informations that were taken on both
sides, in order to a trial in due course of law.   Destiny, one
of the strollers, performed wonders at boxing ; whose great
actions are talked of to this very day in the town of Mans,
according to the faithful account delivered by the two young
men that raised the squabble, whom he particularly engaged, and almost cuffed to death, besides a great many
others of the enemy, whom he disabled with the first blow.
Having lost his patch in the scuffle, people took notice his

face was as fine as his shape. The bloody noses were handsomely washed with clean water : those that had their bands torn, put on others instead of them, cataplasms were applied where need required ; some few stitches served to darn many a torn doublet ; and the household goods were set in their proper places though not so sound and whole as they were before. In short, a moment after there remained nothing of the fight but a great spite and animosity, which appeared in the faces of those of both parties. The poor strollers went out a long while after the combat with La Rappinière, who was still for making speeches. In their way from the tennis-court to the market-place, they were invested by seven or eight bullies with swords in their hands. La Rappinière according to custom, was in a great fright, and indeed not without cause, had not Destiny generously thrust himself between him and a sword which was about to run him through ; however, he could not so well parry the thrust, but that he received a small wound in the arm. Thereupon he drew his rapier, and in the twinkling of an eye beat two swords out of the hands of the enemy, broke two or three skulls, battered and slashed as many faces, and discomfited so dexterously the gentlemen of the ambuscade, that all the bystanders unanimously confessed they never had seen so valiant a champion. This abortive plot had been laid against La Rappinière by two squires, whereof one married the sister of him who began the fight with a great blow with a racket, by which in all likelihood, La Rappinière had been spoiled forever, but for the valiant protector, whom Providence had raised for him in the person of our stout player. This benefit melted his heart of flint, insomuch, that he would not suffer the miserable remains of a scattered company of strollers to lodge in an inn ; but brought them to his own house, where the carter having laid down the strolling furniture, returned home to his village.

HEREIN FARTHER MENTION IS MADE OF MON-
SIEUR LA RAPPINIÈRE; AND OF WHAT
HAPPENED THAT NIGHT AT
HIS HOUSE

MADAM la Rappinière received the company with a great deal of civility, as being the most submissive of wives; she was indifferently handsome, though so very lean and dry, that she never snuffed a candle with her fingers but they presently caught fire. I could relate a thousand curious stories about her, which I pass by for fear of being tedious. The first compliments were scarce over when the two ladies grew so well acquainted that they began with my dear and my dearest. La Rappinière, who was as great a braggadocio as any in the world, was no sooner come into the room, that he bid somebody go to the kitchen and larder, and hasten supper. This was a mere rodomontade; for besides his valet, who likewise dressed his horses, there was nobody in his house but a young maid and an old lame woman, as crazy as a mangy dog. His vanity was punished by an accident that filled him with confusion. He was used to diet at the tavern, at the expense of fools and bubbles, while his wife and his orderly family were reduced to feed on soup and cabbage, according to the custom of that country. Now, being willing to make a show before his guests, and treat them nobly, he was going to slip behind his back some money into the hands of his man, to fetch something for supper; but through the awkwardness either of the servant or the master, the pence fell on the chair he sat on, and from thence to the ground. La Rappinière looked blue upon it; his wife blushed; the man cursed. Cave was uneasy; Rancour perhaps did not mind it; and as for Destiny, I could not well learn what effect it had upon his mind. However, the money was taken up, and while supper was getting ready they engaged in conversation. La Rappinière asked Destiny why he disguised his face with a patch. He answered, he had great reason to do it, and as he had other clothes on

by accident, so he likewise designed to make his face unknown to some enemies he had. At last supper came in,
good or bad. La Rappinière drank so much, that he felt
himself fuddled ; Rancour had his load ; Destiny supped
liked a sober, well-bred man ; Cave like a famished player ;
and Madam la Rappinière like one who had a mind to lay
hold of the opportunity ; that is to say, so very greedily,
that she got a surfeit. While the servants were at supper,
and the beds making, La Rappinière teased his guests with
a thousand stories full of vanity. Destiny lay in a little
room by himself ; Cave in a closet with the chamber-maid ;
and Rancour with the valet I know not where. They all
had a great mind to sleep, some through weariness, others
for having supped too plentifully, and yet they slept but
little ; so true it is, that there is nothing certain in this
world. After her first sleep, Madam la Rappinière had an
inclination to go where kings are forced to go themselves
in person ; her husband waked at the same time, and though
he had not recovered his drunkenness, yet he found himself alone. He called his wife, nobody answered : whereupon he grew jealous, fell in a passion, and instantly rose
out of his bed in a fury. As soon as he was got out of
the chamber, he heard a stamping of feet before him, and
for some time followed the noise through a little gallery
that led to Destiny's room. He found himself so near
what he pursued, that he trod upon its heels, and thinking
it to be his wife he was going to lay hold on her, but his
hands could catch nothing, and his feet stumbling at the
same time, he fell down upon his nose, and felt something that was pointed running into his breast. Thereupon
he cried out after a most hideous manner, " Murder ! murder ! I am stabbed," without letting go his wife, whom he
thought he held by the hair, and was struggling under
him. His cries and oaths set all the house in an uproar,
and everybody ran to his assistance : the maid with a
candle ; Rancour and the valet in their dirty shirts; Cave
in a tattered petticoat ; Destiny with a sword in his hand,
and Madam la Rappinière last of all, who, like all the rest,
was not a little surprised to see her furious husband grap-
pling with a she-goat, which was kept in the house to

suckle some young puppies, whose dam happened to die. No man was ever so much out of countenance as La Rappinière. His wife, who presently suspected the truth of the matter, asked him if he was mad. He answered, without knowing well what he said, that he had taken the goat for a thief; Destiny guessed the business, every one returned to his bed, and made what constructions he thought fit upon the adventure; as for the goat, she was shut up again with her puppies.

HEREIN ARE CONTAINED MANY THINGS NECESSARY TO BE KNOWN FOR THE UNDERSTANDING OF THIS TRUE HISTORY

THE strolling company consisted of Destiny, Olive, and Rancour, who had each of them a servant, who all expected to be one day actors-in-chief. Of those servants, some began to speak without blushing, or being dashed out of countenance. But among the rest, Destiny's man acted indifferently well, understood what he said, and did not want wit. Mrs. Star and Mrs. Cave's daughter played the principal parts. Mrs. Cave acted the queen and the mother, and sometimes Merry Andrew's wife in a farce. Besides all these they had a poet, or an author with them, for all the grocers' shops in the kingdom were stored with his works, both in verse and prose. This great wit followed the company almost against their will; but because he was no sharer, and that he spent his own money with them, they suffered him to act under-parts, which he nevertheless generally murdered. They all perceived well enough that he was in love with one of the two she-players; but however he was so discreet, though a little crack-brained, that it was not yet discovered which of the two he designed to wheedle into compliance, with the fair hopes of making her immortal. He threatened the company with a great many plays of his own writing, but till then had spared them, and they

only knew by conjecture that he was about one called
" Martin Luther," of which they found the first act, which
however he disowned, although it was written with his own
hand. When our strollers first arrived, the women's chamber was continually crowded with the most impertinent fops
and beaux of the town, whose eagerness notwithstanding
was frequently cooled by the indifferent reception they met
with. They talked all together about plays, poetry, poets,
and romances, and there could not possibly have been more
noise unless they had been fighting. The poet, among the
rest, surrounded by three or four, who without doubt were
the top wits of the town, labored to persuade them that
he had seen Corneille, cracked many a bottle with St.
Amant and Beys, and lost a good friend when Rotrou died.
Madam Cave and her daughter Angelica set their goods in
order with as great tranquillity as if there had been nobody
in the room. It is true Angelica's fair hands were now
and then squeezed or kissed ; for these country gentlemen
are ever pulling and hauling ; but a kick on the shins, a
box on the ear, or a biting, according as occasion required,
soon rid her of those hot-spurred lovers, nor was she rude
and impudent neither, but her free and gay humor would
not suffer her to use much ceremony : as for her other
qualities, she had wit and was very honest. Mrs. Star was of
a quite different temper ; for there never was a more modest,
gentle, and good-natured woman in the world, and besides,
she at that time strained her complaisance so far, that she
could not find it in her heart to turn these ogling fops out
of her chamber, though she felt a great pain in her sprained
foot and had therefore occasion for rest. She lay in her
clothes on a bed, surrounded by four or five of these whin-
ing, sighing coxcombs, stunned by abundance of puns and
clinches, which pass for good jests in the country, and
often forcing a smile upon hearing things she did not like.
But this is one of the greatest plagues of that profession,
which together with their being obliged to laugh or weep,
whether they have a mind to it or no, takes very much from
their pleasure of being sometimes emperors and empresses, and
of being styled as fine as angels, though they be little
handsomer than devils, or addressed to as young beauties,

though their hair and teeth be part of their furniture.
There are a great many more things to be said upon this
subject, but we must use them sparingly, and place them
in several stations, for variety's sake. Let us return to
Madam Star, beset with country squires, the most troublesome of men, all great talkers, most of them very impertinent, and among them some newly returned from the
university. Among the rest appeared a little man, who
was a widower, a lawyer by profession, and an officer in a
small court of judicature in the neighborhood. Since the
death of his little wife, he sometimes threatened the women
to marry again, and sometimes the clergy of the province
to turn priest, nay even a preaching prelate. He was the
greatest little fool that ever ran madding about since Or-
lando Furioso. He had studied books all his lifetime; but
though the chief end of scholarship be the knowledge of
truth yet was he as great a liar as a page, proud and obstinate as a pedant, and so bad a poet as to deserve drowning, if the government would but have taken care to rid
the kingdom of such a troublesome race of rhyming fools.
As soon as Destiny and his comrades came into the room,
without giving them the time to know who he was, he
offered to read to them a poem of his own making, called
" The Deeds and Achievements of Charlemagne," in four
and twenty books. This proposal put all the company into
such a fright as made their hair stand on end; but Destiny, who in this general terror preserved a little judgment,
told him smiling, that it was not possible for them to give
him the hearing before supper. " Well," quoth he, " I will
however read you a story taken out of a Spanish book,
which was sent me from Paris, and of which I design to
make a regular play." They shifted the discourse three or
four times on purpose to avoid hearing what they supposed
to be in imitation of " Guy of Warwick," or " Tom Thumb."
But though they often interrupted him, yet did our little
man not lose courage; insomuch that with often beginning
his story he at last forced them to hear him out; which
however they did not repent, because the tale proved to be
a good one, and caused them to alter the ill-opinion they
had of all that came from Ragotin, for so was our Jack-in-

the-Box called. You will find the said story in the following chapter, not such as Ragotin told it, but such as I had it from one of the hearers. Therefore you must know that it is not Ragotin now speaks, but myself.

THE HISTORY OF THE INVISIBLE MISTRESS

DON CARLOS of Arragon was a young gentleman of the family that bore that name. He performed wonders at the public games, which the viceroy of Naples entertained the people with, upon the marriage of Philip the second, third, or fourth, for I have forgot whether. The next day, after a running at the ring, where he bore away the prize, the viceroy gave liberty to the ladies to go about the city in disguise, and to wear masks after the French mode, for the conveniency of strangers, whom the public rejoicings had invited thither. Upon that very day Don Carlos put on his finest clothes, and with many other conquerors of hearts repaired to the church of gallantry. Churches are profaned in these countries as well as in ours; and the house of God serves for an *assemblée* to the beaux and coquets, to the eternal shame of those who have the cursed ambition of drawing customers from other churches to their own. These abuses ought to be reformed, and there should be persons appointed to turn beaux and coquets out of churches, as well as to drive away dogs and bitches. I may be asked, what makes me concern myself about this? Truly you will see more anon. However, let the fool who is offended at it be satisfied, that all men of this world are fools as well as liars, some more, some less; and I myself am perhaps a greater fool than the rest, though I have more frankness in owning it: and moreover my book being but a heap of follies, I hope every fool will find his own character in it, unless he be blinded by self-love. To return to my story. Don Carlos being in a church, with several other Italian and Spanish gentlemen, priding themselves in their fine feathers like proud peacocks three ladies in masks accosted him amid all

2

these fierce and gay Cupids, one of whom spoke to him thus,
or to the same effect : " Signior Don Carlos, there is a lady in
this city to whom you are very much obliged, for at all
the jousts and tournaments her wishes went still along with
you in those exercises wherein you carried the prize."
" What I find most advantageous in this you tell me,"
answered Don Carlos, " is to have it from the mouth of a
lady who seems to be a person of merit ; yet had I so
much as hoped that any of the fair sex had been on my
side, I would have taken more care to deserve her approbation." The unknown lady replied he had given all the
proofs imaginable of his being a most dexterous and accomplished gentleman, and that by his black and white liveries
he had shown he was not in love. " I never was well
acquainted with the meaning of colors," answered Don
Carlos ; " but this I know, that if I am not in love it is
not so much on account of my being indifferent, as because
I am sensible I do not deserve to be beloved." They said
to one another a thousand fine things more which I shall
not relate, because I know nothing of them, and would be
loath to compose fictions, lest I should wrong Don Carlos
and the unknown lady, who had a great deal more wit
than I can pretend to, as I was lately informed by a young
Neapolitan who knew them both. In short, the lady in
the mask declared to Don Carlos that it was she who had
an inclination for him. He desired to see her face, which
she refused, and told him that he must not expect it yet ;
that she would look for a more proper opportunity; and
that, to let him know she feared not to trust herself alone
with him, she would give him a token. At these words
she pulled off her glove, and having showed the Spaniard the
finest hand in the world, presented him with a ring ; which
he received with so great a surprise at the adventure, that
he almost forgot to make a bow and thank her upon her
going from him. The other gentlemen, who out of civility
had left him, being come to him again, he told them what
had happened, and showed them the ring, which was of
considerable value. Every one spoke his thoughts upon
this adventure ; and Don Carlos was upon this as deep in
love with the unknown lady as if he had seen her face, so

great is the power of wit on those who have their share of it. He was eight long days without hearing from this lady; but whether or no he was uneasy at it I could never be well informed. In the meantime he went every day to divert himself at the house of a captain of foot, where several men of quality met to play. One night having not been at play, and going home sooner than ordinary, he was called by his name out of a parlor in a great house. He went near the window, which was latticed, and knew by the voice that called him that it was his invisible mistress, who said to him, "Come near, Don Carlos; I expect you here to decide our controversy." "You are but a braggadocio," said Don Carlos; "you challenge with insolence, and yet hide yourself for eight days together, and then, alas, appear only through a lattice window." "We shall see one another nearer in time," answered she. "It is not for want of courage I have delayed being with you all this while, but I had a mind to know you better before I discovered myself. You know that in duels the combatants ought to fight with arms alike. Now if your heart be not as free as mine, you would fight with advantage, and therefore I have made inquiries after you." "And what information have you got," answered Don Carlos. "That we are much upon the square," returned the invisible lady. "But," said Don Carlos, "there's yet a great inequality betwixt us; for," added he, "you both see and know who I am, whereas I neither see nor know who you are. Now consider, pray, what I can judge of your concealing yourself, since people seldom do so when they have a good design. It is an easy matter to impose at first upon a man that mistrusts nothing, but he is not to be cheated twice; if you make use of me only to give another jealousy, I must freely tell you that I am the most unfit person for it in the world, and that I am good for nothing else besides loving you." "Have you done with your rash suspicions?" said the invisible lady. "You may call them rash if you please," replied Don Carlos; "however, they are not really so." "I would have you to know," said she, "I am sincere; you will find me such in all our intercourse; and I expect you should be so too." "That's but reasonable," answered Don Carlos; "but it is just likewise that I should see you, and know who you are." "You shall be satisfied in that ere it be long," said the invisible lady; "and in the meantime hope with patience; for that's the only way for you to obtain what you expect from me. Now, that you may justify your love to your discretion, I am willing to let you know that my birth is not inferior to yours; that I have a fortune sufficient to make you live with as great magnificence as any prince in the kingdom; that I am rather handsome than ill-favored; and as for wit, you have too much of that yourself not to discover whether I have any or no." She had no sooner made an end of her speech but she withdrew, leaving Don Carlos with his mouth open, ready to answer her; so very much in love with a person he never saw, and so perplexed about this odd way of proceeding, which might prove at last a cheat, that he stood on the same place for above a quarter of an hour, not knowing what to think of this extraordinary adventure. He was not ignorant that there were a great many princesses and ladies of quality in Naples; but knew likewise that there were abundance of greedy courtesans in that city, eager after strangers, great jilts, and the more dangerous as they were handsome. I cannot positively tell whether he had supped at this time or whether he went to bed without a supper.

Neither do I care to imitate the writers of romances, who mark with great exactness all the hours of the day, and make their heroes rise betimes, relate their adventures by dinner-time, eat but little at dinner, then resume the story after dinner, or retire into the thickest part of a wood, in order to entertain their own selves, unless when they have something to say to the rocks and trees. At supper-time they make them repair at the usual hour to the place where they diet; there they sigh and look pensive, instead of eating; and thence go to build castles in the air on some terrace-walk that looks toward the sea, while the trusty squire reveals that his master is such a one, son to such a king; that he is the best prince alive, and though he be still the handsomest of all mortals, that he was quite another man before love had disfigured him.

To return to my story, Don Carlos repaired the next day to his post, where the invisible lady waited his coming. She asked him if he had not been much perplexed about their last conversation, and if he had not doubted the truth of what she told him. Don Carlos, without answering her question, desired her to tell him what danger she feared in discovering herself, since they were upon even terms; and that the end of their amours being honorable, it would have the approbation of everybody. "The danger is very great, and you will have it in time," said the invisible lady. "Once more, be satisfied that I am true, and that in the account I gave you of myself I was rather modest than vain." Don Carlos did not press her any farther; their conversation, which continued some time longer, increased the mutual love they had for each other; and so they parted with promises to meet every day at the appointed hour and place. The next day after there was a great ball at the viceroy's, where Don Carlos hoped to know his invisible charmer. In the meantime, he endeavored to learn at whose house she gave him those favorable audiences, and was told by the neighbors that it belonged to an old lady, widow to a Spanish captain, who had neither daughters nor nieces, and lived very retired. He desired to wait on her, but she sent him word that since her husband died she admitted of no visits, which still perplexed him more and more. Don Carlos went in the evening to the viceroy's, where you may imagine there was a very fine and numerous assembly, and nicely observed all the ladies in hopes to find out his unknown mistress. He engaged in conversation with several, but was disappointed in his search. At last he kept close to the daughter of a marquis of I know not what marquisate, for it was the most difficult thing to know in the world, especially at that juncture, when everybody set up for that quality. She was young and handsome, and had a voice not unlike that of the person he looked after. But at the long run, he found such great disproportion betwixt her wit and that of his invisible, that he was sorry that in so little time he had made such progress with this fine lady, that, without any flattery to himself, he had reason to believe she did not hate him. They danced several times together, and the ball being over, to the great satisfaction of Don Carlos he took his leave of his captive, whom he left full of pride for having had to herself in so fine an assembly a cavalier who was envied by all the men and esteemed by all the women. As soon as he came out of the ball he went in great haste to his house, and from thence to the fatal grate, which was not far off. His lady, who was there already, asked him news of the ball, although she had been there herself. He told her very ingenuously that he had danced with a very beautiful person, and entertained her all the time the ball lasted. She asked him several questions in relation to her, which discovered her jealousy. As for Don Carlos, he let her understand that he began to suspect her quality by reason she had not been at the ball. She having taken notice of it, used all the charms of her wit to remove his suspicions, and favored him as far as was possible in a conversation that passed with a grate between; adding withal, that in a short time she would become visible. Hereupon they parted, Don Carlos very much in doubt whether he ought to believe her, and she somewhat jealous of the fine person he had entertained during the ball. The next day Don Carlos going to hear mass at a certain church, the name of which I have forgot, offered holy water to two veiled ladies who went to take some at the same time with him. She who appeared in the better clothes of the two told him she never accepted of any civility from one with whom she had a quarrel to decide. "If you are not too much in haste," answered Don Carlos, "you may have satisfaction in that this very moment." "Well," said the unknown lady, "follow me then into the next chapel." She led the way, and Don Carlos followed, very much in doubt whether she was his unknown mistress or not; for though her shape was the same, yet he found some difference between their voices, this new lady speaking somewhat thick. This is the substance of what she told him after she had shut herself up with him in the chapel. "All the city of Naples, Signior Don Carlos, talks of the high reputation you have gained during the little time you have been here; and everybody looks upon you as the most accomplished gentleman in the world. The only thing that people wonder at is your not taking notice that there are in this city some ladies of quality and merit who have a particular esteem for you ; they have discovered it to you as far as decency would allow, and though it is their eager desires to make you sensible of it, yet they had rather you had not taken notice of it through insensibility, than that you should have despised their favors through indifference. Among the rest, there's one of my acquaintance who has so much value for you, as to hazard her own reputation by telling you that your night adventures are discovered ; that you rashly engage in an amour with one you do not know, and that since your mistress conceals herself, she must either be ashamed of her lover or conscious of not deserving to be beloved herself. I question not but the object of your contemplative love is a lady of great quality and wit, and that your fancy has framed such a mistress as is worthy of adoration upon all accounts. But, Signior Don Carlos, believe not your imagination at the expense of your judgment ; trust not a person who conceals herself, and engage no more in these night conversations. But why should I disguise myself any longer? I myself am jealous of this phantom of yours. I cannot bear you should speak with her ; and since I have declared my mind so far, I will so thwart all her designs, that I do not much question but I shall carry away the prize, to which I have as much right as she, since I am not inferior to her either in beauty, riches, quality, or anything else that can bespeak love. If you are wise, you will make use of this my advice." When she had spoke these last words she went away without giving Don Carlos time to answer her. He was going to follow her, but met at the church gate a man of quality, who engaged him in a tedious conversation, from which he could not rid himself. He reflected the remainder of the day upon this adventure, and suspected at first the lady at the ball to be the veiled person that had appeared to him. But then calling to mind that she had showed abundance more wit than he had found in this, he was at a loss what to think, and wished almost not to have been engaged with his unknown mis-

tress, that he might give himself entirely up to this. But
then again, considering that he knew her no better than
his invisible, whose wit had charmed him in all the
conversations he had had with her, he firmly resolved to be
constant to his first choice, without minding in the least
the threats of the last lady ; for he was not to be wrought
upon by fear or compulsion. That very night he failed not
to return to the grated window at the usual hour, where in
the height of his conversation with his mistress he was seized
by four strong men in masks, who, having disarmed him,
hurried him by force into a coach that waited for them at
the end of the street. I leave the reader to think how
many abusive names he gave those men in disguise, and
how he reproached them for attacking him so to disadvan-
tage. Nay, he endeavored to win them by promises, but
instead of persuading them he only made them to take more
care of him, and put himself out of hope of being able to show either his strength or courage. In the
meantime the coach and six horses drove on at full trot,
and having got out of the city, after an hour's traveling,
came into a great yard, the gate of which was kept open
to receive it. The four maskers alighted with Don Carlos
holding him under the arms like an ambassador introduced
to salute the grand signior. He was carried up one pair
of stairs in the same manner, where two gentlewomen in
masks came to receive him at the door of a large room,
each with a candlestick in her hand, when the four men in disguise took their leave of him with a profound reverence.
It is probable they left him neither sword nor pistol, and
that he did not forget to thank them for their extraordinary care of his person ; and yet perhaps he never thought
of it ; not but that he was a man of good breeding, but
upon a surprise a slip in point of civility ought to be
forgiven. Neither will I tell you whether the candlesticks
the gentlewomen had in their hands were silver, or only
silver-gilt and engraven. As for the room, it was the most
magnificent in the world, and if you would know it as well
furnished as some apartments in our romances ; namely the
ship of Zelman in " Polexander " the palace of Ibra-
him in the " Illustrious Bassa," or the room wherein the

king of Assyria received Mandoan in "Cyrus," which
together with the others I named before, is certainly
a book that has the best furniture in the world.
Now imagine what surprise our Spaniard was in to find
himself in this stately apartment with two speechless gentlewomen in masks, who having conducted him into another chamber, still better furnished than the great room,
left him there all alone. Had he been of Don Quixote's
humor, he would have found sufficient matter to please his
fancy, and imagined himself to be no less than Esplandian
or Amadis. But our Spaniard was no more concerned than
if he had been in his inn, save only that he had a great
regret for his invisible lady; and as he kept his thoughts
continually employed upon her, he found that chamber
more melancholy than a prison, which never looks pleasant
but on the outside. He was easily persuaded that these
who had provided him so fair a lodging were none of his
enemies; and doubted not but the lady who spoke to him
the day before in the church was the conjurer that had
raised all these enchantments. He admired with himself
the fancies of women, and how soon they put their designs
in execution; as for his part, he resolved to wait patiently
the end of this adventure, and be faithful to his invisible
mistress in spite of all the threats and promises he might
receive in this new lodging. A little while after several
servants in masks, and in very good clothes, came to lay
the cloth, and then served up supper. Everything belonging to it was magnificent; music and perfumes were not
forgotten; and Don Carlos not only gratified his smelling
and hearing, but his taste also; for he eat and drank
more than I thought a man in his condition could have
done. But what's impossible to so great a courage! I
forgot to tell you that he washed his mouth, for I am informed he took great care of his teeth. The music played
a while after supper, but all being withdrawn, Don Carlos
fetched many a turn about the room, reflecting on all these
enchantments, or perhaps on something else. Then came
in two gentlewomen and a dwarf all in masks, who, without asking him whether he had a mind to go to bed or
not, spread a magnificent toilet in order to undress him.

He complied with them in everything. The gentlewomen turned down the bed-clothes and then withdrew. The dwarf pulled off his shoes, stockings, or boots, and then his other clothes; all which being done without exchanging a word, Don Carlos went to bed and slept pretty well for a man in love. At break of day he was waked by the singing of birds that fluttered about in an aviary; the dwarf came to wait upon him, and brought him the finest linen in the world, and the best washed and perfumed. If you think fit, I shall not mention what he did till dinner (which was at least as good as his supper had been), but pass to the first breaking of that profound silence which had been observed to that very hour. A gentlewoman in a mask began to speak by asking him if he would be pleased to see the mistress of that enchanted palace. Don Carlos said she should be welcome. And a little while after she came in, attended by four gentlewomen very richly dressed.

«Such were not Cythera's charms,
  When drest in gay and loose attire,
  She flew to a new lover's arms,
  Upon the wings of soft desire.»

Never had our Spaniard seen a person of more majestic mien than this unknown Urganda. He was so transported and surprised at the same time, that he stumbled at every bow and step he made, as he led her into the next room, whither she directed him.

All the fine things he had seen in the other rooms I mentioned before were nothing in comparison to what he found in this last, which still received a new brightness from the lady in a mask. They walked on the finest foot-carpet that ever was seen since foot-carpets have been in fashion. There the Spaniard was placed in an arm-chair in spite of himself, and the lady sitting by herself, on I know not how many fine cushions over against him, she ravished his ears with a voice as sweet as a harpsichord, speaking to him to this effect: " I doubt not, Signior Don Carlos, but you are much surprised at what has happened to you in my house since yesterday; but if all that is not able to move you, yet by it you may see I am as good as my word; and from what I have done, you may guess what I am able to do. Perhaps my rival, both by her artifice and the advantage she has of having attacked you first, has made herself absolute mistress of that heart which I nevertheless pretend to dispute my right to with her; but a woman is not to be discouraged by the first disappointment; and if my fortune, which is not to be despised, with all that goes along with my person, cannot persuade you to love me, yet shall I have the satisfaction of not concealing myself out of shame or deceit, and choose to be despised through my defects, rather than be beloved through my artifice." As she spoke these last words she pulled off her mask, and showed Don Carlos the heavens with all their glories, or if you please, a heavenly miniature: the finest head in the world, supported by the best shape he ever admired before; in short, a person all over divine. By the freshness of her complexion one would not have thought her to have been above sixteen years of age; but by a certain free and majestic air, which young persons generally want, she appeared to be near twenty. Don Carlos paused a while before he answered her, being almost angry with his invisible lady, who hindered him from surrendering himself entirely to the finest person he ever saw, and dubious what he should say or do. At last, after an inward conflict, which lasted so long as to make the mistress of the enchanted palace uneasy, he took a firm resolution not to conceal from her his inmost thoughts; which, without any manner of question, was the best thing he ever did in his life. This is the answer he gave her, which some have found a little too blunt. "Madam, I could not but own myself extremely happy in your esteem, if my stars would but suffer me to love you. I see well enough that I leave the finest person in the universe for one who perhaps is only such in my fancy; but, madam, would you think me worth your affection if you found me capable of infidelity? and how can I be faithful if I love you? Therefore, madam, pity me, but blame me not; or rather let us pity each other and complain both; you of not obtaining what you desire, and I of not seeing what I love."

He uttered these words with such a melancholy air that
the lady might easily perceive he spoke his true sentiments. She used all the arguments she could think of to
persuade him to alter his mind, but he was deaf to her
prayers and unconcerned at her tears. She renewed the
attack several times, but met still with a stout resistance.
At last she began to revile and reproach him, and told
him,

> « What rage and jealousy suggest,
> When they possess a lovesick breast, »

and then she left him, not to pick straws, but to curse a
hundred times his misfortune, which proceeded only from
being too happy. A gentlewoman came a little while after
to acquaint him that he had the liberty to walk in the
garden. He traversed all these fine apartments without
meeting with anybody, till he came to the staircase, at the
foot of which he saw ten men in masks, who kept the
door, armed with partisans and carbines. As he was crossing the court to go into the garden, one of the gentlemen
of the guard accosted him without looking him in the face,
and told him, as though he feared to be overheard, that
an old gentleman had trusted him with a letter which he
had promised to deliver into his own hands, though his
life must answer for it if he should be discovered ; but
that a present of twenty pistoles, and a promise of as many
more, made him to run all hazards. Don Carlos promised
him secrecy, and went straight into the garden, where he
read the letter which was as follows :

"You may judge what pains I have felt since I lost you,
by those you ought to feel yourself, if you love me as
much as I do you. However, my uneasiness is something
abated by being informed of the place where you are. It
is the Princess Porcia who stole you away ; she is a
woman that sticks at nothing to please herself, and you
are not the first Rinaldo of that dangerous Armida. But I
will soon break all her enchantments and disengage you
from her arms, to receive you into mine, which favor you
will deserve, if you are as constant as I wish you to be.

"THE INVISIBLE LADY."

Don Carlos was so transported with joy to receive this news from his lady, with whom he was really in love, that he kissed the letter a hundred times over, and came back to the garden door to recompense the messenger with a fine diamond ring he had on his finger. He walked a little longer in the garden, still wondering at the Princess Porcia, whom. he often heard people report to be a young rich lady of the best family in the kingdom; but as he was a person of strict virtue, he conceived such an aversion for her, that he resolved to break out of his prison even at the hazard of his life. As he came out of the garden, he met a gentlewoman unmasked (for from that time forward everybody went barefaced in the palace), who came to ask if he would be pleased to have her mistress eat with him; and I leave you to think whether he answered, she should be welcome. A little while after they served up supper, or dinner for I have forgot which of the two it ought to have been. Porcia appeared more bright and handsome, I said just now, than Venus Citherea, and it will not be amiss if, for variety sake, I now say, than an angel: she was charming in every respect, and during the time they were at table the Spaniard discovered so much wit in her, that he was in a manner sorry to find so many excellent qualities so ill-bestowed on a person of so high a degree. He did all he could to appear in good humor and force a pleasing countenance, although he was continually thinking upon his unknown mistress, and burned with impatience to return to the lattice-window. As soon as the table was cleared they were left by themselves, and because Don Carlos spoke not a word, either out of respect or only to oblige the lady to speak first, she broke silence in these words: "I know not whether I ought to hope something from the gayety I fancy I have discovered in your face; and whether mine, which you have seen already, does seem handsome enough to make you doubt whether that of your invisible mistress has more charms to captivate your heart. I do not conceal what I designed to present you with, because I would not have you repent the accepting my present; and though a person who has been used to be instructed by others be apt to be

offended at a denial, yet will I forgive you, provided you
repair your past offense by giving me what I have more
right to than your invisible : therefore tell me your last
resolution, that if in case it be not in my behalf, I may at
least find out new reasons strong enough to combat those
which I think I had to love you." Don Carlos thought she
would have gone on with her speech ; but observing she
spoke no more, and that with eyes fixed on the ground
she expected her doom from his mouth, he resumed his
former resolution of telling her frankly that he could never
be hers, which he did in these words. "Madam, before I
answer what you would know of me, I must desire you,
that with the same frankness you expect from me, you
would be pleased to tell me your sentiments about what I
am going to propose to you. Suppose," added he, "you
had engaged a man to love you, and that by all the favors
a lady can grant without wronging her virtue you had
obliged him to swear an inviolable fidelity ; would you not
account him the basest and most treacherous of mankind
if he should fail in his promise? and were I not that villain,
and that traitor, if I should leave for you a person who has
reason to think I love her? " He was going to frame abundance of logical arguments in order to convince her ; but
she did not give him time, and rising abruptly from her
seat, told him that she plainly saw the drift of his discourse ; that she could not but admire his constancy, though
so much opposite to her own quiet that she would set him
at liberty, and that she only desired him to stay till night
to go back in the same manner he came. While she was
speaking, she held her handkerchief to her eyes as though
she designed to conceal her tears, and afterward left the
Spaniard a little concerned ; yet so transported with
joy that he was to be again at liberty, that he had not
been able to conceal it had he been the greatest hyprocrite
in the world ; and I verily believe, that had the lady taken
notice of it, she would certainly have scolded at him for
it. I know not whether it was long before night came, for
as I told you before, I don't trouble myself about marking
the time or hours. You must be contented to know that
night came at last, and that he went into a close coach,

and was set down at his lodgings after a pretty long journey. As he was the best master in the world, so his servants were like to die with joy at the sight of him, and almost stifled him with their embraces; but they did not enjoy him long; for having provided himself with arms, and taken two of his stoutest men along with him, he presently went to the grated window in such great haste, that those who accompanied him had much ado to keep pace with him. He had no sooner given the usual signal but his invisible deity communicated herself to him; when they exchanged such soft and tender expressions, that I cannot forbear weeping whenever I think of them. At last the lady told him she had been lately affronted in that house, and therefore had sent for a coach in order to leave it; but because it might be a long while a coming, she desired him to send for his, which might be sooner got ready; and that she would carry him to a place where she would no longer conceal her face from him. The Spaniard needed no farther entreaty, but ran like a madman to his men, whom he had left at the end of the street, and sent for his coach in all haste. The coach being come, the invisible lady kept her word, and went into it with Don Carlos. She directed the coachman which way he should drive, and bid him stop at a great house, into the courtyard of which the coach went by the light of several flambeaus, which were lighted at their arrival. The cavalier leading his lady, went up stairs into a very large room, where he was a little uneasy because she did not pull off her mask. At last several gentlewomen being come to receive them, with each a candlestick in their hands, the lady was invisible no longer; but pulling off her mask, let Don Carlos see that the lady at the grated window and the Princess Porcia were but one person. I will not endeavor to describe the pleasant surprise of the Spaniard. The fair Neapolitan told him she had stolen him away a second time to know his last resolution; that the lady at the lattice had made over to her all her pretensions, and added a thousand expressions no less obliging than ingenious. Don Carlos threw himself at her feet, embraced her knees, and devoured, as one may say, her hands with kisses; by that means avoid-

ing all the impertinence and nonsense which people generally speak when they are transported with joy. The
raptures of his passion being over, he used all his wit and
eloquence to extol the agreeable caprice of his mistress,
and expressed himself so well to her advantage, that he
confirmed her she was not mistaken in her choice. She
told him she had been unwilling to trust anybody but herself
in a thing, without which she could never have loved him ;
and that she would never have bestowed herself upon a
man less constant than himself. Thereupon the Princess
Porcia's relations came in, having had notice given them of
her design. And as they were the chief men in the kingdom, they easily obtained a dispensation from the arch-
bishop for their marriage. The same night the ceremony
was performed by the parson of the parish, who was an
honest priest and a good preacher ; and so 'twere needless
to ask whether he made a fine exhortation upon the subject. It is said they got up late the next day, which I
am inclined to believe. The news was soon spread about,
at which the viceroy, a near relation of Don Carlos's was
so overjoyed, that the public rejoicings began anew in
Naples, where to this day they talk of Don Carlos of Arragon and his invisible mistress.

HOW RAGOTIN RECEIVED A BLOW ON THE FIN-
GERS WITH A BUSK

RAGOTIN's story had a general applause, and he valued
himself as much upon it as if it had been his own ;
which swelling his natural pride, he began to treat
the men players with contempt, and afterward accosting
the women, squeezed their hands without their consent,
and offered to feel their breasts ; a piece of country gallantry which favors more of the satyr than gentleman.
Mistress Star contented herself to force her soft, fair hands
from his dirty rough clutches ; but Mrs. Angelica, her companion, gave him, withal smiling, a rap on the fingers with
her busk. He left them abruptly, without so much as

speaking a word, glowing with rage and confusion, and returned to the men's company, where everyone spoke as fast as he could without minding what the rest said. Ragotin silenced most of them by demanding of them, with a superior voice, what they thought of his novel. A young man, whose name I have forgot, answered him bluntly, it was no more his than anybody else's in the company, since he had it out of a book; whereupon seeing one stick out of Ragotin's pocket he pulled it out, which the little man perceiving, scratched his hands to get it from him; but in spite of Ragotin he put it in another man's hands, from whom Ragotin endeavored to snatch it, to as little purpose as before. The book having got by this time into a third man's hands after the same manner, passed to five or six different hands more; which Ragotin however could not reach, because he was the shortest man in the company. At last, having stretched himself five or six times in vain, torn half a dozen pairs of cuffs, scratched as many hands, and the book still traveling about through the middle region of the chamber, poor Ragotin, who saw everybody laugh at his expense, rushed like a madman upon the first author of his confusion, and dealt him several blows on his belly and thighs, not being able to reach higher. The hands of his adversary, who had the advantage of the place, fell five or six times so perpendicular and heavy on the top of his head, that the crown of his hat sunk down to his very chin; which so shook the seat of his reason, that the poor little man did not for some time know where he was. To complete his defeat, his antagonist at parting gave him a sound kick on the head, which after a very sudden retrogradation, made him fall on his breech, at the women players' feet. Now, if possible, I would have you to conceive the rage and fury of a little man, more proud than all the sieurs in the kingdom, at a time when he was cock-a-hoop about his story; and that too before players to whom he designed to make love, as you shall see anon, though he was yet ignorant which of them had the greater title to his heart. To speak the truth, his little body thus tumbled on his breech, did so lively represent the fury of his soul by the different motions of his arms

3

and legs, that though his face could not be seen, because his whole head was encased into his hat, yet all the company though fit to join and form as it were a barrier betwixt Ragotin and his adversary; who by this means got away, while the charitable women players raised the poor little man, roaring like a lion in his hat, which stopped his eyes and mouth, and almost hindered him from fetching his breath. Now the difficulty was, how to pull off this hat of his; for its crown being in the form of a butter-pot, and the mouth of it narrower than the bottom, God knows whether a head that got inself into it by force, and whose nose was so excessively large, was able to get out the same way. This misfortune had a good effect; for his anger being now at the highest, without doubt its effects had been answerable, had not his hat, which suffocated him, made him to consult his own preservation rather than contrive the destruction of another. He did not cry out for help, because he had not the use of his tongue; but when the company perceived he lifted up in vain his trembling hands to his head in order to set it at liberty, and stamped on the floor with rage and indignation, biting his nails to no purpose, they all bent their thoughts on his relief. The first efforts they used to pull off his hat were so violent, that he thought they had been going to pluck off his head from his shoulders. At last, being almost spent, he made signs with his fingers to have it cut with a pair of scissors. Mistress Cave unclasped those she wore on her girdle; and Rancour, who was to perform the operation, having made a show of making the incision over against his face (which did not a little fright him), at last he slit his hat behind his head from top to bottom. As soon as he had given vent to his face, all the company fell a laughing to see it bloated, as if it had been ready to burst, upon account of the vast quantity of spirits that had flushed to it; and besides, his nose was a little excoriated. However the jest had gone no father, had not a bungling tailor advised him to get his hat fine-drawn. This unseasonable advice so revived his anger, which was not entirely extinguished, that he laid hold of one of the andirons, and threatened to throw it at the company; which put the stoutest of them all into

such a fright, that every one ran to the door in order to
avoid the impending blow. They pressed so far upon one
another that not above one was able to get out; and he
too by a fall, his sparred legs having entangled themselves
with those of the rest. Ragotin fell a laughing in his turn,
which gave all the company fresh courage; they returned
him his book, and the players lent him an old hat. He
fell into a violent passion against the man who used him
so scurvily; but being somewhat more vain than revenge-
ful, he told the players, with the air of one that was going
to promise some extraordinary thing, that he had a mind
to make a play out of this story of his, and would contrive
it so well, that he was sure to get as much reputation by
that single piece as other poets had in all their lives gained
by several. Destiny told him the story he had related was
very entertaining, but would by no means fit the stage.
"Sure," said Ragotin, "you won't pretend to teach me? I
would have you to know that my mother was seamstress to
the poet Garnier, and I myself have one of his ink-horns at
home." Destiny replied that even Garnier would get no
reputation by it, if he was to do it himself. "But what
difficulty do you find in it?" asked Ragotin. "The difficulty," answered Destiny, "is in that it cannot be brought
into a regular play without committing a great many faults,
both in point of decorum and judgment." "As for that,"
said Ragotin, "a man of my parts may make new rules
whenever he pleases. Pray consider," added he, "what a
new and magnificent thing it would be to represent a great
church-gate in front of the stage, before which twenty beaux,
more or less, with as many ladies, should appear and speak
a thousand fine things to one another; would it not ravish
all the spectators with admiration, think you? I am so far
of your opinion," continued he, "that one ought to observe
decorum and good manners, and therefore would not make
my actors talk in the church." Destiny interrupted, to ask
him where they could get so many gentlemen and ladies.
"And how do they in colleges," said Ragotin, "where
they fight pitched battles? I myself played at La Flèche
the overthrow at the Bridge of Cé," added he; "above a
hundred soldiers of the queen-mother's party appeared on

the stage, besides those of the king's army, which was more numerous; and I remember, that by reason of a great shower that fell that day and spoiled the sport, it was reported that all the feathers of the country gentry, which had been borrowed on this occasion, would never come to themselves again." Destiny, who took great delight in hearing him utter all these judicious things, replied that colleges had scholars enough for that purpose, whereas their company did never consist in all of above seven or eight persons. Rancour, who, you know, had ever been a malicious dog, sided with Ragotin in this matter, the better to help to make him ridiculous, and told his comrade he was not of his opinion; that he had been a player before him; that a church-gate would be the finest scene that ever was seen; and as for the necessary number of gentlemen and ladies, that they might have some flesh and blood, and represent the rest with pasteboard. This fine expedient of pasteboard, invented by Rancour, set all the company a laughing. Ragotin laughed with the rest, and swore he knew that contrivance well enough, but had a mind to keep it to himself. "As for coaches," added he, "will it not be a novelty in a play? I formerly personated Toby's dog, and did it so to the life, that the whole audience was highly pleased with my performance, taking me to be a real dog. As for my part," continued he, "if we may judge of things by the effects they work upon our minds, I never saw 'Pyramus and Thisbe' acted in my life, but I was less concerned at Pyramus's death than frightened by the roaring of the lion." Rancour backed Ragotin's reasons with others as ridiculous, and by that means ingratiated himself so far into him, that Ragotin took him to supper. All the other impertinents left likewise the players at liberty; who it is probable had much rather go to supper than entertain these idle coxcombs of the town.

THIS CONTAINS WHAT YOU'LL FIND, IF YOU'LL BUT TAKE THE PAINS TO READ IT

RAGOTIN carried Rancour to a tavern, where he called for the best things the house could afford. It is thought he would not carry him to his own house, because his commons were but indifferent; but I will say nothing about that, for fear of passing rash judgment; neither did I care to inquire much into the truth of the business, because I did not think it worth my while, especially having matters of far greater importance to relate. Rancour, who was a person of great discernment and knew his men at first sight, no sooner saw a brace of partridges and a capon served up for two people, then he began to think that Ragotin had some design or other, and did not treat him so well, either upon account of his own merit, or to repay the civility he had received from him in maintaining his story to be a good subject for a play. He therefore expected to hear some new extravagance from Ragotin, who, however, did not discover his thoughts at first, but continued talking about his novel. Notwithstanding he at length repeated several lampoons he had made upon most of his neighbors, some cuckolds that were nameless, and other women. He sang drunken catches, and showed Rancour abundance of acrostics and anagrams, which are generally the first things with which your paltry rhymers begin to plague men of sense. Rancour made him a complete coxcomb by crying up all he heard, with eyes lifted to heaven, and swore like a losing gamester, that he never heard anything so fine in his life: nay, he was so transported, that he made a show of pulling off his hair in an ecstasy of pleasure. He told him now and then, "It is a great misfortune both for you and us, that you do not leave off all other business and write for the stage; for in such case, in two or three years time, Corneille would be no more talked of than Alexander Hardy is now. I am," added he, "an absolute stranger to flattery; but to encourage you, must needs own I no sooner saw you but

I read in your face that you were a great poet ; and you may be satisfied by my comrades what I told them about it. I am seldom mistaken ; I can smell a poet at two miles' distance ; and therefore as soon as ever I cast my eyes on you, I was acquainted with your genius as well as if I had brought you up." All this fulsome stuff went down with Ragotin as glib as several glasses of wine, which he drank at the same time, and which intoxicated his brain as much as Rancour's commendations swelled his vanity. As for Rancour, he eat and drank very heartily, crying out now and then, " For God's sake, Monsieur Ragotin, improve your talent. Once more let me tell you, you are much to blame not to make your fortune and ours. For my part, I scrawl a little paper sometimes as well as other people, but if I could make verses half so good as those you have been reading to me, I should not have been so hard put to it to keep life and soul together, but would live upon my income as well as Mondori. Therefore, Monsieur Ragotin, once more pray write ; and if this next winter we do not eclipse the companies of the Hôtel de Bourgogne and des Marez, may I never tread the stage more without breaking one of my arms or legs. I will say no more, and so let's drink." He was as good as his word ; for having put a double quantum into a glass, he drank Monsieur Ragotin's health to Monsieur Ragotin himself, who pledged him after the same manner, and returned his civility with drinking the health of the women players. This he drank cap in hand, and in such a rapture, that as he set the glass down on the table he broke its foot, without taking notice of it ; however, he afterward attempted three or four times to set it upright, but finding it impossible, he at last flung it over his head ; when pulling Rancour by the sleeve, he let him know he had had the honor of breaking a glass in drinking the players' health. It vexed him a little that Rancour did not laugh at it ; but, as I said before, he was rather an envious than a risible animal. Rancour asked him what he thought of their women.—— The little man blushed without giving an answer. But Rancour putting the same question to him again, at last, what by his stuttering, blushing, and broken speech, he gave Rancour

to understand that he liked one of the players extremely.
"But which of them?" quoth Rancour. The little man
was so disordered for having said so much, that he answered, "I don't know." "Nor I neither," said Rancour.
This reply cast him into greater disorder; insomuch that
with a bewildered look he said, "It is, it is"——He repeated the same words five or six times over again; at
which the stroller growing impatient, cried, "I like your
choice, she is a very beautiful person." This put him
quite out of countenance, insomuch that he could never
tell which he loved most; though it may be he knew
nothing of the matter himself, or that his passion was
rather lust than love. At last Rancour naming Mrs. Star,
he said it was she with whom he was in love. For my
part, I verily believe that had he named either Angelica
or her mother Cave, he would have forgot the blow he had
received with a busk from the one, and the age of the
other, and given himself body and soul to the very first
that Rancour had named, so great was the confusion of
goatish Ragotin. The stroller however made him drink a
good bumper, which carrying off part of it, pledged him
with another; which done, looking about the room, he
whispered, as though it were a great secret he was about
to tell, though there were nobody. "Well, your wound is
not mortal," quoth Rancour; "and you have addressed
yourself to one who is able to cure you, provided you will
be but ruled by him and keep counsel; not but your enterprise is a little difficult, for Mrs. Star is a very tigress,
and her brother Destiny a lion. But still, she does not
see men every day like you, and I know not what I can
do. Let's drink out our liquor, and to-morrow will be
day." They drank each a glass of wine, which interrupted
their conversation for a while. After this Ragotin recounted all his accomplishments and riches, and told Rancour that a nephew of his was clerk to a financier; that
this nephew had contracted great friendship with the Partisan de Ralliere during the time he was at Mans to settle
an excise office there, by the means of which nephew's
interest he endeavored to give him hopes that he would procure him such a pension from the king as his players in

ordinary had. He told him likewise, that if any of his relations had children, he could prefer them in the Church,
by reason his niece had married the brother of a certain
miss, kept by the steward of an abbot of that province,
who had good livings in his gift. While Ragotin was
thus relating what great interest he had, Rancour, who
the more he drank the more thirsty he grew, was still filling both the glasses, which were emptied in an instant,
Ragotin not daring to refuse anything from the hands of a
man from whom he expected such a great piece of service.
In short, they swilled it about till they had both their
fill. Rancour, according to his custom, grew more serious,
but Ragotin became so dull and heavy, that he laid down
his head on the table and fell asleep. Rancour called one
of the maids to make a bed ready for him, because
nobody was up at his inn. The maid told him she
had as good make two, for she was sure Monsieur
Ragotin wanted one as well as he. In the meantime, he
slept and snored as heartily as ever he had done in
his life, for all the noise they made while they were
putting clean sheets on two of the three beds that were in
the room. But when the maid came to wake him, and
acquaint him his bed was ready, he called her a thousand
flirts, and threatened to beat her. At last Rancour,
having turned him in his chair toward the fire, at which
the sheets were aired, he rubbed and opened his eyes, and
suffered himself to be undressed without repining. They
got him into his bed as well as they could ; and Rancour,
having first made the chamber-door fast, went into his.
About an hour after Ragotin got up, to what purpose I
never yet could learn. He rambled a long time about the
room, not knowing where he was ; and having overturned
all the chairs and tables he met in his way, and tumbled
himself down several times, without being able to find his
bed again, he went at last to Rancour's and pulling his
bed-clothes, made him to start out of his sleep. Rancour
asked him what he would have. " I am looking for my
bed," said Ragotin. " It is on the left-hand of mine,"
replied Rancour. The little drunken man, however, took to
the right, and thrust himself betwixt the rug and mattress

of the third bed, which had neither feather-bed, quilt, nor sheets, and there he slept all night very quietly. Rancour got up and dressed himself before Ragotin waked ; when he asked him whether it was to do penance that he had left his bed to sleep on straw. Ragotin was positive that he never got up, and that the room must be haunted. The innkeeper hearing this, stood up for the reputation of his house, and picking a quarrel with Ragotin, threatened to sue him for giving it an ill name. But I have sufficiently exercised your patience with this tedious story of Ragotin's debauch, and therefore let us return to the strollers' inn.

A COMBAT IN THE NIGHT

I AM too much a man of honor not to advertise the courteous reader, that if he be offended at all the silly trifles he has already found in this book, he will do well not to go on with the reading of it; for, upon my conscience, he must expect nothing else, although the volume should swell to the bigness of that of the Grand Cyrus : and if from what he has read he doubts what will follow, perhaps I am in the same quandary as well as he. For one chapter draws on another, and I do with my book as some do with their horses, putting the bridle on their necks, and trusting to their good conduct. But perhaps I have a fixed design, and without filling my chapters with examples for imitation, shall instruct with delight after the same manner as a drunken man creates in us an aversion for drunkenness, and yet may sometimes divert us with his merry impertinence. Let us end this moral reflection, and return to our strollers, whom we left in the inn. As soon as their room was cleared, and Rancour had got thither with Ragotin, the doorkeeper they left at Tours came into the inn with a horseload of goods, and sat down to supper with them. By this person, and what they had learned from one another, they understood how the intendant of the province could do them

no harm, having had much ado to escape the hands
of the boisterous mob, with his fusiliers. Destiny told
his comrades how he had got away in his Turkish
habit, with which he designed to represent Mairet's "Soli-
man"; and that being informed that the plague was at
Alencon, he was come to Mans with Cave and Rancour,
with the same equipage we have described in the beginning
of these most true, though little heroical adventures. Mrs.
Star acquainted them also with the good offices she had received from a lady at Tours, whose name never came to
my knowledge, and how by her means she had been
conducted as far as a village near Bonnestable, where she
sprained her foot as she alighted off her horse. She added
that hearing the company was gone to Mans, she got herself carried thither in a litter, which the lady of that village had lent her with a great deal of civility. After
supper, Destiny alone stayed in the lady's chamber. Cave
loved him as if he had been her own son; Mrs. Star
was no less dear to her; and her daughter and only heiress,
Angelica, loved Destiny and Star like a brother and sister.
She did not yet exactly know who they were, nor upon
what account they had turned players; but she had taken
notice, that though they called one another brother and
sister, yet were they better friends than near relations; that
Destiny paid to Star the greatest respect imaginable; that
she was extremely modest and virtuous: and as Destiny
had a great deal of wit, and seemed to have a liberal education, so Mrs. Star looked more like a young lady of
quality than a stroller. Now Destiny and Star were beloved by Cave and her daughter, because they really deserved their love both by their good qualities and the
mutual friendship which they naturally had for two players, who had as much merit as any in France, though they
never had the good fortune to tread either of the two
theatres in Paris, which are the *non plus ultra* of French
players. Those who do not understand these three little
Latin words (which come so pat in my way, that I could
not refuse to place them here) may be pleased to ask some
Latinist of their acquaintance the meaning of them. To
end this digression: Destiny and Star did not scruple to

express their mutual fondness before Cave and Angelica, and show the extreme joy they had to see each other after so long an absence. They related, as pathetically as ever they could, how uneasy they were about each other; and Destiny acquainted Mrs. Star, that the last time they acted at Tours, he thought he had spied their inveterate persecutor among the crowd of their auditors, although he had his cloak about his face : and that as he went out of the city, not finding himself able to resist him if he should have offered to attack him, he had disguised himself by putting a great patch on his face. While Destiny was speaking, poor Mrs. Star could not forbear shedding some few tears : Destiny was sensibly touched with them ; and having comforted her as well as he could, added, that if she would but suffer him to use the same endeavors in seeking out their enemy as he had used till then in avoiding him, he would soon free her from his persecutions, or lose his life in the attempt. These last words redoubled her grief : Destiny had not courage enough to forbear grieving likewise ; and Cave and her daughter, who were of a tender and compassionate temper, grieved also, either out of complaisance or through contagion. I cannot tell whether Destiny wept, but this I know, the women and he were silent a long while ; and in the meantime every one wept as they thought fit. At last Cave renewed the conversation which tears had interrupted, and reproached Destiny and Star, that though during the time they had lived together they might have been convinced how much she was their friend, yet they reposed so little confidence in her and her daughter, that they were still unacquainted with their birth and quality ; adding, she had not met with crosses enough in her life to enable her to advise unfortunate persons such as they two seemed to be. To which Destiny answered, that their not discovering themselves to her was not out of any distrust, but because he thought the recital of their misfortunes could not but be very tedious; telling her withal, that he would be ready to entertain her with the story of their adventures whenever she was willing to throw any time away upon the hearing of it. Cave was glad of this opportunity to satisfy her curiosity ; and her daughter, who had the same inclination, being sat near her on Star's

bed, Destiny was about to begin his story, when they heard
a great noise in the next chamber. Destiny stood listening
a while; but the noise and squabble increasing, and somebody crying out, " Murder! help! murder! "— he with three
leaps got out of the chamber at the expense of his doublet,
which Cave and Angelica had torn as they were going to
stop him. He went into the chamber from whence the
noise came, which was so dark that he could not see his
own nose; and where the fisticuffs, boxes on the ears, and
several confused voices of fighting men and women,
together with the hollow noise of naked feet stamping on
the floor, made a hideous and frightful uproar. He ran
very rashly among the combatants, and in one moment
received a cuff on one side, and a box on the ear on the
other; which changed his good intention of parting those
hobgoblins into a violent thirst for revenge. He began to
set his hands agoing, and made a flourish with his two
arms, by which many a maimed chops were belabored, as
it afterward appeared by his bloody fists. The scuffle
lasted so long that he received twenty cuffs more, which he
however returned with double the number. In the heat of
the fight he felt himself bit on the calf of the leg, when
clapping his hands to the place, he met with something
hairy, which he for that reason took to be a dog; but Cave
and her daughter, who appeared at the chamber door at
that interim with a candle, like the fire of St. Helmo after
a storm, discovered to Destiny that he was amid seven
persons in their shirts, who having been in close conflict
before, began to let one another go as soon as the light
appeared. This tranquillity however did not last long.
The innkeeper, who was one of the naked combatants,
grappled the poet anew; Olive, who was also among
them, was attacked by the innkeeper's man, another of the
combatants; Destiny went to part them; whereupon the
hostess, who was the animal that had bit him, and whom
he had taken for a dog by reason she was bare-headed and
had short hair, flew at his face, assisted by two maids, as
naked and bare-headed as herself. The shrieks and cries
filled the air once more, the cuffs and boxes made the room
to ring again, and the fight grew still warmer and warmer.

At last several persons who waked at the noise came into
the field of battle, parted the combatants, and procured a
second suspension of arms. Now the question was to
know the occasion of the quarrel, and what fatal accident
had brought seven naked persons into one room. Olive,
who seemed the least concerned, said that the poet being
gone out of the room, he saw him come running back as
fast as he could, followed by the innkeeper, who seemed to
have a mind to beat him; that the hostess followed her
husband, fell foul of the poet; that as he was going to part
them, a servant and two maids fell upon him; and that the
light happening to go out at the same time, made the fight
last longer than it would otherwise have done. Now it
was the poet's turn to speak for himself. He said that
having made two of the finest stanzas that ever was written
since stanzas were in fashion, and fearing to lose them, he
went to the maid of the inn for a candle, which she scorn-
fully refused to give him; whereupon the innkeeper called
him rope-dancer, which he returned by calling him
cuckold. He had no sooner spoke this last word but the
host, who was within reach, gave him a good slap on the
chops; you would have thought they had made a fighting
concert together; for as soon as the box on the ear was
given, the innkeeper's wife, his man, and his maids rushed
upon the strollers altogether, who received them with
sound cuffs. This last encounter was more fierce and obstinate than either of the other two. Destiny having
closed with a lusty wench and tucked up her skirts, gave
her a thousand slaps; Olive, who saw the company pleased
with it, did the same to the other maids. The innkeeper
was busy with the poet; and the hostess, the most furious
of all the combatants, was seized by some of the spectators; which made her to fly into such a passion, that she
cried out "Thieves! thieves!" Her cries woke La Rappinière, who lived over against the inn. He caused the
door to be broken open, and judging by the noise he
heard that there could be no less than seven or eight people killed, he parted the fray in the king's name; and
having learned the cause of all the disturbance, exhorted
the poet not to make any more verses in the night-time,

and was like to have beaten the innkeeper and his wife for giving a hundred abusive names to the players, whom they called jack-puddings and tumblers, swearing, withal, to turn them out of doors the next day ; but La Rappinière, to whom the innkeeper owed money, threatening to arrest him, his mouth was soon stopped. La Rappinière after the fray went home, the rest returned to their chambers, and Destiny to that of the players, where Cave desired him not to defer any longer relating the history of his and his sister's adventures. He told her he was ready to satisfy her curiosity, and began his relation after the manner you shall find in the following chapter.

THE HISTORY OF DESTINY AND MRS. STAR

I WAS born in a village near Paris, and might make you believe I came of a very illustrious family, since nobody can disprove what a stranger says of himself ; but I am too generous, and too much a lover of truth, to deny the meanness of my extraction. My father was one of the topping and most substantial men in his village, whom I have often heard to say that he was a poor gentleman's son ; that he had spent his youth in the wars, where having got nothing but dry blows and empty pockets, he betook himself to the service of a rich Parisian lady in the quality of her gentleman usher ; and that having scraped together a sum of money in this place (because he was also the steward and caterer of the house, and had the knack of emptying his mistress's purse to fill his own pockets) he married an old waiting-woman of the family, who died soon after, and left him all she had got in her service. Being soon weary of the condition of a widower, and no less of that of a servant, he married a country-woman, who furnished his lady's house with bread. And it is to this last marriage that I owe my birth. My father was called Gariquet ; what country he was of I could never yet learn ; and as for my mother's name, it signifies nothing to my story. Let it

suffice that she was more covetous than my father, and
my father more covetous than she, and that they had both
a pretty large conscience. My father had the honor of
being the inventor of the piece of flesh tied with a string
to the pot-handle, which having boiled a considerable time,
may be taken out again, and serve several times to make
soup. I could tell a hundred more particulars of his good
husbandry, which gained him, with justice, the reputation
of a man of wit and invention; but for fear of being too
tedious, I will content myself with relating only two,
which may seem incredible, though they are most certainly
true. He had bought up a great quantity of corn, with
design to sell it very dear in case the year should prove
bad; but the harvest being plentiful, and corn falling in
its price, he was so possessed with despair and the devil,
that he had an inclination to hang himself. One of the
neighbors who happened to be in the room when he entered upon that noble design, and had hid herself for fear
of being seen (for what reason I know not), was not a
little surprised when she saw him hang dangling on one of
the joists of the ceiling. She immediately ran to him,
crying out "Help! help!" and began to cut the rope; and
by the help of my mother, who came in at the noise, got
it from his neck. Perhaps they repented the doing of so
good an action, for he beat them both to mummy, and
made that poor woman pay for the rope she had cut, by
stopping some money he owed her. His other prank is no
less strange. He grudged himself whatever he ate, and his
wife being brought to bed of a boy, the fancy took him in
the crown that she had milk enough to nourish both his
son and himself; and hoped that by sucking his wife he
should save bread and live upon a food of easy digestion.
My mother's wit was much inferior to his, though her
avarice was as great; but though she did not invent things
as my father did, yet having once conceived them she put
them in execution with more exactness than he could. She
therefore tried to nourish both her son and her husband
with her own milk, and ventured also to feed upon it herself, with so much obstinacy, that the little innocent creature was soon starved to death; and my father and mother

were so weakened and famished, that when they returned
to meat they surfeited themselves, and fell both sick upon
it. Sometime after my mother went with child with
me, and having happily brought forth a most unhappy
creature, my father went to Paris to desire his mistress to
stand godmother to his son, together with an honest
churchman, residing at his village, where he had a bene-
fice. As he was returning home in the evening to avoid
the heat of the day, and passed through a great street in
the suburbs, the houses whereof were for the most part
a-building, he saw afar off by the moonshine somewhat
that glittered in his eyes, as he was crossing the street.
He did not think it worth while to inquire what it was;
but hearing the groans of one in pain at the same place
where what he had seen vanished out of his sight, he
boldly entered one of those unfinished buildings, where he
found a woman sitting alone on the ground. The place
she was in received sufficient light from the moon to let
my father perceive that she was very young and very
richly clad, having on a gown of silver tissue, which was
the glittering thing my father saw the moment before.
You must not question that my father, who did not want
resolution, was less surprised than the young lady; for she
was in a condition that nothing worse could happen to her.
This consideration gave her the assurance to speak first
and tell my father that if he was a Christian he would
take pity on her; that she was in labor ready to be
brought to bed, and that the maid she had sent for a
trusty midwife not returning, she had slipped away from
her house without waking anybody, her maid having left
the door open that she might come in again without making any noise. She had scarce made an end of this short relation but she was delivered of a child, which my father
received into the lappet of his cloak. He acted the midwife
as well as he could, and the young lady conjured him to
carry away the creature with all speed, to take care of it,
and not to fail two days after to go to an old churchman
she named to him, who would give him money and all
necessary orders for nursing of the child. At this word
money my father, who had a penurious soul, was going to

display all the eloquence of a gentleman usher, but she would not give him time ; she put into his hands a ring for a token to the priest he was to go to from her ; caused him to swaddle the young creature in her neck-handkerchief, and sent him away in haste, notwithstanding his unwillingness to leave her in the condition she was in. I am inclined to believe she had much ado to get home again ; as for my father, he returned to his village, gave the child to his wife, and did not fail two days after to go to the old priest and show him the ring. He learned from him that the child's mother was a young lady of a very good family, and very rich ; that she had had this child by a Scotch lord, who was gone into Ireland to raise soldiers for the king's service ; and that this foreign nobleman had promised her marriage. Moreover the priest told him that by reason of her precipitate delivery she was fallen desperately sick, and being in that extremity had confessed all to her father and mother, who instead of chiding her endeavored to comfort her, by reason she was an only child ; that the thing was yet a secret in the house, and therefore assured my father that if he would but take care of the child and keep counsel, his fortune should be made. Thereupon he gave him fifty crowns and a bundle of all sorts of things necessary for a child. My father returned home after he had well dined with the priest. I was put out to nurse, and the stranger kept at home in my stead. A month after the Scotch lord came back, and having found his mistress so very ill that she could not live much longer, he married her one day before she died, and so was no sooner a husband than a widower. He came two or three days after to our town with the parents of his wife. There they began to weep afresh, and were like to stifle the child with kisses. My father had reason to be thankful to the Scotch lord for his generosity, and the relations of the child did not forget him besides. They returned to Paris very much satisfied with the care my father and mother took of the boy, whom they would not yet take home with them because the marriage was still kept secret, for some reasons which never came to my knowledge. As soon as I was able to walk, my father took me home to

4

keep the young Earl of Glaris company (for so he was
called by his father's name). The natural antipathy said
to have been between Jacob and Esau in the very womb
of their mother was never greater than that which was
between the young earl and me. My father and mother
loved him tenderly, and had an aversion for me, though I
was the more hopeful boy of the two. There appeared
nothing but what was mean in him. As for me, I seemed
to be what I was not, and rather an earl's son than
Gariquet's; and if I am at last no more than a wretched
player, it is undoubtedly because fortune had a mind to be
revenged upon nature for designing to make me something
without her help; or, if you please, because nature is sometimes willing to favor those whom fortune is unkind to.
I shall pass over in silence the infancy of two young
clowns (for Glaris was such by education as well as myself),
since our most memorable adventures were nothing but
abundance of fisticuffs. In all the quarrels we had I
always got the better of him, except when my father and
mother sided with him, which they did so often and with
so much heat that my godfather, Monsieur Saint Sauveur
by name, was highly offended at it, and demanded me of
my father. He made him a present of me with great joy,
and my mother had yet less regret than he to part with
me. Thus I was at my godfather's well clad, well fed,
much caressed, and never beaten. He spared no costs to
make me read and write; and as soon as I was fit to
learn Latin, he obtained of the lord of our village, who
was a very civil gentleman and very rich, that I should
study with two of his sons under a learned man he had
from Paris, and to whom he gave a very good salary.
This gentleman, the Baron d'Arques by name, took great
care to have his sons well educated. The eldest, called
Saint Far, was a handsome gentleman, but as untractably
rough and brutish in his nature as ever man was; to make
amends, the younger brother was both handsomer than
Saint Far, and had a vivacity of mind and greatness of
soul equal to the beauty of his body. In short, I do not
think there ever was a more hopeful young gentleman than
Vervelle, for this was the younger brother's name. He

honored me with his friendship, and as for me, I loved him like a brother and ever respected him as a master. As for Saint Far, he had none but ill-inclinations, and I cannot better express the sentiments he had both for his brother and me, than by telling you that he loved not his brother more than me, for whom he had a great indifference; and that he hated me no more than he did his brother, whom he loved but little. His diversions were different from ours, for he loved nothing but hunting, and hated books of morality; whereas Vervelle seldom went out a hunting, and took great delight in reading; wherein I agreed wonderfully with him, as I did in everything else, without being put to the trouble of doing anything out of complaisance, as in duty I ought. The Baron d'Arques had a large library of romances. Our tutor who had never read any in his college, and who at first forbade us the reading of them, having condemned them a hundred times before the Baron d'Arques to render them as odious to him as he found them delightful, grew at last so much in love with them himself, that having devoured both the old and the new ones, he confessed that the reading of good romances was as instructive as pleasant, and no less proper to inspire young people with noble sentiments than the reading of Plutarch. He therefore encouraged us to read them as earnestly as he had discouraged us before, and first of all advised us to peruse the modern; but these were not yet suitable to our palates; and till we were fifteen we were much more delighted with reading *Amadis de Gaul* than *Astrea*, and other fine romances that have been made since, by which the French have shown to the world, as they have by a thousand things besides, that if they do not invent so much as other nations, yet do they nevertheless bring the inventions of others to a far greater perfection. We therefore bestowed upon the reading of romances the greatest part of the time we had allowed us for diversion. As for Saint Far, he called us the Ruyters, and went abroad every day either to hunt or to beat the poor country fellows, which he did with wonderful success. The inclination I had to do well gained me the favor of the Baron d'Arques, who loved me no less than if I had

been his near relation. He would not suffer me to leave
his sons when he sent them to the academy, but sent me
thither along with them, and that rather as a companion
than a servant. There we stayed about two years to learn
our exercises, at the end of which a man of quality, related
to the Baron d'Arques, raising soldiers for the Venetians,
Saint Far and Vervelle persuaded their father to let them
go to Venice with their kinsman. The good old gentleman
desired I would still accompany them, and Monsieur de
Saint Sauveur, my godfather, who loved me extremely, gave
me very generously bills of exchange for a considerable
sum, to make use of in case those I had the honor to
accompany should be unwilling to bear my charges. We
went the longest way about on purpose to see Rome and
the other fine cities of Italy, in each of which we stayed
a considerable time, excepting those which are in the
Spaniards' hands. I fell sick at Rome, and the two
brothers went on their journey; the gentleman under
whose conduct they were being willing to lay hold of the
opportunity of the pope's galleys, which were putting out
to sea to join the Venetian army near the Straits of the
Dardanelles, where they waited for the Turks. Vervelle
was extraordinarily sorry to leave me, and I almost mad to
part from him, at a time when by my services I might in
some measure have deserved the love he had for me. As
for Saint Far, I believe he left me with as much indifference as if he had never seen me; and I never thought
of him, but only because he was brother to Vervelle, who
left me as much money as he could spare; but whether
Saint Far was consenting I cannot tell. Thus I was left
sick at Rome, having no other acquaintance besides my
landlord, a Fleming apothecary, who took extraordinary
care of me during my illness, and who, as far as I can
judge, had more skill in physic than the Italian doctor
who looked after me. At last I recovered, and gathered
strength enough to go and view the most remarkable
places in Rome, where strangers find abundantly where-
withal to entertain their curiosity. I took a singular
delight in viewing the vines (thus are called several
gardens, finer than the Tuileries in Paris, which cardinals

and other persons of quality keep with much cost in Rome, rather out of vanity than for their own entertainment, since they never, or at least very seldom, go there themselves). One day, as I was walking in one of the finest, I saw at the turning of the wall two women very genteelly dressed, whom two young Frenchmen stopped and would not let go, unless the youngest of them unveiled her face. One of those two Frenchmen, who looked like the master of the other, had even the insolence to offer to unveil her by force, while his man held the other, who was bare-faced. I was not long debating what I should do on this occasion, but presently told those rude men that I was resolved not to suffer them to offer violence to those ladies. They were both very much surprised, for I spoke with such a resolution as would have daunted them had they had their swords as well as myself. The two ladies came over to me, and the young Frenchman choosing rather to be baulked than beaten, told me as he went off: "Sir, for all your hectoring we shall meet you in some other place, where our swords shall not hang all one side." I answered I would not hide myself. His man followed him, and so I stayed with the two women. She that had no veil on looked to be about five and thirty: she returned me thanks in good French, without any mixture of Italian, and told me among other things, that if all Frenchmen were like me the Italian women would not scruple to live after the French fashion. After that, to reward the service I had done them, she added, that since I hindered that rude Frenchman from seeing her daughter against her will, it was reasonable I should see her of her own accord. "Therefore," said she, "Leonora, lift up your veil, and let the gentleman see that we are not altogether unworthy of the honor of being under his protection." She had scarce done speaking but her daughter put aside her veil, or rather discovered a sun which dazzled my eyes. I never beheld so beautiful an object in my whole life. She cast three or four times her eyes on me, as it were by stealth, and as they still met with mine, the innocent blushes which overspread her face made her to look as handsome as an angel. I perceived the mother was very fond of her, for she seemed to share the pleasure

I had in gazing upon her. Now by reason I was little used to these adventures, and that young people are easily dashed out of countenance in strange company, I made them but indifferent compliments when they went away, and gave them perhaps but an indifferent opinion of my wit. I was angry with myself for not asking their habitation, and that I did not offer to wait upon them thither; but it was preposterous to run after them. I went to the doorkeeper to inquire whether he knew them; but we were a long while before we could understand one another, because he spoke no better French than I did Italian. At last, rather by signs than otherwise, he gave me to understand that they were unknown to him, at least he would not own he knew them. I returned to my Fleming apothecary in a very different disposition of mind from what I was in when I came out; that is to say, very amorous, and very much in pain to know whether that beautiful Leonora was a courtesan or an honest woman, and if she had as much wit as her mother, who seemed to have a great deal. I abandoned myself to thought, and flattered myself with a thousand fair hopes which entertained me awhile, but disquieted me much more when I considered the impossibility of my wishes. Having framed a thousand frivolous designs, I resolved at last to seek them out, not thinking it possible for them to remain long invisible in Rome (which is not a populous city), especially to a man so much in love as I was. That very day I looked for them wherever I thought it most likely to find them, and returned home at night more tired and uneasy than I was when I went out. The next day I sought them still with more diligence, yet did nothing but tire and disquiet myself. By my peeping through the lattice-windows, and my hasty running after all the women that bore the least resemblance of my Leonora, I was taken a hundred times, both in the streets and in the churches, for the greatest fool among those Frenchmen who have contributed most to their disparaging their nation at Rome. It is a matter of wonder how I could gather strength at a time when I suffered like one in hell. However my body recovered, while my sick mind remained so divided betwixt honor and love, which kept me at Rome,

that I often doubted whether I should obey the frequent
letters I received from Vervelle, who conjured me by the
ties of friendship to come to him, without using the right
he had to command me. At last all my endeavors to find
out my unknown lady proving ineffectual, I paid my landlord,
and got my little equipage ready in order to depart. The
day before I was set out, Signior Stephano Vanberge (for
so was my landlord called) told me he designed to give me
a dinner at a mistress's house of his, and at the same time
make me confess that he had not made an ill-choice for a
Fleming; adding, withal, that he would not carry me to
her before I was to go away, because he was a little jealous.
I promised to wait on him rather out of complaisance than
inclination; and accordingly we went about dinner-time.
The house we went into had neither the appearance nor
furniture of an apothecary's mistress. Having traversed a
very fine parlor, we entered a magnificent room, where
we were received by Leonora and her mother. You may
imagine how much I was agreeably surprised. The mother
of that beautiful daughter came toward me to be saluted
after the French way; and I must needs own that she
kissed me rather than I her. I was so amazed that I
scarce could see anything, neither did I hear one word of
the compliment she made me. At last I recovered both my
senses and sight, and saw Leonora more beautiful and
charming than before, but had not the assurance to salute
her. I was sensible of my fault as soon as I had committed it; but instead of repairing it, blushed as much out of
shame as she did out of modesty. Her mother told me she
designed to return me thanks before I went away for the
pains I had taken to find out their habitation; and this
still increased my confusion. She pulled me into an alcove
adorned after the French fashion, where her daughter did
not follow us, because, I suppose, she did not think it worth
her while to join conversation with so dull a fellow as I
seemed to be. She stayed with Signior Stephano, while
with her mother I acted the part of a clown to the life.
She was so civil to find matter to keep up the conversation
herself, which she did very ingeniously, though nothing
can be more difficult than to show one's wit with those that

have none. For my part I never was such a blockhead in my life ; and if she was not tired with me then, she never could be with anybody. Among other things, to which I scarce answered yes or no, she told me she was a French-woman born, and that Signior Stephano would inform me of the reasons which kept her in Rome. By this time, dinner being ready, she was fain to pull me along to the table as she had pulled me before to the alcove ; for I was so disordered that I did not know how to set one foot before the other. I was the same dull loggerhead both before and after dinner, during which the only thing I did with assurance was to stare upon Leonora. I fancy she was uneasy at it, and therefore to punish me for it never lifted up her eyes all the while. Had the mother been silent the dinner had been like a Carthusian meal ; but she discoursed with Signior Stephano about the affairs of Rome, at least I fancy so, for I am not very sure of it. At last we rose from table, to the great comfort of every-body, except myself, whose distemper grew worse and worse every moment. When we went to take our leave they said a thousand obliging things to me, which I only answered with the ordinary compliments used at the bottom of a letter. However I did something more at parting than I did when I came in ; for I saluted Leonora, and by that means completed my ruin. Stephano was not able to get one single word from me all the way home. I locked myself up in my room without pulling off either my cloak or sword. There I revolved in my mind what-ever had happened to me. Leonora presented herself to my fancy more beautiful than ever she had appeared to my sight. I remembered how dull and silly I was before the mother and the daughter ; and as often as I thought of it was so ashamed, that I could not forbear blushing. I wished to be rich, cursed my mean extraction, and then fancied to myself a thousand lucky adventures, advan-tageous both to my fortune and love. At last, having nothing in my thoughts but how to frame a plausible pre-tense to stay, and not finding any to my liking, I grew so desperate as to wish to fall sick again, to which I had already no small disposition. I designed to write to

Leonora; but all my pen could produce did not please me, and so I put into my pocket the beginning of a letter, which perhaps I had not dared to send had it been finished. Thus having disquieted myself to little purpose, and not being able to banish Leonora from my thoughts, I resolved to go by the vine where she appeared to me first, to abandon myself entirely to my passion, and pass by her door once for all. This vine was well situated in one of the remotest parts of the city, and in the midst of several old uninhabited buildings. As I passed along, pensive and melancholy, under the ruins of a portico, I heard somebody stalk behind me, and at the same time felt myself run through under the reins. I presently faced about, and instantly drew my sword; and finding I had to do with the servant of the young Frenchman I mentioned before, I was like to return him at least as good a pass as he had made at me by treachery: but as I pushed at him without being able to close with him, because he maintained a running fight, and endeavored to parry, his master came out from among the ruins of the portico, and attacking me behind, dealt me such a stunning blow on the head, and a great thrust in the thigh, as made me to fall down. There was no likelihood of my escaping at so cheap a rate; but because in an ill action people seldom preserve a presence of mind, the servant wounded his master in the right hand; and at the same time two Minime friars of the Trinity of the Mount passing by, and seeing me treacherously assaulted, ran to my assistance; whereupon my assassins made their escape, and left me wounded in three several places. Those good friars happened to be Frenchmen, to my great comfort; for in so remote a place, had an Italian seen me in the condition I was in, he would rather have avoided than succored me, lest being found doing me a good office he were suspected of being himself my murderer. While one of these charitable friars received my confession, the other ran to my lodging to acquaint my landlord with my disaster. He came instantly to me, and caused me to be carried, half-dead, to my bed. With so many wounds, and so much love, it was no wonder if I soon fell into a most

violent fever. My life was despaired of by all, and I had
no reason to hope better than the rest. In the meantime
my passion for 'Leonora was so far from abating that it
was rather increased, though my strength grew still
weaker and weaker. Wherefore, not being able to support
so heavy a burden, without easing myself of it, nor resolved to die without letting Leonora know that it was
for her sake only that I wished to live, I called for a pen
and ink. They thought I was light-headed ; but I was so
earnest in protesting that they would drive me into despair
in case they should deny me what I requested, that Signior
Stephano, who had taken notice of my passion, and was so
clear-sighted as to guess at my design, gave orders that I
should have all things necessary to write ; and as he knew
my intention, he stayed all alone in the room. I perused
what I had scribbled a little before, with design to make
use of some thoughts which came then into my head upon
the same subject, and then wrote thus to Leonora :

" I no sooner saw you, but it was out of my power to
forbear loving you ; my reason did not oppose my passion,
but told me, as well as my eyes, that you were the most
lovely person in the world ; whereas it should have represented to me how unworthy I was of your heart. However, that would have served only to exasperate my disease
with unprofitable remedies, and after having struggled a
while, I must at last have yielded to the irresistible
necessity of loving you, which you impose on all that see
you. Well, I love you, my charming Leonora, but with so
much respect, that you ought not to hate me for it,
although I have the boldness to discover it to you. But
how is it possible to die for you without boasting of it?
And how can you refuse to pardon a crime with which
you can not reproach me long? I own your being the
cause of a man's death is recompense not to be merited but
by a great number of services, and you will perhaps envy
me a happiness which you procure me without design.
But do not grudge it me, lovely Leonora, since it is
no more in your power to make me lose it, and that it
is the only favor I ever received from fortune, who will

never sufficiently reward your merit, but by procuring you adorers as much above me as all other beauties in the world are below yours. Therefore I am not so vain as to think that you will bestow the least sentiment of pity on ——»

I was not able to make an end of my letter; my strength failed me on the sudden; the pen fell from my hand, for my mind went so fast, that my body could not keep pace with it; else that long beginning you have heard had been but a small part of my letter; so much was my imagination warmed by my fever and my love. I was a long time in a fainting fit without giving the least sign of life, which Signior Stephano perceiving, he opened the chamber-door to send for a priest. At that very moment Leonora and her mother came to visit me, having, it seems, been informed of my being wounded. Now as they thought this accident befell me upon their account, and for that reason that they were the innocent cause of my death, they did not scruple to come to see me in the condition I was in. My trance lasted so long that they went away before I was come to myself, very much afflicted, as one may imagine, and fully persuaded that I would never recover. They read what I had been writing; and the mother being more curious than the daughter, perused also the papers I had left on the bed; among which there was a letter from my father. I was a long time struggling betwixt life and death; but at length youth getting the upper hand, in a fortnight's time I was out of danger: and in five weeks' time began to walk about the room. My landlord entertained me often about Leonora. He acquainted me with the charitable visit she and her mother had made me, at which I was overjoyed: and if I was a little troubled at their reading my father's letter, I was highly pleased that my own had been read also. As often as I happened to be alone with Stephano I could talk of nothing but Leonora. One day calling to mind what her mother told me, that he could inform me who she was, and what reasons obliged her to stay in Rome, I desired him to acquaint me with what he knew of the matter. He acquainted me that she came to Rome with the French ambassador's lady; that a man of quality, a near relation of the ambassador's, had fallen in love with her; that in time she loved him too, and that, being married clandestinely, she had the beautiful Leonora by him. He informed me likewise that that nobleman had fallen out with all his relations upon this account, which obliged him to leave Rome and go to Venice with Madame la Boissière (for this was her name) till the time of the embassy should be expired; that having brought her back to Rome, he furnished her a house, and gave her all necessaries to live like a person of quality while he stayed in France, whither his father had called him back, and whither he durst not carry his mistress, or, if you please, his wife, well knowing that none of his relations would approve his match. I must confess I could not sometimes forbear wishing that Leonora were not the legitimate daughter of a person of quality, that the blemish of her birth might excuse the meanness of mine; but however I soon repented so criminal a thought, and wished her fortune answerable to her merit. This last thought cast me into despair; for as I loved her more than my life, I plainly foresaw that I could never be happy without enjoying her, nor enjoy her without making her unhappy. When I began to recover, and that there was no other remains of my distemper than a great paleness in my cheeks, occasioned by the vast quantity of blood I had lost, my young masters returned from the Venetian army, the plague which infected all the Levant not suffering them to signalize their courage there any longer. Vervelle had still the same affection he ever had for me, and Saint Far did not yet show he hated me, as he has done since. I recounted to them all my adventures except my falling in love with Leonora; both expressed a great desire of being acquainted with her, which my exaggerating the merit both of the mother and the daughter increased. A man ought never to commend the person he loves before those who may love her also, since love enters at the ears as well as the eyes. This folly has often been pernicious to those who have been guilty of it, which my own experience will justify, as you shall see anon. Saint Far asked me every day when I

designed to carry him to Madame la Boissière. One day, when
he was more pressing than ordinary, I answered I could not
tell whether she would admit of his visit or not, because
she lived very retired. " Nay," replied he, " I now plainly
see you are in love with her daughter ; " and adding he
knew how to go see her without me, after a very blunt manner. I was so daunted, that he then firmly believed what
he barely suspected before. Afterward he passed a hundred silly jests upon me, and dashed me so out of countenance, that Vervelle pitied me. He took me away from
his unmannerly brother, and carried me to the boulevard,
where I was extremely melancholy, though Vervelle, out
of a kindness extraordinary in a person of his age, and so
much above me by his quality, used all possible means to
divert me. In the meantime, the ill-natured Saint Far endeavored to satisfy himself, or rather to ruin me. He went
straight to Madame la Boissière, where they took him at
first for me, because he had my landlord's servant with him,
who had often accompanied me thither ; but had it not been
for that, I believe he never had been admitted. Madame
la Boissière was very much surprised to see a man she did
not know. She told Saint Far she could not imagine upon
what score a stranger did her the honor of a visit. Saint
Far replied very humbly that he was the master of a young
fellow who was so happy as to be wounded in her service.

Having begun his compliment with an account, which,
as I was informed since, pleased neither the mother nor the
daughter, and these two ingenuous persons being unwilling
to hazard the reputation of their wit with a person who at
first dash discovered he had little, the rude impertinent was
meanly diverted by them, and they very much tired with
him. But what made him almost mad was his being denied the satisfaction of seeing Leonora's face, though he
had begged her a thousand times to lift up the veil she
commonly wore, as all unmarried ladies do at Rome. At
last this accomplished courtier, being tired with tiring of
them, rid them of his troublesome visit, and returned to
Signior Stephano's with little advantage from the ill office
he had done me. Ever since that time, as it is ordinary
with ill-natured people to hate those whom they have

injured, he despised me to that degree, and disobliged me so often, that I had a hundred times forgot the respect I owed to his quality if Vervelle, by his constant friendship and repeated kindnesses, had not made me amends for his brother's brutality. I was not yet acquainted with the ill office he had done me, though I often felt the effects of it. I found indeed, Madame la Boissière more reserved to me than when we were first acquainted; but being still as civil as before, I did not take notice of my being troublesome. As for Leonora, she appeared very thoughtful before her mother; but when not observed by her, methought she was not so melancholy, and cast on me more favorable looks than I could have expected.

Destiny was thus relating his story, and the actresses listening very attentively, without showing the least inclination to sleep, when they heard the clock strike two (in the morning). Mrs. Cave put Destiny in mind that the next day he was to accompany Monsieur la Rappinière to a house about two or three leagues out of town, where he promised to give them the diversion of hunting. This made Destiny take his leave of the players and retire to his own chamber, where in all probability he went to bed. The other players did the same, and the remaining part of the night was spent in quiet: the poet, as luck would have it, having made no new stanzas to disturb the general repose.

SOME REFLECTIONS WHICH ARE NOT AMISS. RAGOTIN'S NEW DISGRACE, AND OTHER THINGS

LOVE, which makes the young to undertake anything and the old to forget everything; love, which occasioned the wars of Troy, and many others besides, which I do not think worth while to mention here, would needs make it known in the city of Mans that he is as much to be dreaded in a pitiful inn as in the brightest palace whatsoever. He was not therefore contented with depriving the

amorous Ragotin of his appetite, but likewise inspired La
Rappinière with a thousand irregular desires, a man very
susceptible of them, and made Roquebrune likewise to
languish for the operator's wife, adding a fourth folly to his
vanity, bravery, and poetry; or rather obliging him to
commit a double infidelity; for he had made his amorous
addresses a long while before, both to Star and Angelica,
who often advised him to desist, and not throw away his
courtship. But all this is nothing to what I shall now
relate; love triumphed likewise over the insensibility and
misanthropy of Rancour, who became enamored of the
operator's wife too, and by consequence a rival to the poet
Roquebrune, a punishment for his sins, and an atonement
for the cursed writings he had published. This woman's
name was Donna Inezilla del Prado, a native of Malaga,
and her husband, or he that was reputed such, Signior
Ferdinando Ferdinandi, a gentleman of Venice, born at
Caen in Normandy. There were several others in the inn
besides the above named, who were infected with the same
disease, as dangerously, if not more than those whose
secrets I have revealed; but they shall be discovered too in
due time and place. La Rappinière fell in love with
Madam Star when she acted Climene, and intended then to
have declared his distemper to Rancour, whom he thought
capable of doing anything for money. The heavenly bard
Roquebrune designed the conquest of a Spanish lady
worthy his courage. But as for Rancour, I cannot imagine by what potent charms this foreign lady could inflame the heart of one with love, who hated all the world.
This worn-out stroller, being in hell before his time, I
mean in love before his death, was still in bed when Ragotin, troubled with his passion, as it were the bellyache,
came to desire him to mind his business and take pity on
him. Rancour assured him, that ere that day were over,
he would do him a notable piece of service with his
mistress. La Rappinière entered Rancour's chamber at the
same time, who was still dressing himself. Having taken
him aside, he confessed his infirmity to him, and vowed,
that if he could bring him into favor with Madam Star,
there was nothing in his power, but he would do for him,

even to the making him one of his assistants, and bestowing his niece in marriage on him, whom he designed to
make sole heiress after his death, because he had no children of his own.

The cheating rogue promised him yet more than he had
done Ragotin, which put this hangman's purveyor in good
hopes. Roquebrune came likewise to consult the same
oracle. He was the most incorrigible, presumptuous coxcomb that ever came from the banks of Garonne, and one
who thought everybody believed what he romanced about
his good family, riches, poetry, and valor, insomuch that
he slighted all the dry jests and bobs that Rancour perpetually cast at him, presuming that what he did was only
for conversation's sake; and besides, he understood raillery
as well as any man alive, and bore it like a Christian
philosopher, even when it touched to the very quick. He
therefore imagined he was admired by all the players, nay,
even by Rancour himself, who had experience enough to
admire but few things, and was so far from having a good
opinion of this poor brother of the quill that he made a
full inquiry into his extraction, thereby to discover whether
those bishops and great lords, his countrymen, whom he
quoted ever and anon for his relations, were the true
branches of that genealogic tree, this fool of noble alliances
and coats of arms, together with many other things, had
caused to be drawn in an old roll of parchment. He was
very sorry to find Rancour in company, though he had less
need to be troubled at that time than any one besides, it
being his ill custom to be ever whispering in people's ears,
and to make a secret of everything, sometimes of nothing.
However, he took Rancour in a corner, and at first very
gravely desired to know whether the operator's wife was a
person of a great deal of wit or not, because he had loved
women of all nations but Spaniards, and if she were worth
his labor he should not be much the poorer if he presented
her with a hundred pistoles, which he as often mentioned
upon every trifling occasion as the great family from
whence he was descended. Rancour told him he was not
so well acquainted with Donna Inezilla, as to answer for
her wit, though he had often met her husband in the

chiefest cities of the kingdom, where he sold his antidotes; but if he desired so much to be informed about it, it was but joining conversation with her, since she began to speak French tolerably well, and he might soon be satisfied. Roquebrune would needs entrust him with his pedigree in parchment, that he might dazzle the Spanish Donna with the splendor of his race; but Rancour told him his pedigree would sooner make him a Knight of Malta than a happy lover. Whereupon Roquebrune with a smiling countenance added, "Well, Sir, you know what I am."

"Yes," replied Rancour, "I know well enough what you are now, and what you will ever be, to your dying day."

The poet went away as he came, and Rancour, his rival and confidant at the same time, drew near to La Rappinière and Ragotin, who were rivals also, though unknown to each other. As for old Rancour, besides that we naturally hate any one that endeavors to rob us of what we design for ourselves, and the general quarrel he had against all mankind; besides all this, I say, he ever had a particular aversion to the poet, which this discovery was not likely to abate. Rancour therefore absolutely resolved, from that time forward, to do him all the mischief he possibly could, to which moreover his apish nature prompted him, and fitted him for it. And not to lose time, he began that very day, by basely borrowing money of him, wherewith he new clothed himself from top to toe, and besides stocked himself well with linen. He had before been a sloven all his lifetime; but love, which works far greater miracles than anything else, now made him more curious of his dress in his declining days. In a word he changed his linen oftener than became a stroller, and began to wash, powder, and color his gray hair, and likewise to trim himself so carefully, that his comrades took notice of it. The players had that day a play bespoke, as one of the chiefest citizens of Mans, who made a great treat, and gave a ball at his niece's wedding, whose guardian he had been. The nuptials were kept at a very fair country-house of his, about a league from the city; but whether eastward, westward, northward or southward, I cannot tell. The decorator belonging to

the strollers, and a carpenter were sent in the morning
early to erect a stage. The whole company of players
followed in two coaches, about eleven o'clock, that they
might get thither by dinner-time. Donna Inezilla, the
Spanish lady, made one, at the earnest entreaty of the
actresses and Rancour. Ragotin being informed of the
business, went to an inn at the end of the suburb, where
he waited the coming of the coaches, and tied a very fine
steed which he had borrowed, to the grate of the parlor
that looked into the street. He was scarce sat down to
dinner, when word was brought him, that the coach was
in sight. He flew to his horse on the wings of love, with
a great sword by his side, and a carabine dangling at his
breech like a bandoleer. He would never confess what
his fancy was, to go to a wedding with such store of
offensive and defensive weapons; neither could Rancour
his confidant ever persuade him to discover it. By that
time he had untied his horse's bridle, the coaches were so
near, that he had not time to look for a jossing-block,
that he might appear in state on his steed like pretty
Saint George. And being none of the best horsemen, and
unprepared to show his nimble disposition, he did it but
very awkwardly; for his horse's legs were as much too long,
as his were too short. However, he stoutly reared himself
in the stirrup, and threw his right leg over the saddle; but
the girths being loose, it occasioned a strange disaster; for
this made the saddle to turn round, while he was bestriding
the steed. Yet all things went hitherto well enough, but
the cursed carabine which hung on a belt about his neck
like a collar, got so unfortunately betwixt his legs before
he was aware, that his breech could not reach his saddle,
which was an old-fashioned one, the carabine lying across
from the pummel to the crupper. Thus he sat in a very
uneasy posture, as not being able with the tip of his toe so
much as to touch the stirrups. Therefore his heels being
armed with spurs, he kicked the horse's side in a place he
was never used to be pricked in, which made him to start
more briskly than was necessary for a little rider in that
posture, having nothing but the carabine to rest upon.
This made him to cling his legs close to the horse's sides,

which made the horse to fling up his hinder legs; when Ragotin following the nature of all heavy bodies, fell into the horse's neck, whereby he got a bruised nose, the steed lifting up his head suddenly at a jerk he gave him with the bridle very preposterously. Now thinking to repair his oversight, he let go the reins; but giving the horse his head, he at that very instant gave such a great leap, and cast his rider quite over the saddle upon the crupper, with the carabine still between his legs. The horse not being used to carry anything behind makes a croupade, which places Ragotin in the saddle again. The unskilled horseman clapped his heels close to his sides afresh, and then the horse flung up his hinder legs more than at first, which pitched the unfortunate Ragotin just upon the pummel, where we must leave him as on a pinnacle to rest ourselves a while; for upon the honor of a gentleman this description has cost me more pains, than all the book besides, and yet I am not well satisfied with it neither.

RAGOTIN'S FALL OFF HIS HORSE, AND SOMETHING OF THE LIKE NATURE WHICH HAPPENED TO ROQUEBRUNE

WE LEFT Ragotin planted on the pummel of a saddle, not knowing how to behave himself, and much perplexed how he should get off. I scarce believe the defunct Phaeton, of unhappy memory, was ever more troubled with his father's four fiery steeds, than was at this time our little lawyer, with this one tit, on which he nevertheless sat as quiet as a lamb. That it did not cost him his life, as it did Phaeton, he was beholden to Fortune, whose caprices would be a fit subject for me to expatiate on, were I not in conscience obliged to release Ragotin from the imminent danger he is in, having besides many more things to treat of concerning our strollers, during their residence at Mans. As soon as the disastrous Ragotin felt what an uneasy cushion he had under the two most fleshy parts of his body,

on which he used to sit, as all other rational creatures are
won't; I mean, as soon as he found how narrow his seat was,
he quitted the briddle like a man of discretion, and laid hold
of the horse's mane, who at the same time ran away full speed.
Thereupon the carabine went off. Ragotin thought he had
been shot, his horse undoubtedly believed the same, and
therefore made such a foul stumble, that the little man lost
his seat; insomuch, that for a time, he hung by the horse's
mane, with one foot entangled by his spur in the saddle-
cloth, and the other, with the rest of his body, hanging
dangling toward the earth in expectation of a fall, as soon
as his spur should break loose; together with his sword,
carabine, and bandoleer. At length his foot being disengaged, his hands let go the mane, and down he tumbled,
though with more grace and skill than he had got up. All
this happened in sight of the coaches, that stopped on purpose to see what would become of him; or rather to have
the pleasure of laughing at him. He cursed the horse, who
stood still, as soon as he had laid down his load. But to
comfort him, they took him into one of the coaches in the
poet's room, who was willing to ride, that he might flutter
about the coach, and court Inezilla, who sat in the boot.
Ragotin resigned his sword and fire-arms to him, which he
put on as dexterously as any son of Mars could have done.
He lengthened his stirrups, fitted the bridle, and without
doubt went to get up more methodically than Ragotin had
done. But surely there had some spell been cast upon that
uulucky horse that day, for the saddle being too loosely
girted, as before, turned round with the poet, as it had done
with Ragotin; and the string of his breeches breaking, the
horse ran a pretty way with him, while he had but one
foot in the stirrup, his other serving the beast as a fifth
leg whereby his back-parts became exposed to all the company, his breeches dangling all the way about his heels.
None of the spectators laughed much at Ragotin's mishap,
because they were afraid he would hurt himself, but Roquebrune's accident was attended with loud shouts and laughter
from the coaches. The coachmen stopped to laugh their
bellies full, and altogether halloaed at Roquebrune, which
drove him, having disengaged himself, into a house for

shelter, leaving the horse to his own discretion, who very wisely trotted back again to town. Ragotin, knowing he was responsible for the beast, alighted out of the coach and went after him; when the poet having cased up his posteriors, returned to the coach much troubled, and no less troublesome to the company by Ragotin's martial equipage, who had undergone this third disgrace in his mistress's presence.

A CONTINUATION WHICH PERHAPS WILL NOT BE FOUND VERY ENTERTAINING

THE players were very well received by the master of the house, who was a good, honest man, and one of the most considerable in those parts. They had two chambers allotted them to lay their clothes in and make themselves ready for the play, which was put off till after supper. They dined in private, and after dinner, those that had a mind to walk, had the choice of a grove and a fine garden to do it in. A young counselor of the Parliament of Rennes, and near kinsman to the master of the house, accosted our players, having discovered Destiny to be a person of more than vulgar judgment, and the actresses, besides their great beauty, to be such as could say more than just the parts they had learned by heart. They discoursed of matters relating to their profession, as plays, dramatic writers, etc. This young counselor said among other things, that there was scarce any remarkable subject for the stage, that had not been blown upon; that all history was almost exhausted, and that modern authors would at last be constrained to waive those nice rules of unity of time, and stretch it beyond four and twenty hours; that the generality of people did not apprehend what those severe rules of the stage were good for, being rather pleased with action and representation than recitals; and therefore such plots might be contrived as would meet with applause, without either falling into the extravagances of the Spaniards, or being tied up to the strict precepts of Aristotle.

From plays, they proceeded to talk of romances. The counselor said that nothing could be more diverting than our modern romances; that the French alone knew how to write good ones; however, that the Spaniards had a peculiar talent to compose little stories, which they called *Novelas*, which are more useful, and more probable patterns for us to follow, than those imaginary heroes of antiquity, who grow oftentimes tedious and troublesome, by being over-civil, and over-virtuous. In short, that those examples which may be imitated, are at least as beneficial as those that exceed all probability and belief; from all which he concluded, that, if a man could write as good novels in French, as those of Miguel de Cervantes, they would soon be as much in vogue as ever heroic romances have been. Roquebrune was not of the same opinion. He affirmed very positively that there could be no pleasure in reading romances unless they contained the adventures of princes, nay, and of great princes too, and that for that reason, "Astrea" only pleased him here and there.

"In what histories can one find kings and emperors enough to make new romances?" said the counselor.

"We must feign them," replied Roquebrune, "as they usually do in fabulous stories, which have no foundation in history."

"I perceive, then," returned the counselor, "that 'Don Quixote' is very little in your favor."

"It is the silliest book that ever I read," replied Roquebrune, "though it be cried up by a great many men of wit."

"Have a care," said Destiny, "it be not rather for want of wit in you, than any defect in the book, that you entertain so indifferent an opinion of it."

Roquebrune would not have failed to answer Destiny, had he but heard what he had spoken. But he was so taken up with telling his fears to some ladies, who were come near the players, that he minded him not, but promised that fair sex he would write a romance in five parts, every part to contain five volumes, which should eclipse all the Cassandras, Cleopatras, and Cyruses in the world, though this last had the surname of Great, as well as the son of Pepin. During this the counselor was telling Destiny and the actresses that he had written some novels in imitation of the Spaniards, and promised he would communicate them to them. Thereupon Inezilla told them, in a sort of French that had more of the Gascon than the Spanish in it, that her first husband had the character of a tolerable writer in the court of Spain, having composed several novels that were much esteemed ; some whereof she had in manuscript, which, in her opinion, deserved to be translated into French. The young counselor being extremely curious in such kind of compositions, told the Spanish lady she would do him a great favor in letting him have the perusal of them, which she very civilly consented to do : adding withal, that nobody was better stored with novels than herself ; for as some women in her country would sometimes attempt to write both in verse and prose, so she had made it her pastime, and could entertain them with some novels of her own making. Roquebrune confidently, according to custom, offered to turn them into French. Inezilla, who was perhaps the sharpest Spaniard that had ever come over the Pyrenees, replied, that to do as he pretended, it was not only requisite he should understand the French tongue well, but be equally acquainted with the Spanish also ; and that therefore she could not give him her novels to translate, till she was so well acquainted with the French, as to be able to judge whether he was qualified for the undertaking. Rancour, who had been silent all the while, said, there was no doubt to be made of his ability, since he had been corrector to a printing-house. He had no sooner popped out these words, but he remembered Roquebrune had lent him money, which made him pursue his jest no farther ; to which the poet, dashed out of countenance at Rancour's words, replied, that he could not deny but that he had corrected some few sheets, but then they were nothing but what he had published of his own. Madam Star, to shift the discourse, told Donna Inezilla, that since she was mistress of so many fine stories, she could not be angry if she often importuned her to relate some of them. The Spanish lady replied she was ready to give her satisfaction presently. They took her at her word, and all the company having seated themselves round her, she began a story, though not in the very same words you will find in the following chapter; yet so intelligibly, as made them guess she was mistress of a great deal of wit in Spanish, since she discovered so much in a language to whose delicacies she was a perfect stranger.

THE IMPOSTER OUTWITTED

A YOUNG lady of the city of Toledo, named Victoria, descended from the ancient family of Portocarrero, had retired to a house she had on the banks of the Tagus, about half a league distant from that city, in the absence of her brother, who was a captain of a troop of horse in the Low Countries. She became a widow at seventeen, having been wedded to an old gentleman that had got a great estate in the Indies, but who six months after his marriage, perished in a storm at sea, leaving much wealth to his wife. This fair widow after the death of her husband, kept house constantly with her brother, where she lived in such repute that at the age of twenty all the mothers proposed her for a pattern for their children, the husbands to their wives, and the lovers to their desires, as a conquest worthy their ambition. But as her retirement had cooled the love of many so, on the other hand, it increased the esteem the whole world had for her. In this country house she enjoyed at liberty all the innocent pleasures of a rural life; when one morning her shepherds brought to her a couple of men, whom they had found stripped of all their clothes, and bound safe to a tree, to which they had been tied the whole night. They had lent each of them a scurvy shepherd's coat to cover their nakedness; and in this fine equipage they appeared before the fair Victoria. So mean a habit did not hide from her the noble mien of the younger, who made her a genteel compliment, and told her he was a gentleman of Cordova, Don Lopes de Gongora by name, who traveling from Seville to Madrid about business of great importance, and having overstayed his time at play, about half a day's journey from Toledo, where he had dined the day before, the night surprised them ; and both he and his man falling asleep, expecting a mule driver who stayed behind, some thieves finding them in that condition, tied them to a tree, having first stripped them. Victoria doubted not the truth of his relation, his good mien pleading in his favor ; however thought it would be a great piece of generosity in her to relieve a stranger reduced to this sad extremity. It happened by good luck, that among the clothes her brother had left in her custody, there were some suits, for the Spaniards never part with their old clothes, though they make new ones. They chose the finest, and that which fitted best the master's shape ; and his man was also clothed with what they could find next at hand. Dinner-time being come, this stranger whom Victoria had invited to her table, appeared so accomplished, and entertained her with so much wit, that she thought the relief she had afforded him could never have been better bestowed. They conversed together the remaining part of the day, and were so much taken with each other's perfections, that neither of them slept so quietly that night as they had done before. The stranger would needs send his man to Madrid, to fetch him money, and buy him some clothes, or at least he pretended to do so ; but the fair widow would by no means suffer him, promising to lend him as much as would carry him to his journey's end. He made some overtures of love to her the very same day, and she gave him a favorable audience. In fine, in a fortnight's time, the opportunity of the place, the equal merit of these two persons, a great many oaths and vows on one side, too much frankness and credulity on the other, a promise of marriage rendered, and their reciprocal faith plighted in the presence of an old gentleman-usher and waiting-woman, made her to commit a fault she had hitherto been thought incapable of, and put this happy stranger in possession of the most beautiful lady of Toledo. For eight days together it was nothing but love and dear, fire and flames, and the like, betwixt these two lovers. But now part they must and tears will succeed. Victoria indeed had right to stay him, but the stranger pretended he lost a great deal by not going; however professed, that since he had been so happy as to win her heart, he would mind no more either his lawsuit at Madrid, or his preferment at court. Hereupon she grew impatient to have him gone; her passion it seems not having blinded her reason so much as to make her prefer the pleasure of his company to that of his advancement. She got new clothes made for him and his man at Toledo, furnished him with as much money as he desired; and so he set forward on his journey to Madrid, mounted on a good mule and his man on another. The poor lady was full of real grief at his departure, and he was no less afflicted, or at least pretended to be so, with the greatest hypocrisy in the world. The same day he took his journey the chambermaid, making his bed, found a picture-case wrapped in a letter; she carried them immediately to her mistress, who found in the case the portraiture of a most beautiful young lady, and reading the letter, it contained these words, or others to the same effect: —

" DEAR COUSIN,
    " Here inclosed I send you the picture of the beautiful Elvira de Sylva, but when you shall see her, you will be apt to confess how infinitely the resemblance falls short of the original; and how much brighter her beauty is, than that the painter could draw for her. Her father, Don Pedro de Sylva, expects you with impatience. The articles of marriage betwixt you and her are already drawn up according to your wishes, and in my opinion, very much to your advantage. All this, I hope, will be sufficient to hasten your journey. Farewell.
                    " DON ANTONIO DE RIBERA.
    " MADRID," etc.

This letter was directed to Ferdinand de Ribera at Seville. Now imagine, I beseech you, Victoria's astonishment at the reading of this epistle, which in all probability, could be written to no other than her false Lopes de Gongora. She now perceived, but too late, that this stranger, whom she had so highly and so hastily obliged, had disguised his name; and thereby was fully assured of his infidelity and treachery. The beauty of the lady in the picture made her to feel all the torments of jealousy, and the articles of marriage already drawn up, almost distracted her with despair. Never was any mortal creature more sensibly afflicted; her sighs went near to burst her heart, and she shed such a flood of tears that her head ached most intolerably. " Miserable, abandoned woman that I am," said she to herself (and sometimes would also bemoan herself before her old gentleman-usher, and waiting-woman, who had both been witnesses of her marriage) " have I thus long been so discreet and reserved to commit at last a most irreparable fault? And have I refused so many men of quality of my acquaintance, who would have thought themselves but too happy in the enjoyment of me, to throw myself away upon a stranger, who perhaps laughs at my easy credulity now he has ruined my fame, and made me forever miserable? What will they say of me at Toledo; nay, what will they say over all Spain? Can a young, base, cheating pretender, be discreet? Why did I let him know I loved him, before I was assured of the sincerity of his heart? Would he have changed his name, if he had meant to keep his flattering promises? Or can I hope, after all this, that he will not reveal his easy conquest over me? What will not my brother be provoked to do to me, for what I have done against myself? And to what purpose is he now courting glory and fame in Flanders, if I must disgrace him thus in Spain? No, no, Victoria, thou must do anything to repair this crime. But before I proceed to vengeance and desperate remedies, I must try to regain by craft what I have lost by my imprudence. It will then be time enough to have recourse to desperate methods, when all other means prove ineffectual." Victoria had, it seems, a great spirit, and presence of mind, since she could fix on so good a resolution at such a plunge. Her old gentle-man-usher, and her waiting-woman, would have both given her advice; but she told them she knew as much as they could say, and that actions and not words must now

do her business. The very same day, a couple of carts
were laden with household stuff and necessaries, Victoria
giving out among her domestics that she had pressing
occasions concerning her brother, which called her to
Court. She took coach with her squire and woman, and
hastened to Madrid, whither her goods were appointed to
follow. As soon as she arrived there, she inquired for
Don Pedro de Sylva's house, and being informed where-
abouts it was, hired one for herself in the same street.
Her gentleman-usher's name was Roderigo Santillane, who
from his youth had been bred by Victoria's father, which
made him to love his mistress as if she had been his own
sister. Having much acquaintance in Madrid, where he
had spent his youthful days, he soon discovered that Don
Pedro de Sylva's daughter was to be wedded to a gentleman of Seville named Ferdinand de Ribera, which match
had been made up by a cousin of his of the same name,
and was so near a conclusion that Don Pedro was already
providing servants for his daughter. The very next day
Roderigo Santillane, in a plain, but decent garb, Victoria in
the habit of a widow of mean condition, accompanied by
Beatrix the waiting-woman, who was to personate her
mother-in-law, and Roderigo's wife, went all together to
Don Pedro's and desired to speak with him. Don Pedro
received them very civilly, whom Roderigo acquainted
with much assurance that he was a decayed gentleman of
the mountains of Toledo, and having but one only daughter
by his first wife, which was Victoria, whose husband died
not long since at Seville, and finding his own and his
daughter's fortune very low, he had brought her to Court
to get some good service ; and moreover, having been
informed that he was about settling his daughter's family
upon her marriage, he hoped he would not take it un-
kindly that he came to proffer the young widow's service
to him, she being a person very fit to be a duenna to the
bride ; adding, his daughter's merit gave him the greater
confidence to present her to him, not doubting but that
her breeding and good qualities would procure her a little
better title to her mistress's favor than the small stock
of beauty she had to recommend her. Before I proceed

any further, I must advertise those that are unacquainted with it, that the ladies in Spain keep duennas in their houses, and that those duennas are much the same with our governantes or ladies of honor belonging to persons of quality. I must add to this, that the duennas in Spain are severe and troublesome animals, no less dreadful than a domineering mother-in-law is esteemed among us. To go on with my story, Roderigo played his part so well, and Victoria, beautiful as she was, appeared so agreeable in her modest and plain attire, and had such a promising look in her face, that Don Pedro de Sylva accepted of her immediately to govern his daughter. He proffered Roderigo and his wife an employment in his house likewise; but he excused himself, and told him he had some reasons not to accept of the honor he intended him; but having a honse in the same street, he would be ready to wait on him at any time he should command it. Thus was Victoria entertained in Don Pedro's house, infinitely beloved both by him and his daughter, and no less envied by all the other servants. Don Antonio de Ribera, who had contrived the match between his faithless cousin and Don Pedro de Sylva's daughter, came often to bring Don Pedro news that his kinsman was on his journey, and had written to him of his setting forth from Seville, and yet this cousin did not appear. This very much perplexed him, nor could Don Pedro and Elvira tell what to make of it. But still Victoria was the most concerned. However, Don Ferdinand was not able to come so soon. For the very same day he parted from Victoria, heaven had in some measure punished his treachery; for as he passed through Illescas, a fierce dog running out of a house unawares, affrighted his mule so terribly that his leg was sorely bruised against a wall, he thrown down, and his knee put out of joint, which pained him so exceedingly that he could not prosecute his journey. He was seven or eight days under the surgeons' hands, who were none of the most skillful; when his ailment growing worse and worse, he at length acquainted his cousin with his misfortune, desiring him withal to send him a horse-litter. The news of his friend's fall afflicted no less

than the knowledge of his being so nigh pleased them.
Victoria, who still loved him, was not a little disquieted.
Don Antonio sent a litter to convey Don Ferdinand to
Madrid, where, being arrived, while they were providing
clothes for him and his retinue, which was to be very magnificent, he being the eldest son of the family, and wealthy
enough, the surgeons of Madrid, more skillful than those
at Illescas, cured him perfectly well. Don Pedro de Sylva
and his daughter Elvira had notice of the day when Don
Antonio de Ribera was to bring his cousin Don Ferdinand
to them. It is probable the young Elvira did not neglect
herself upon that occasion, nor that Victoria was without
concern at this intended interview. She saw her faithless
lover enter, tricked up like a bridegroom; and if he was so
charming in a poor naked deshabille, what must he be now
in his wedding-clothes? Don Pedro was very well satisfied
with him, and his daughter must have been very nice had
she not been fully pleased. All the servants of the house
stared with all the eyes they had upon their young lady's
bridegroom, and every one of the family was overjoyed at
the match, except the poor Victoria, whose heart you may
imagine was oppressed with grief. Don Ferdinand was
charmed with Elvira's beauty, and confessed to his cousin
that she was yet more beautiful than her picture, according to what he had hinted in his letter. His first compliments displayed a great deal of wit, and he very skillfully
avoided those impertinent fooleries, and starched nonsense,
which most men are guilty of in their first addresses to a
father-in-law and a mistress. Don Pedro de Sylva locked
himself up in a closet with the two kinsmen and a lawyer,
to adjust somewhat that was left unfinished in the articles.
In the meantime Elvira stayed in her chamber, surrounded
by her women, who all expressed their joy at the good
mien and noble air of her lover. Only Victoria stood cold
and silent, while the rest were in their raptures. Elvira
observed this, therefore took her aside to tell her that she
admired she said nothing of the happy choice her father
made of a son-in-law who seemed so deserving; adding, that
either out of complaisance or civility she ought at least to
wish her joy.

"Madam," replied Victoria, "your lover's mien speaks so much to his advantage, that it were needless for me to add my commendations; the coldness you have taken notice of does not proceed from any indifference; and I were unworthy of the favors you have vouchsafed me should I not share in everything that concerns you; and therefore should be no less transported with joy at your marriage, than all the rest about you are, were I not so well acquainted with the gentleman you are about to wed. My own husband was an inhabitant of Seville, whose house was not far off from your lover's. He is, I confess, of a good family, rich, handsome, and, I believe, a man of wit. In fine, he is worthy a lady such as you are. But withal I must tell you, Madam, you desire a man's entire affection, which he cannot bestow on you, because his heart is divided. I could waive a discovery which may perhaps displease you: but I should be wanting in my duty should I not reveal all I know of Don Ferdinand in a business which so nearly concerns the happiness or unhappiness of your whole life."

Elvira was amazed at her duenna's words, and entreated her not to defer any longer the clearing of those doubts she had started.

Victoria replied it was neither to be done before her women, nor in few words. Elvira pretended she had some business of privacy in her chamber, when as soon as they were alone, Victoria told her, that Ferdinand de Ribera was in love at Seville with one Lucretia de Monsalva, a very beautiful lady, though of a very mean fortune, by whom he had three children, upon promise of marriage; and that during Ribera's father's life it was kept secret; after whose death Lucretia, having claimed his promise, he grew indifferent to her, whereupon she had left the business to the management of two gentlewomen, her relations, who had made so much noise in Seville that Don Ferdinand, through his friend's persuasion, absented himself for a while, to shun the rage of Lucretia's kindred, who sought for nothing so much as blood and revenge. "In this posture were his affairs," added she, "when I left Seville, which is about a month ago, at which time it was also reported that Don Ferdinand was going to Madrid to be married." Elvira could

not forbear asking, whether that Lucretia were a great
beauty? Victoria told her she wanted nothing but a fortune; so left her extremely pensive, and firmly resolved to
give her father instantly an account of the discovery. At
the same moment, she was called to entertain her lover, the
business for which he had retired into the closet with her
father being concluded. Elvira went to him, while Victoria
stayed in the withdrawing-room, where the same fellow
came to her that attended on him when she so generously
received them into her house near Toledo. This servant
brought a packet of letters for his master, which he had
taken up at the post-office from Seville, and not knowing
Victoria, so much her widow's weeds disguised her, he desired to be admitted to the speech of his master, to deliver
him his letters. She told him it would be a good while
before he could conveniently speak with him; but if he
durst trust her with his packet, she would be sure to give
it him as soon as she possibly could. The fellow made no
scruple in the matter, but having left the packet in her
custody, went about his business. Victoria, who was resolved to leave no stone unturned to revenge herself, goes
up to her own chamber, opens the packet, and in a moment seals it up again, together with a letter of her own,
which she had written in haste. In the meantime, the
two kinsmen made an end of their visit, and took their
leave. Elvira, espying the packet in her governante's hands,
asked what it was? Victoria coldly answered, that Don
Ferdinand's servant had left a packet of some letters with
her to deliver to his master, which she was going to send
after him, not being in the way when he went out. Elvira
said it would give them some farther light about the discovery she had made, and therefore she would open them.
This being what was desired, Victoria breaks open the
seal a second time: Elvira looked upon all the letters, and
fixing her eye upon one which seemed to be written by a
woman, addressed to Don Ferdinand de Ribera at Madrid, she
read the following lines:—

"Your absence, and the news I hear of your marriage at
Court, will soon deprive you of a person that valued you

above her own life, unless you suddenly return, and make good your promise; which you can neither defer any longer, nor deny me without a manifest indifference or breach of faith. If what I hear be true, that you regard your vows and promises so little, which you have made both to me and our children, I advise you to take care of your life; which my relations are resolved to take for your treachery, whenever your ungrateful usage shall prompt me to call upon them for my just revenge, since you enjoy it now only at my request. LUCRETIA DE MONSALVA.

"SEVILLE," etc.

Elvira having read this letter was thoroughly persuaded of the truth of what her governante had told her. Moreover she showed it to her father, who could not but admire that a gentleman of his quality could be so base as to be treacherous to a lady of equal birth with him, after he had had so many children by her. Thereupon he went to a gentleman of Seville for farther information, being a friend of his, and one that had before given him an account of Ferdinand's wealth and circumstances. He was scarce gone out of doors, when Don Ferdinand came to inquire for his packet, attended by his servant, who told him that his mistress's governante had promised to deliver it into his hands. He found Elvira alone in the parlor, and told her that though the engagement which was between her and him might excuse two visits in one day, yet he now only came for the letters his man had told him he had left with her duenna. Elvira freely told him that she had taken them from her, and had had the curiosity to break them open; not doubting but a man of his years had some amorous engagements in so great a city as Seville; and though her curiosity afforded her but little satisfaction, yet had she met with this caution in recompense; that it was dangerous for people to be married together before they were thoroughly acquainted; adding, she would not debar him any longer of the pleasure of perusing his letters; and therefore immediately restored him his packet, together with the counterfeit letter: and after making him a slight curtesy, left him without waiting for his answer. Don

6

Ferdinand was strangely surprised at his mistress's discourse. He perused the supposed letter, and quickly perceived it was a trick to hinder his marriage. He addressed himself to Victoria, who remained in the outward room, and told her, without taking much notice of her face, that either some rival or malicious person had contrived that letter to abuse him.

"I a wife in Seville!" cried he with amazement: "I children! If this be not the most impudent imposture that ever was set on foot, I'll forfeit my head!"

Victoria told him he might possibly be innocent; however, Elvira in common discretion could do no less than make a farther inquiry into the truth; and that therefore the marriage would certainly be put off till her father, Don Pedro, could be convinced by a gentleman of Seville, a friend of his (whom he was then gone to seek on purpose), that this was only a pretended intrigue.

"With all my heart," answered he; "and if there be but a lady of the name of Lucretia de Monsalva in all Seville, let me forfeit the honor and reputation of a gentleman. And let me entreat you," added he, "to let me know, if you are so far in your lady's favor as I suppose you to be, that I may bespeak your good offices on this occasion."

"Truly," answered Victoria, "I believe, without vanity, that she will not do a thing upon anybody's account that she has refused to do on mine. But withal I know her humor to be such that she is not easily appeased when she thinks herself disobliged. And as all the hopes of mending my fortune depend on the kindness she has for me, I shall never offer to contradict her out of complaisance to you, nor hazard her displeasure by endeavoring to work her out of the ill opinion she has of your sincerity. I am but poor," added she, "and not to get anything were to lose a great deal. If what she has promised to give me in case I marry a second time should fail, I might live a widow all the rest of my days, though I am yet young enough and not so deformed but that somebody or other may like me. But it is an old saying, and a true one, that without money ——— "

She was thus going on with a true governante's tedious tale — for to act her part to the life she must talk a great deal — when Don Ferdinand, interrupting her, said : " Do me but one piece of service I shall require of you, and I will put you above the hopes of your mistress's reward. And," added he, "to convince you that my promises are not empty words, give me but pen, ink, and paper, and you shall immediately have what you will under my hand."

" Jesu ! Signior," said the feigned governante, " a gentleman's word is as good as his bond, but to obey you, I will fetch you what you desire." She returned again with materials enough to have drawn a bond for a million of gold, and Don Ferdinand was so gallant, or at least had such a month's mind to Elvira, that he signed her a blank, leaving her to fill it up as she pleased, thereby to engage her to serve him with the greater zeal. This raised Victoria up to the clouds. She promised wonders to Don Ferdinand, and moreover told him she wished herself the unhappiest of all her sex if she did not act in this business as if she herself had been a party concerned. In this she spoke a great truth. Don Ferdinand left her full of hopes ; and Roderigo Santillane, who went for her father, being come to visit her, to learn how her intrigue advanced, she gave him an account of all, and showed him the blank paper subscribed ; for which he with her gave thanks to heaven, finding now that all things seemed to contribute to her happiness. To lose no time, he went home to the house that Victoria had hired not far from Don Pedro's, as I have before related, where he filled up the blank Don Ferdinand had given, with a promise of marriage attested by witnesses, and dated about the same time that Victoria received this faithless man into her country-house. He was as skillful a penman as any in Spain, and had studied Don Ferdinand's hand so exactly well in a copy of verses of his own writing, that even Don Ferdinand himself would have been mistaken in the forgery, and thought it to have been his own hand. Don Pedro de Sylva could not meet with the gentleman he sought to be informed by about Don Ferdinand's amours, therefore left a note for him, and so came back to his house ; where

that same night Elvira unbosomed her secrets to her governante, and vowed she would sooner disobey her father
than ever marry Don Ferdinand, confessing withal that she
had been pre-engaged to one Don Diego de Maradas a long
while before, and had in all reason complied enough with
her father's commands and her own duty, by putting a
constraint on her inclinations, to satisfy him ; but since
heaven had ordered it so that Ferdinand's treachery was discovered, she thought, by refusing him, she obeyed the divine
pleasure, which seemed to allot her another husband. You
may imagine Victoria fortified Elvira in these good resolutions,
and spoke quite contrary to Don Ferdinand's expectations.

"Don Diego de Maradas," said then Elvira to her, "is
much dissatisfied with me for having paid this obedience to
my father ; but the least inviting look from me will however be sure to bring him back, were he at as great a
distance from me as Don Ferdinand is from his Lucretia."

"Write to him, madam," quoth Victoria, "and I will
willingly be your messenger."

Elvira was overjoyed to find her governante so favorable
to her designs ; she commanded the coach to be made
ready for Victoria, who immediately went away with a
billet-doux for Don Diego, and being alighted at her father
Santillane's, sent the coach back again, telling the coachman she would walk the rest of the way whither she
designed to go. Honest Santillane showed her the promise
of marriage he had drawn up, whereupon she immediately
wrote two little notes, one to Don Diego de Maradas, the
other to Don Pedro de Sylva, her lady's father, wherein
she entreated both of them to repair to her house about
business, with the direction where she dwelt, and subscribed herself Victoria Portocarrero. While these notes
were carrying, Victoria strips off her black weeds, puts on
very rich clothes, pulls out her locks (which I have been
told were of the finest colored hair that could be), and
dressed her head as nicely as if she had been going to
Court. Don Diego de Maradas came a while after, to
know what concern a lady to whom he was a perfect
stranger could have with him. She received him very
civilly, and they were scarce set down, when it was told

her that Don Pedro de Sylva was come likewise to wait upon her. She entreated Don Diego to conceal himself in her alcove, assuring him it concerned him very much to hear the discourse she should have with Don Pedro. He easily complied with the desire of a lady of so much beauty and so good a mien, and Don Pedro was admitted into Victoria's chamber, not knowing her, so much had her headdress and rich attire changed her face and heightened her majestic air. She desired him to place himself in a chair, whence Don Diego might easily hear all they said, and then she began in these words : —

"I think, sir, I ought in the first place to inform you who I am, because in all probability you are impatient to know it. I am of the family of the Portocarreros, born in the city of Toledo, where I was married at the age of sixteen, and became a widow about six months after. My father was a knight of the order of St. Jago, and my brother of the order of Callatrava."

Don Pedro interrupted her, to let her know her father was his intimate friend.

"What you tell me rejoices me extremely," answered Victoria, "for I shall have occasion for a great many friends in the affair I design to acquaint you with." After this she informed Don Pedro of all that passed between her and Don Ferdinand, and put into his hands the promise of marriage counterfeited by Santillane. He had no sooner read it, but she went on thus : "You know, sir, what honor obliges persons of my quality to do in these cases ; for though justice should be partially denied me, yet have my friends power and credit enough to prosecute my interest to the highest. I thought, sir, it became me to let you know my pretensions, that you might put a stop to that match you had designed for your daughter. She deserves better than to be thrown away upon a faithless man ; and I believe you are more discreet than to procure her a husband whom another has a right to dispute with her."

"Were he a grandee of Spain," replied Don Pedro, " I would have nothing to do with him if he were unjust and false as you say he is. I shall therefore not only refuse him my daughter, but likewise forbid him my house. As for yourself, madam," continued he, "both my friends and interest are at your service. I had notice given me before, that he was a man that pursued his pleasure even to the hazard of his reputation; and being of that temper, though you had no title to him, yet should he never have my daughter, who, I hope in God, shall not want a husband in the Court of Spain."

Don Pedro took his leave of Victoria, perceiving she had no more to say to him; and then she called Don Diego out of the alcove, where he had overheard all the conversation she had with her mistress's father. This spared her the labor of repeating her story to him. She delivered Elvira's letter to him, which transported him with joy; and lest he should be in pain to know how she came by it, she intrusted him with her metamorphosis into a duenna, knowing he was as much concerned as herself to keep it secret. Don Diego, before he left Victoria, wrote an answer to his mistress's letter, wherein the infinite joy he expressed for his revived hopes plainly discovered the real affliction he had been in ever since he thought them quite lost. He parted from the fair widow, who presently put on her governante's habit, and returned to Don Pedro's.

In the interim Don Ferdinand de Ribera was come to wait on his mistress, and had taken his cousin Don Antonio along with him to endeavor to set all to rights again, which had been charged against him by Victoria's feigned letter. Don Pedro found them with his daughter, who knew not what to answer when they both desired no better justification than only a due inquiry whether there ever were in Seville such a lady as Lucretia de Monsalva. They renewed the same plea to Don Pedro to clear Don Ferdinand; to which he answered that if that engagement with the lady of Seville was a supposition, it was so much the easier to be cleared; but that he came from a lady of Toledo, named Victoria Portocarrero, to whom Don Ferdinand had promised marriage, and to whom he was still more engaged by having been so generously assisted by her when a mere stranger to her; which he could not deny, since she had under his hand and seal a promise of marriage; adding withal, that a person of honor ought not

to court a wife at Madrid, while he had one already at
Toledo. At these words he showed the two cousins the
promise of marriage in due form. Don Antonio knew his
cousin's writing, and Don Ferdinand, mistaking it, though
he were confident he had never given any such, yet was
quite confounded at the sight of it. The father and
daughter withdrew, after they had coldly bid them farewell. Don Antonio quarreled with his cousin for employ-
ing him in this treaty when he had another on foot
before. They took coach together, where Don Antonio,
having made him confess his unhandsome proceeding with
Victoria, reproached him a thousand times with the
heinousness of the fact, and withal represented to him the
evil consequence that was like to attend it. He told him
he must not think of getting a wife either at Madrid or in
any part of Spain after this rate; and that he were happy
if he could get off by marrying Victoria without forfeiting
his life with his honor, Victoria's brother being a person
not used to put up so foul affronts without full satisfaction. It was Don Ferdinand's part to be silent, while his
cousin continued his reproaches. His conscience sufficiently
accused him of treachery and falsehood to a lady that had
so highly obliged him; but this promise of marriage however almost distracted him, not knowing by what strange
enchantment they had made him to grant it. Victoria,
being come back to Don Pedro's in her widow's weeds,
delivered Don Diego's letter to Elvira, who told her how
the two kinsmen had been there to justify themselves; but
that Don Ferdinand had been charged with other-guess prac-
tices than his amour with the lady of Seville. She afterward
related what Victoria knew better than herself, though she
pretended to admire at and detest Don Ferdinand's baseness.

The same day Elvira was invited to a play at one of her
relations. Victoria, whose thoughts still ran upon her own
affairs, hoped, if Elvira would follow her counsel, that this
play might prove favorable to her design. She told her
young lady that, if she had a mind to meet her lover, Don
Diego, there was nothing more easy, her father's house
being the most convenient that could be; and that,
since the play was not to begin till midnight, she might

go out a little earlier, and have time enough to speak
with Don Diego, and after go to her relation's. Elvira,
who really loved Don Diego, and had consented to marry
Don Ferdinand merely out of respect to her father's commands, showed no reluctance to do what Victoria had pro-
pounded. They therefore took coach as soon as ever Don
Pedro was gone to bed, and went to Victoria's house.
Santillane, as master of the family, and Beatrix, who personated the mother-in-law, welcomed them very kindly.
Elvira wrote a *billet* to Don Diego, which was delivered
immediately; while Victoria despatched another privately
to Don Ferdinand in Elvira's name, to let him know
it was in his power to complete the match, on which
his extraordinary merit engaged her to adventure, as
not desiring to make herself unhappy forever by losing
him, only to please a father's crabbed suspicious humor. In the same note she gave him such particular
directions how to find the house, that it was impossible
he should miss it. This note was carried a little while
after that other from Elvira to Don Diego. Victoria wrote
a third likewise, which Santillane carried himself to Don
Pedro de Sylva, by which she informed him, as a trusty
governante, that his daughter, instead of going to the play,
would needs stop at her father's house, and had sent for
Don Ferdinand to consummate her nuptials with him;
which she believing to be contrary to his consent, thought
herself obliged to give him notice of it, to the end he might
be sensible he was not at all mistaken in the good opinion
he had entertained of her honesty, when he chose her for
his daughter's governante. Santillane likewise told Don
Pedro that his daughter had charged him not to come
thither by any means without bringing an alguazil with
him, which is an officer much like to a commissary in Paris.
Don Pedro, then being in bed, hastened to put on his clothes
in a great passion. But while he is dressing, and sending
for a commissary, let us go back and see what they are
doing at Victoria's. By good fortune the notes came safe
to the brace of lovers' hands. Don Diego, who had received
his first, came first to the assignation. Victoria met him at
the door, and conducted him into a chamber, where she

left him with Elvira. I will not trouble you with the relation
of all the endearments that passed betwixt these two young
lovers ; and if I would, Don Ferdinand's knocking at the
door will not give me time to do it. Victoria lets him in
herself, after having magnified the great service she had
done him on this occasion ; for which the amorous spark
returned her a thousand thanks, promising he would yet do
more for her than all his former promises engaged him to.
She leads him into a chamber, where she desired him to
stay a while for Elvira, who was coming, and so locked
him in without light, telling him his mistress would needs
have it so, but that it would not be long before he should
be visible again ; adding that a young lady's modesty would
not suffer her to bear, without blushing, the sight of a
man for whom she had committed so bold an action. This
done, Victoria, with all the haste she could, attired herself
as well and as nicely as the short time would permit. She
goes into the chamber where Don Ferdinand was, who had
not the least suspicion but that she was Elvira, being no
less young than she, and having such perfumes about her,
according to the Spanish fashion, as would have made a
chambermaid pass for a woman of quality.

In this interim Don Pedro, the alguazil, and Santillane
arrive. They enter the chamber where Elvira was in private
with her lover ; at which they both were not a little surprised. Don Pedro, blinded by the first transports of his
passion, was ready to run the person through whom he
took for Don Ferdinand. The commissary, discovering it
was not he, but Don Diego, held his arm, bidding him to
have a care what he did, since it was not Don Ferdinand
de Ribera that was with his daughter, but Don Diego de
Maradas, a person of no less quality and riches. Don Pedro
at this behaved himself like a discreet gentleman, and raised
his daughter, who had cast herself at his feet. He wisely considered that if he should cross her inclination by opposing this
match, he would create both her and himself a great deal of
trouble ; and besides could not pitch upon a better son-in-
law, though he had the choosing of one himself. Santillane
desired Don Pedro, the alguazil, and all that were with
them in the room, to follow him, when he led them to

the chamber where Don Ferdinand was shut up with Victoria. They commanded the door to be opened in the King's name. Don Ferdinand letting them in, and seeing DonPedro, attended by the commissary, told them, with a great deal of confidence, that he was with his wife Elvira de Sylva. Don Pedro answered he was mistaken, his daughter being married to another ; " and as for you," added he, " you cannot deny but that Victoria Portocarrero is your lawful wife." Victoria then discovered herself to her faithless gallant, who remained full of confusion. She expostulated his ingratitude with him, to whom his silence was his only plea, as well as to the commissary, who told him he could do no less than carry him to prison. In short, his remorse of conscience, and fear of imprisonment, together with Don Pedro's exhortations, who minded him of his honor and reputation, joined to Victoria's tears and beauty, nothing inferior to that of Elvira, and, above all the rest, some sparks of generosity still remaining in his heart, notwithstanding his debaucheries and youthful follies, made him at length, with reason and justice, to yield to Victoria's bright charms. He tenderly embraced her, she being likely to swoon in his arms, which no doubt but his warm kisses preserved her from. Don Pedro, Don Diego, and fair Elvira shared in Victoria's happiness, and Santillane and Beatrix were ready to die for joy. Don Pedro very much commended Don Ferdinand for thus nobly repairing the wrongs he had committed. The two young ladies embraced each other with as great testimonies of love as if they had hugged their own husbands. Don Diego de Maradas made a thousand protestations of his obedience to his father-in-law, or he that should be so in a short time. Don Pedro, before he went home with his daughter, made them to promise that they would all come and dine the next day at his house, where for fifteen days together he endeavored, by solemn rejoicings, to dispel the thoughts of their past troubles. The alguazil was invited too, who promised to be there. Don Pedro took him along with him ; and Don Ferdinand remained with Victoria, who now had as much reason to bless her good fortune, as she formerly had to curse her evil.

SENTIMENT

VOLNEY

THE RUINS OF EMPIRES

SENTIMENT

COUNT VOLNEY

VOLNEY'S work, here represented, is a thoroughly French inspiration, peculiarly illustrative of the tone and temper of the later eighteenth century thought, and of the affected style of the day. Behind its sounding periods there is nobility of conception and great power of expression. The author was a man of mark in more ways than one.

Constantin François Chasseboeuf Volney, born in 1757, was able to spend several early years in Egypt and Syria, where his studies qualified him for the writing of scholarly books and for active work as a member of the States-General. "The Ruins of Empires" appeared in 1791. The writer finds himself among the ruins of Palmyra, which move him to ponder the rise of nations to greatness and the causes of their decadence and extinction. Biased though he was by the dominant cast of philosophic thought of his time, there is a loftiness of view and utterance in his meditations that cannot but impress the reader with admiration and respect. The theme is as fascinating now as ever and the moral awaits consideration by the wisest in the nations.

Volney tried the experiment of developing trade in colonial products, buying an estate in Corsica for that purpose. His zeal for political reforms landed him in prison, where he spent ten months during the reign of terror. Later he became professor of history in the École Normale, and published his lectures, which had conspicuous merit and courage. Then he visited the United States, the only printed outcome being a work on the soil and climate.

(93)

As a scholar, rather than for his political eminence, Napoleon made Volney a count and senator. Later honors came to him in being made a member of the Institute and Academy and a peer of France. He died in 1825, leaving a fund to insure the publication of his philosophical essays, in which he urged the promotion of the study of Oriental languages as the surest means of bringing the nations into closer, if not fraternal, relations.

THE RUINS OF EMPIRES

THE JOURNEY

IN THE eleventh year of the reign of Abd-ul-Hamid, son of Ahmid, emperor of the Turks; when the Nogais-Tartars were driven from the Crimea, and a Mussulman prince of the blood of Gengis-Kahn became the vassal and guard of a Christian woman and queen, I was traveling in the Ottoman dominions, and through those provinces which were anciently the kingdoms of Egypt and Syria.

My whole attention bent on whatever concerns the happiness of man in a social state, I visited cities, and studied the manners of their inhabitants; entered palaces, and observed the conduct of those who govern; wandered over fields, and examined the condition of those who cultivated them: and nowhere perceiving aught but robbery and devastation, tyranny, and wretchedness, my heart was oppressed with sorrow and indignation.

I saw daily on my road fields abandoned, villages deserted, and cities in ruin. Often I met with ancient monuments, wrecks of temples, palaces and fortresses, columns, aqueducts, and tombs. This spectacle led me to meditate on times past, and filled my mind with contemplations the most serious and profound.

Arrived at the city of Hems, on the border of the Orontes, and being in the neighborhood of Palmyra of the desert, I resolved to visit its celebrated ruins. After three days journeying through arid deserts, having traversed the Valley of Caves and Sepulchres, on issuing into the plain,

I was suddenly struck with a scene of the most stupendous ruins — a countless multitude of superb columns, stretching in avenues beyond the reach of sight. Among them
were magnificent edifices, some entire, others in ruins ; the
earth every where strewed with fragments of cornices, capitals, shafts, entablatures, pilasters, all of white marble, and
of the most exquisite workmanship. After a walk of three-
quarters of an hour along these ruins, I entered the enclosure of a vast edifice, formerly a temple dedicated to the
Sun ; and accepting the hospitality of some poor Arabian
peasants, who had built their hovels on the area of the
temple, I determined to devote some days to contemplate at
leisure the beauty of these stupendous ruins.

Daily I visited the monuments which covered the plain ;
and one evening, absorbed in reflection, I had advanced to
the Valley of Sepulchres. I ascended the heights which
surround it from whence the eye commands the whole
group of ruins and the immensity of the desert. The sun
had sunk below the horizon : a red border of light still
marked his track behind the distant mountains of Syria ;
the full-orbed moon was rising in the east, on a blue
ground, over the plains of the Euphrates ; the sky was
clear, the air calm and serene ; the dying lamp of day still
softened the horrors of approaching darkness : the refresh-
ing night breezes attempered the sultry emanations from
the heated earth ; the herdsmen had given their camels to
repose, the eye perceived no motion on the dusky and uniform plain ; profound silence rested on the desert ; the
howlings only of the jackal, and the solemn notes of the
bird of night, were heard at distant intervals. Darkness
now increased, and through the dusk could only be discerned the pale phantasms of columns and walls. The solitude of the place, the tranquillity of the hour, the majesty
of the scene, impressed on my mind a religious pensiveness.
The aspect of a great city deserted, the memory of times
past, compared with its present state, all elevated my mind
to high contemplations. I sat on the shaft of a column,
my elbow reposing on my knee, and head reclining on my
hand, my eyes fixed, sometimes on the desert, sometimes
on the ruins, and fell into a profound reverie.

THE REVERIE

H ERE, said I, once flourished an opulent city; here was the seat of a powerful empire. Yes! these places now so wild and desolate, were once animated by a living multitude; a busy crowd thronged in these streets, now so solitary. Within these walls, where now reigns the silence of death, the noise of the arts, and the shouts of joy and festivity incessantly resounded; these piles of marble were regular palaces; these fallen columns adorned the majesty of temples; these ruined galleries surrounded public places. Here assembled a numerous people for the sacred duties of their religion, and the anxious cares of their subsistence; here industry, parent of enjoyments, collected the riches of all climes, and the purple of Tyre was exchanged for the precious thread of Serica; the soft tissues of Cassimere for the sumptuous tapestry of Lydia; the amber of the Baltic for the pearls and perfumes of Arabia; the gold of Ophir for the tin of Thule.

And now behold what remains of this powerful city: a miserable skeleton! What of its vast domination: a doubtful and obscure remembrance! To the noisy concourse which thronged under these porticoes, succeeds the solitude of death. The silence of the grave is substituted for the busy hum of public places; the affluence of a commercial city is changed into wretched poverty; the palaces of kings have become a den of wild beasts; flocks repose in the area of temples, and savage reptiles inhabit the sanctuary of the gods. Ah! how has so much glory been eclipsed? how have so many labors been annihilated? Do thus perish then the works of men — thus vanish empires and nations?

And the history of former times revived in my mind; I remembered those ancient ages when many illustrious nations inhabited these countries; I figured to myself the Assyrian on the banks of the Tigris, the Chaldean on the banks of the Euphrates, the Persian reigning from the Indus to the Mediterranean. I enumerated the kingdoms of Damascus and Idumea, of Jerusalem and Samaria, the warlike states of the Philistines, and the commercial republics of Phœnicia. This Syria, said I, now so depopulated, then contained a hundred flourishing cities, and abounded with towns, villages, and hamlets. In all parts were seen cultivated fields, frequented roads, and crowded habitations. Ah! whither have flown those ages of life and abundance? —whither vanished those brilliant creations of human industry? Where are those ramparts of Nineveh, those walls of Babylon, those palaces of Persepolis, those temples of Balbec and of Jerusalem? Where are those fleets of Tyre, those dock-yards of Arad, those work-shops of Sidon, and that multitude of sailors, of pilots, of merchants, and of soldiers? Where those husbandmen, harvests, flocks, and all the creation of living beings in which the face of the earth rejoiced? Alas! I have passed over this desolate land! I have visited the palaces, once the scene of so much splendor, and I beheld nothing but solitude and desolation. I sought the ancient inhabitants and their works, and found nothing but a trace, like the foot-prints of a traveler over the sand. The temples are fallen, the palaces overthrown, the ports filled up, the cities destroyed; and the earth, stripped of inhabitants, has become a place of sepulchres. Great God! whence proceed such fatal revolutions? What causes have so changed the fortunes of these countries? Wherefore are so many cities destroyed? Why has not this ancient population been reproduced and perpetuated?

Thus absorbed in meditation, a crowd of new reflections continually poured in upon my mind. Every thing, continued I, bewilders my judgment, and fills my heart with trouble and uncertainty. When these countries enjoyed what constitutes the glory and happiness of man, they were inhabited by infidel nations: It was the Phœnician, offering human sacrifices to Moloch, who gathered into his stores the riches of all climates; it was the Chaldean, prostrate before his serpent-god, who subjugated opulent cities, laid waste the palaces of kings, and despoiled the temples of the gods; it was the Persian, worshiper of fire, who received the tribute of a hundred nations; they were the inhabitants of this very city, adorers of the sun and stars, who erected so many monuments of prosperity and luxury.

Numerous herds, fertile fields, abundant harvests — whatsoever should be the reward of piety — was in the hands of these idolaters. And now, when a people of saints and believers occupy these fields, all is become sterility and solitude. The earth, under these holy hands, produces only thorns and briers. Man soweth in anguish, and reapeth tears and cares. War, famine, pestilence, assail him by turns. And yet, are not these the children of the prophets? The Mussulman, Christian, Jew, are they not the elect children of God, loaded with favors and miracles? Why, then, do these privileged races no longer enjoy the same advantages? Why are these fields, sanctified by the blood of martyrs, deprived of their ancient fertility? Why have those blessings been banished hence, and transferred for so many ages to other nations and different climes?

At these words, revolving in my mind the vicissitudes which have transmitted the sceptre of the world to people so different in religion and manners from those in ancient Asia to the most recent of Europe, this name of a natal land revived in me the sentiment of my country; and turning my eyes toward France, I began to reflect on the situation in which I had left her in 1782.

I recalled her fields so richly cultivated, her roads so admirably constructed, her cities inhabited by a countless people, her fleets spread over every sea, her ports filled with the produce of both the Indies: and then comparing the activity of her commerce, the extent of her navigation, the magnificence of her buildings, the arts and industry of her inhabitants, with what Egypt and Syria had once possessed, I was gratified to find in modern Europe the departed splendor of Asia; but the charm of my reverie was soon dissolved by a last term of comparison. Reflecting that such had once been the activity of the places I was then contemplating, who knows, said I, but such may one day be the abandonment of our countries? Who knows if on the banks of the Seine, the Thames, the Zuyder-Zee, where now, in the tumult of so many enjoyments, the heart and the eye suffice not for the multitude of sensations, — who knows if some traveler, like myself, shall not one day sit on their silent ruins, and weep in solitude over the ashes of their inhabitants, and the memory of their former greatness.

At these words, my eyes filled with tears : and covering my head with the fold of my mantle, I sank into gloomy meditations on all human affairs. Ah ! hapless man, said I in my grief, a blind fatality sports with thy destiny ! A fatal necessity rules with the hand of chance the lot of mortals ! But no : it is the justice of heaven fulfilling its decrees ! — a God of mystery exercising his incomprehensible judgments ! Doubtless he has pronounced a secret anathema against this land : blasting with maledictions the present, for the sins of past generations. Oh ! who shall dare to fathom the depths of the Omnipotent ?

And sunk in profound melancholy, I remained motionless.

SOURCES OF THE EVILS OF SOCIETY

IN TRUTH, scarcely were the faculties of men developed, when, inveigled by objects which gratify the senses, they gave themselves up to unbridled desires. The sweet sensations which nature had attached to their real wants, to endear to them their existence, no longer satisfied them. Not content with the abundance offered by the earth or produced by industry, they wished to accumulate enjoyments, and coveted those possessed by their fellow men. The strong man rose up against the feeble to take from him the fruit of his labor ; the feeble invoked another feeble one to repel the violence. Two strong ones then said :—

" Why fatigue ourselves to produce enjoyments which we may find in the hands of the weak? Let us join and despoil them ; they shall labor for us, and we will enjoy without labor."

And the strong associating for oppression, and the weak for resistance, men mutually afflicted each other ; and a general and fatal discord spread over the earth, in which the passions, assuming a thousand new forms, have generated a continued chain of misfortunes.

Thus the same self-love which, moderate and prudent, was a principle of happiness and perfection, becoming blind and disordered, was transformed into a corrupting poison; and cupidity, offspring and companion of ignorance, became the cause of all the evils that have desolated the earth.

Yes, ignorance and cupidity! these are the twin sources of all the torments of man! Biased by these into false ideas of happiness, he has mistaken or broken the laws of nature in his own relation with external objects; and injuring his own existence, has violated individual morality; shutting through these his heart to compassion, and his mind to justice, he has injured and afflicted his equal, and violated social morality. From ignorance and cupidity, man has armed against man, family against family, tribe against tribe; and the earth is become a theatre of blood, of discord, and of rapine. By ignorance and cupidity, a secret war, fermenting in the bosom of every state, has separated citizen from citizen; and the same society has divided itself into oppressors and oppressed, into masters and slaves; by these, the heads of a nation, sometimes insolent and audacious, have forged its chains within its own bowels; and mercenary avarice has founded political despotism. Sometimes, hypocritical and cunning, they have called from heaven a lying power, and a sacrilegious yoke; and credulous cupidity has founded religious despotism. By these have been perverted the ideas of good and evil, just and unjust, vice and virtue; and nations have wandered in a labyrinth of errors and calamities.

The cupidity of man and his ignorance,—these are the evil genii which have wasted the earth! These are the decrees of fate which have overthrown empires! These are the celestial anathemas which have smitten these walls once so glorious, and converted the splendor of a populous city into a solitude of mourning and of ruins! But as in the bosom of man has sprung all the evils which have afflicted his life, there he also is to seek and to find their remedies.

ORIGIN OF GOVERNMENT AND LAWS

IN FACT, it soon happened that men, fatigued with the evils they reciprocally inflicted, began to sigh for peace; and reflecting on their misfortunes and the causes of them, they said : —

"We are mutually injuring each other by our passions; and, aiming to grasp every thing, we hold nothing. What one seizes to-day, another takes to-morrow, and our cupidity reacts upon ourselves. Let us establish judges, who shall arbitrate our rights, and settle our differences. When the strong shall rise against the weak, the judge shall restrain him, and dispose of our force to suppress violence; and the life and property of each shall be under the guarantee and protection of all; and all shall enjoy the good things of nature."

Conventions were thus formed in society, sometimes express, sometimes tacit, which became the rule for the action of individuals, the measure of their rights, the law of their reciprocal relations; and persons were appointed to superintend their observance, to whom the people confided the balance to weigh rights, and the sword to punish transgressions.

Thus was established among individuals a happy equilibrium of force and action, which constituted the common security. The name of equity and of justice was recognized and revered over the earth; every one, assured of enjoying in peace, the fruits of his toil, pursued with energy the objects of his attention; and industry, excited and maintained by the reality or the hope of enjoyment, developed all the riches of art and of nature. The fields were covered with harvests, the valleys with flocks, the hills with fruits, the sea with vessels, and man became happy and powerful on the earth. Thus did his own wisdom repair the disorder which his imprudence had occasioned; and that wisdom was only the effect of his own organization. He respected the enjoyments of others in order to secure his own; and cupidity found its corrective in the enlightened love of self.

Thus the love of self, the moving principle of every individual, becomes the necessary foundation of every association; and on the observance of that law of our nature has depended the fate of nations. Have the factitious and conventional laws tended to that object and accomplished that aim? Every one, urged by a powerful instinct, has displayed all the faculties of his being; and the sum of individual felicities has constituted the general felicity. Have these laws, on the contrary, restrained the effort of man toward his own happiness? His heart, deprived of its exciting principle, has languished in inactivity, and from the oppression of individuals has resulted the weakness of the state.

As self-love, impetuous and improvident, is ever urging man against his equal, and consequently tends to dissolve society, the art of legislation and the merit of administrators consists in attempering the conflict of individual cupidities, in maintaining an equilibrium of powers, and securing to every one his happiness, in order that, in the shock of society against society, all the members may have a common interest in the preservation and defense of the public welfare.

The internal splendor and prosperity of empires then, have had for their efficient cause the equity of their laws and government; and their respective external powers have been in proportion to the number of persons interested, and their degree of interest in the public welfare.

On the other hand, the multiplication of men, by complicating their relations, having rendered the precise limitation of their rights difficult, the perpetual play of the passions having produced incidents not foreseen — their conventions having been vicious, inadequate, or nugatory — in fine, the authors of the laws having sometimes mistaken, sometimes disguised their objects; and their ministers, instead of restraining the cupidity of others, having given themselves up to their own; all these causes have introduced disorder and trouble into societies; and the viciousness of laws and the injustice of governments, flowing from cupidity and ignorance, have become the causes of the misfortunes of nations, and the subversion of states.

GENERAL CAUSES OF THE PROSPERITY OF ANCIENT STATES

SUCH, O man who seekest wisdom, such have been the causes of revolution in the ancient states of which thou contemplatest the ruins! To whatever spot I direct my view, to whatever period my thoughts recur, the same principles of growth or destruction, of rise or fall, present themselves to my mind. Wherever a people is powerful, or an empire prosperous, there the conventional laws are conformable with the laws of nature — the government there procures for its citizens a free use of their faculties, equal security for their persons and property. If, on the contrary, an empire goes to ruin, or dissolves, it is because its laws have been vicious, or imperfect, or trodden under foot by a corrupt government. If the laws and government, at first wise and just, become afterward depraved, it is because the alternation of good and evil is inherent to the heart of man, to a change in his propensities, to his progress in knowledge, to a combination of circumstances and events; as is proved by the history of the species.

In the infancy of nations, when men yet lived in the forest, subject to the same wants, endowed with the same faculties, all were nearly equal in strength; and that equality was a circumstance highly advantageous in the composition of society: as every individual, thus feeling himself sufficiently independent of every other, no one was the slave, none thought of being the master of another. Man, then a novice, knew neither servitude nor tyranny; furnished with resources sufficient for his existence, he thought not of borrowing from others; owning nothing, requiring nothing, he judged the rights of others by his own, and formed ideas of justice sufficiently exact. Ignorant, moreover, in the art of enjoyments, unable to produce more than his necessaries, possessing nothing superfluous, cupidity remained dormant; or if excited, man, attacked in his real wants, resisted it with energy, and the foresight of such resistance ensured a happy balance.

Thus original equality, in default of compact, maintained freedom of person, security of property, good manners, and order. Every one labored by himself and for himself; and the mind of man, being occupied, wandered not to culpable desires. He had few enjoyments, but his wants were satisfied; and as indulgent nature had made them less than his resources, the labor of his hands soon produced abundance — abundance, population; the arts unfolded, culture extended, and the earth, covered with numerous inhabitants, was divided into different dominions.

The relations of man becoming complicated, the internal order of societies became more difficult to maintain. Time and industry having generated riches, cupidity became more active; and because equality, practicable among individuals, could not subsist among families, the natural equilibrium was broken; it became necessary to supply it by a factitious equilibrium; to set up chiefs, to establish laws; and in the primitive inexperience, it necessarily happened that these laws, occasioned by cupidity, assumed its character. But different circumstances concurred to correct the disorder, and oblige governments to be just.

States, in fact, being weak at first, and having foreign enemies to fear, the chiefs found it their interest not to oppress their subjects; for, by lessening the confidence of the citizens in their government, they would diminish their means of resistance — they would facilitate foreign invasion, and by exercising arbitrary power, have endangered their very existence.

In the interior, the firmness of the people repelled tyranny; men had contracted too long habits of independence; they had too few wants, and too much consciousness of their own strength.

States being of a moderate size, it was difficult to divide their citizens so as to make use of some for the oppression of others. Their communications were too easy, their interest too clear and simple: besides, every one being a proprietor and cultivator, no one needed to sell himself, and the despot could find no mercenaries.

If, then dissension arose, they were between family and family, faction and faction, and they interested a great

number. The troubles, indeed, were warmer; but fears from
abroad pacified discord at home. If the oppression of a party
prevailed, the earth being still unoccupied, and man, still in
a state of simplicity, finding every where the same advantages, the oppressed party emigrated, and carried elsewhere
their independence.

The ancient states then enjoyed within themselves numerous
means of prosperity and power. Every one finding his own
well-being in the constitution of his country, took a lively
interest in its preservation. If a stranger attacked it, having to defend his own field, his own house, he carried into
combat all the passions of a personal quarrel; and, devoted
to his own interests, he was devoted to his country.

As every action useful to the public attracted its esteem
and gratitude, every one became eager to be useful; and
self-love multiplied talents and civic virtues.

Every citizen contributing equally by his talents and
person, armies and funds were inexhaustible, and nations
displayed formidable masses of power.

The earth being free, and its possession secure and easy,
every one was a proprietor; and the division of property
preserved morals, and rendered luxury impossible.

Every one cultivating for himself, culture was more
active, produce more abundant; and individual riches became public wealth.

The abundance of produce rendering subsistence easy,
population was rapid and numerous, and states attained
quickly the term of their plentitude.

Productions increasing beyond consumption, the necessity
of commerce arose; and exchanges took place between
people and people; which augmented their activity and reciprocal advantages.

In fine, certain countries, at certain times, uniting the
advantages of good government with a position on the
route of the most active circulation, they became empori-
ums of flourishing commerce and seats of powerful domination. And on the shores of the Nile and Mediterranean,
of the Tigris and Euphrates, the accumulated riches of
India and of Europe raised in successive splendor a hundred different cities.

The people, growing rich, applied their superfluity to works of common and public use; and this was in every state, the epoch of those works whose grandeur astonishes the mind; of those wells of Tyre, of those dykes of the Euphrates, of those subterranean conduits of Media,* of those fortresses of the desert, of those aqueducts of Palmyra, of those temples, of those porticoes. And such labors might be immense, without oppressing the nations;

* From the town or village of Samouât the course of the Euphrates is accompanied with a double bank, which descends as far as its junction with the Tigris, and from thence to the sea, being a length of about a hundred leagues, French measure. The height of these artificial banks is not uniform, but increases as you advance from the sea; it may be estimated at from twelve to fifteen feet. But for them, the inundation of the river would bury the country around, which is flat, to an extent of twenty or twenty-five leagues; and even notwithstanding these banks, there has been in modern times an overflow, which has covered the whole triangle formed by the junction of this river to the Tigris, being a space of country of one hundred and thirty square leagues. By the stagnation of these waters an epidemical disease of the most fatal nature was occasioned. It follows from hence, 1. That all the flat country bordering upon these rivers, was originally a marsh; 2. That this marsh could not have been inhabited previously to the construction of the banks in question; 3. That these banks could not have been the work but of a population prior as to date; and the elevation of Babylon, therefore, must have been posterior to that of Nineveh, as I think I have chronologically demonstrated in the memoir above cited.

The modern Aderbidjân, which was a part of Medea, the mountains of Koulderstan, and those of Diarbekr, abound with subterranean canals, by means of which the ancient inhabitants conveyed water to their parched soil in order to fertilize it. It was regarded as a meritorious act and a religious duty prescribed by Zoroaster, who, instead of preaching celibacy, mortifications, and other pretended virtues of the monkish sort, repeats continually in the passages that are preserved respecting him in the Sad-der and the Zendavesta: —

«That the action most pleasing to God is to plow and cultivate the earth, to water it with running streams, to multiply vegetation and living beings, to have numerous flocks, young and fruitful virgins, a multitude of children,» etc., etc.

Among the aqueducts of Palmyra it appears certain, that, besides those which conducted water from the neighboring hills, there was one which brought it even from the mountains of Syria. It is to be traced a long way into the Desert where it escapes our search by going under ground.

because they were the effect of an equal and common contribution of the force of individuals animated and free.

Thus ancient states prospered, because their social institutions conformed to the true laws of nature; and because men enjoying liberty and security for their persons and their property, might display all the extent of their faculties,— all the energies of their self-love.

GENERAL CAUSES OF THE REVOLUTIONS AND RUIN OF ANCIENT STATES

CUPIDITY had nevertheless excited among men a constant and universal conflict, which incessantly prompting individuals and societies to reciprocal invasions, occasioned successive revolutions, and returning agitations.

And first, in the savage and barbarous state of the first men, this audacious and fierce cupidity produced rapine, violence, and murder, and retarded for a long time the progress of civilization.

When afterward societies began to be formed, the effect of bad habits, communicated to laws and governments, corrupted their institutions and objects, and established arbitrary and factitious rights, which depraved the ideas of justice, and the morality of the people.

Thus one man being stronger than another, their inequality — an accident of nature — was taken for her law;* and the strong being able to take the life of the weak, and yet sparing him, arrogated over his person an abusive right of property; and the slavery of individuals prepared the way for the slavery of nations.

*Almost all the ancient philosophers and politicians have laid it down as a principle that men are born unequal, that nature has created some to be free, and others to be slaves. Expressions of this kind are to be found in Aristotle, and even in Plato, called the divine, doubtless in the same sense as the mythological reveries which he promulgated. With all the people of antiquity, the Gauls, the Romans, the Athenians, the right of the strongest was the right cf nations; and from the same principle are derived all the political disorders and public national crimes that at present exist.

Because the head of a family could be absolute in his house, he made his own affections and desires the rule of his conduct; he gave or resumed his goods without equality, without justice; and paternal despotism laid the foundation of despotism in government.*

In societies formed on such foundations, when time and labor had developed riches, cupidity restrained by the laws, became more artful, but not less active. Under the mask of union and civil peace, it fomented in the bosom of every state an intestine war, in which the citizens, divided into contending corps of orders, classes, families, unremittingly struggled to appropriate to themselves, under the name of SUPREME POWER, the ability to plunder every thing, and render every thing subservient to the dictates of their passions; and this spirit of encroachment, disguised under all possible forms, but always the same in its object and motives, has never ceased to torment the nations.

* Upon this single expression it would be easy to write a long and important chapter. We might prove in it, beyond contradiction, that all the abuses of national governments, have sprung from those of domestic government, from that government called patriarchal, which superficial minds have extolled without having analyzed it. Numberless facts demonstrate, that with every infant people, in every savage and barbarous state, the father, the chief of the family, is a despot, and a cruel and insolent despot. The wife is his slave, the children his servants. This king sleeps or smokes his pipe, while his wife and daughters perform all the drudgery of the house, and even that of tillage and cultivation, as far as occupations of this nature are practiced in such societies; and no sooner have the boys acquired strength than they are allowed to beat the females, and make them serve and wait upon them as they do upon their fathers. Similar to this is the state of our own uncivilized peasants. In proportion as civilization spreads, the manners become milder, and the condition of the women improves, till, by a contrary excess, they arrive at dominion, and then a nation becomes effeminate and corrupt. It is remarkable that parental authority is great in proportion as the government is despotic. China, India, and Turkey are striking examples of this. One would suppose that tyrants gave themselves accomplices and interested subaltern despots to maintain their authority. In opposition to this the Romans will be cited, but it remains to be proved that the Romans were men truly free; and their quick passage from their republican despotism to their abject servility under the emperors, gives room at least for considerable doubt as to that freedom.

Sometimes, opposing itself to all social compact, or breaking that which already existed, it committed the inhabitants of a country to the tumultuous shock of all their
discords ; and states thus dissolved, and reduced to the
condition of anarchy, were tormented by the passions of all
their members.

Sometimes a nation, jealous of its liberty, having appointed agents to administer its government, these agents
appropriated the powers of which they had only the guar-
dianship : they employed the public treasures in corrupting
elections, gaining partisans, in dividing the people among
themselves. By these means, from being temporary they
became perpetual ; from elective, hereditary ; and the state,
agitated by the intrigues of the ambitious, by largesses
from the rich and factious, by the venality of the poor and
idle, by the influence of orators, by the boldness of the
wicked, and the weakness of the virtuous, was convulsed
with all the inconveniences of democracy.

The chiefs of some countries, equal in strength and
mutually fearing each other, formed impious pacts, nefarious associations ; and, apportioning among themselves all
power, rank, and honor, unjustly arrogated privileges and
immunities ; erected themselves into separate orders and
distinct classes ; reduced the people to their control ; and,
under the name of ARISTOCRACY, the state was tormented
by the passions of the wealthy and the great.

Religious impostors, in other countries, tending by other
means to the same object, abused the credulity of the ignorant. In the gloom of their temples, behind the curtain of
the altar, they made their gods act and speak ; gave forth
oracles, worked miracles, ordered sacrifices, levied offerings,
prescribed endowments ; and, under the names of theocracy
and of religion, the state became tormented by the passions
of the priests.

Sometimes a nation, weary of its dissensions or of its
tyrants, to lessen the sources of evil, submitted to a single
master ; but if it limited his powers, his sole aim was to
enlarge them ; if it left them indefinite, he abused the trust
confided to him ; and, under the name of monarchy, the
state was tormented by the passions of kings and princes.

Then the factions, availing themselves of the general discontent, flattered the people with the hope of a better master; dealt out gifts and promises, deposed the despot to take his place; and their contests for the succession, or its partition, tormented the state with the disorders and devastations of civil war.

In fine, among these rivals, one more adroit, or more fortunate, gained the ascendency, and concentrated all power within himself. By a strange phenomenon, a single individual mastered millions of his equals, against their will and without their consent; and the art of tyranny sprung also from cupidity,

In fact observing the spirit of egotism which incessantly divides mankind, the ambitious man fomented it with dexterity, flattered the vanity of one, excited the jealousy of another, favored the avarice of this, inflamed the resentment of that, and irritated the passions of all; then, placing in opposition their interests and prejudices, he sowed division and hatreds, promised to the poor the spoils of the rich, to the rich the subjection of the poor; threatened one man by another, this class by that; and insulating all by distrust, created his strength out of their weakness, and imposed the yoke of opinion, which they mutually riveted on each other. With the army he levied contributions, and with contributions he disposed of the army: dealing out wealth and office on these principles, he enchained a whole people in indissoluble bonds, and they languished under the slow consumption of despotism.

Thus the same principle, varying its action under every possible form, was forever attenuating the consistence of states, and an eternal circle of vicissitudes flowed from an eternal circle of passions.

And this spirit of egotism and usurpation produced two effects equally operative and fatal: the one of division and subdivision of societies into their smallest fractions, inducing a debility which facilitated their dissolution; the other, a preserving tendency to concentrate power in a single hand,*

* It is remarkable that this has in all instances been the constant progress of societies; beginning with a state of anarchy or democracy, that is, with a great division of power they have passed to aristocracy,

which, engulfing successively societies and states, was fatal to their peace and social existence.

Thus, as in a state, a party absorbed the nation, a family the party, and an individual the family ; so a movement of absorption took place between state and state, and exhibited on a larger scale in the political order, all the particular evils of the civil order. Thus a state having subdued a state, held it in subjection in the form of a province ; and two provinces being joined together formed a kingdom ; two kingdoms being united by conquest, gave birth to empires of gigantic size ; and in this conglomeration, the internal strength of states, instead of increasing, diminished ; and the condition of the people, instead of ameliorating, became daily more abject and wretched, for causes derived from the nature of things.

Because, in proportion as states increased in extent, their administration becoming more difficult and complicated, greater energies of power were necessary to move such masses ; and there was no longer any proportion between the duties of sovereigns and their ability to perform their duties :

Because despots, feeling their weakness, feared whatever might develop the strength of nations, and studied only how to enfeeble them :

Because nations, divided by the prejudices of ignorance and hatred, seconded the wickedness of their governments ; and availing themselves reciprocally of subordinate agents, aggravated their mutual slavery :

Because, the balance between states being destroyed, the strong more easily oppressed the weak.

Finally, because in proportion as states were concentrated, the people, despoiled of their laws, of their usages, and of the government of their choice, lost that spirit of personal identification with their government, which had caused their energy.

and from aristocracy to monarchy. Does it not hence follow that those who constitute states under the democratic form, destine them to undergo all the intervening troubles between that and monarchy ; but it should at the same time be proved that social experience is already exhausted for the human race, and that this spontaneous movement is not solely the effect of ignorance.

And despots, considering empires as their private domains, and the people as their property, gave themselves up to depredations, and to all the licentiousness of the most arbitrary authority.

And all the strength and wealth of nations were diverted to private expense and personal caprice ; and kings, fatigued with gratification, abandoned themselves to all the extravagancies of factitious and depraved taste.* They must have gardens mounted on arcades, rivers raised over mountains, fertile fields converted into haunts for wild beasts ; lakes scooped in dry lands, rocks erected in lakes, palaces built of marble and porphyry, furniture of gold and diamonds. Under the cloak of religion, their pride founded temples, endowed indolent priests, built, for vain skeletons, extravagant tombs, mausoleums, and pyramids ;† millions of hands

* It is equally worthy of remark, that the conduct and manners of princes and kings of every country and every age, are found to be precisely the same at similar periods, whether of the formation or dissolution of empires. History every where presents the same pictures of luxury and folly ; of parks, gardens, lakes, rocks, palaces, furniture, excess of the table, wine, women, concluding with brutality.

The absurd rock in the garden of Versailles has alone cost three millions. I have sometimes calculated what might have been done with the expense of the three pyramids of Gizeh, and I have found that it would easily have constructed, from the Red Sea to Alexandria, a canal one hundred and fifty feet wide and thirty deep, completely covered in with cut stones and a parapet, together with a fortified and commercial town, consisting of four hundred houses, furnished with cisterns. What a difference in point of utility between such a canal and these pyramids !

† The learned Dupuis could not be persuaded that the pyramids were tombs ; but besides the positive testimony of historians, read what Diodorus says of the religious and superstitious importance every Egyptian attached to building his dwelling eternal, b. 1.

During twenty years, says Herodotus, a hundred thousand men labored every day to build the pyramid of the Egyptian Cheops. Supposing only three hundred days a year, on account of the Sabbath, there will be 30 millions of days' work in a year, and 600 millions in twenty years ; at 15 sous a day, this makes 450 millions of francs lost, without any further benefit. With this sum, if the king had shut the isthmus of Suez by a strong wall, like that of China, the destinies of Egypt might have been entirely changed. Foreign invasions would have been prevented, and the Arabs of the desert would neither have conquered nor harassed that country. Sterile labors ! how many mil-

8

were employed in sterile labors; and the luxury of princes, imitated by their parasites, and transmitted from grade to grade to the lowest ranks, became a general source of corruption and impoverishment.

And in the insatiable thirst of enjoyment, the ordinary revenues no longer sufficing, they were augmented; the cultivator, seeing his labors increase without compensation, lost all courage; the merchant, despoiled, was disgusted with industry; the multitude, condemned to perpetual poverty, restrained their labor to simple necessaries; and all productive industry vanished.

The surcharge of taxes rendering lands a burdensome possession, the poor proprietor abandoned his field, or sold it to the powerful; and fortune became concentrated in a few hands. All the laws and institutions favoring this accumulation, the nation became divided into a group of wealthy drones, and a multitude of mercenary poor; the people were degraded with indigence, the great with satiety, and the number of those interested in the preservation of the state decreasing, its strength and existence became proportionally precarious.

On the other hand, emulation finding no object, science no encouragement, the mind sunk into profound ignorance.

The administration being secret and mysterious, there existed no means of reform or amelioration. The chiefs governing by force or fraud, the people viewed them as a faction of public enemies; and all harmony ceased between the governors and governed.

And these vices having enervated the states of the wealthy part of Asia, the vagrant and indigent people of the adjacent deserts and mountains coveted the enjoyments of the fertile plains; and, urged by a cupidity common to all, attacked the polished empires, and overturned the thrones of their despots. These revolutions were rapid and easy; because the policy of tyrants had enfeebled the subjects, razed the fortresses, destroyed the warriors; and be-

lions lost in putting one stone upon another, under the forms of temples and churches! Alchymists convert stones into gold; but architects change gold into stone. Woe to the kings (as well as subjects) who trust their purse to these two classes of empirics!

cause the oppressed subjects remained without personal interest, and the mercenary soldiers without courage.

And hordes of barbarians having reduced entire nations to slavery, the empires, formed of conquerors and conquered, united in their bosom two classes essentially opposite and hostile. All the principles of society were dissolved : there was no longer any common interest, no longer any public spirit ; and there arose a distinction of castes and races, which reduced to a regular system the maintenance of disorder ; and he who was born of this or that blood, was born a slave or a tyrant — property or proprietor.

The oppressors being less numerous than the oppressed, it was necessary to perfect the science of oppression, in order to support this false equilibrium. The art of governing became the art of subjecting the many to the few. To enforce an obedience so contrary to instinct, the severest punishments were established, and the cruelty of the laws rendered manners atrocious. The distinction of persons establishing in the state two codes, two orders of criminal justice, two sets of laws, the people, placed between the propensities of the heart and the oath uttered from the mouth, had two consciences in contradiction with each other ; and the ideas of justice and injustice had no longer any foundation in the understanding.

Under such a system, the people fell into dejection and despair ; and the accidents of nature were added to the other evils which assailed them. Prostrated by so many calamities, they attributed their causes to superior and hidden powers ; and, because they had tyrants on earth, they fancied others in heaven ; and superstition aggravated the misfortunes of nations.

Fatal doctrines and gloomy and misanthropic systems of religion arose, which painted their gods, like their despots, wicked and envious. To appease them, man offered up the sacrifice of all his enjoyments. He environed himself in privations, and reversed the order of nature. Conceiving his pleasures to be crimes, his sufferings expiations, he endeavored to love pain, and to adjure the love of self. He persecuted his senses, hated his life ; and a self-denying and anti-social morality plunged nations into the apathy of death.

But provident nature having endowed the heart of man with hope inexhaustible, when his desires of happiness were baffled on this earth, he pursued it into another world. By a sweet illusion he created for himself another country — an asylum where, far from tyrants, he should recover the rights of nature, and thence resulted new disorders. Smitten with an imaginary world, man despised that of nature. For chimerical hopes, he neglected realities. His life began to appear a troublesome journey — a painful dream; his body a prison, the obstacle to his felicity; and the earth, a place of exile and of pilgrimage, not worthy of culture. Then a holy indolence spread over the political world; the fields were deserted, empires depopulated, monuments neglected, and deserts multiplied; ignorance, superstition, and fanaticism, combining their operations, overwhelmed the earth with devastation and ruin.

Thus agitated by their own passions, men, whether collectively or individually taken, always greedy and improvident, passing from slavery to tyranny, from pride to baseness, from presumption to despondency, have made themselves the perpetual instruments of their own misfortunes.

These, then, are the principles, simple and natural, which regulated the destiny of ancient states. By this regular and connected series of causes and effects, they rose or fell, in proportion as the physical laws of the human heart were respected or violated; and in the course of their successive changes, a hundred different nations, a hundred different empires, by turns humbled, elevated, conquered, overthrown, have repeated for the earth their instructive lessons. Yet these lessons were lost for the generations which have followed! The disorders in times past have reappeared in the present age! The chief of the nations have continued to walk in the paths of falsehood and tyranny — the people to wander in the darkness of superstition and ignorance!

Since then, continued the Genius, with renewed energy, since the experience of past ages is lost for the living — since the errors of progenitors have not instructed their descendants, the ancient examples are about to reappear;

the earth will see renewed the tremendous scenes it has forgotten. New revolutions will agitate nations and empires; powerful thrones will again be overturned, and terrible catastrophes will again teach mankind that the laws of nature and the precepts of wisdom and truth cannot be infringed with impunity.

WILL THE HUMAN RACE IMPROVE?

A T THESE words, oppressed with the painful sentiment with which their severity overwhelmed me: Woe to the nations! cried I, melting in tears; woe to myself! Ah! now it is that I despair of the happiness of man! Since his miseries proceed from his heart; since the remedy is in his own power, woe forever to his existence! Who, indeed, will ever be able to restrain the lust of wealth in the strong and powerful? Who can enlighten the ignorance of the weak? Who can teach the multitude to know their rights, and force their chiefs to perform their duties? Thus the race of man is always doomed to suffer! Thus the individual will not cease to oppress the individual, a nation to attack a nation; and days of prosperity, of glory, for these regions, shall never return. Alas! conquerors will come; they will drive out the oppressors, and fix themselves in their place; but, inheriting their power, they will inherit their rapacity; and the earth will have changed tyrants, without changing the tyranny.

Then, turning to the Genius, I exclaimed: —

O Genius, despair hath settled on my soul. Knowing the nature of man, the perversity of those who govern, and the debasement of the governed — this knowledge hath disgusted me with life; and since there is no choice but to be the accomplice or the victim of oppression, what remains to the man of virtue but to mingle his ashes with those of the tomb?

The Genius then gave me a look of severity, mingled with compassion; and after a few moments of silence, he replied: —

Virtue, then, consists in dying! The wicked man is indefatigable in consummating his crime, and the just is discouraged from doing good at the first obstacle he encounters! But such is the human heart. A little success intoxicates man with confidence; a reverse overturns and confounds him. Always given up to the sensation of the moment, he seldom judges things from their nature, but from the impulse of his passion.

Mortal, who despairest of the human race, on what profound combination of facts hast thou established thy conclusion? Hast thou scrutinized the organization of sentient beings, to determine with precision whether the instinctive force which moves them on to happiness is essentially weaker than that which repels them from it? or, embracing in one glance the history of the species, and judging the future by the past, hast thou shown that all improvement is impossible? Say! hath human society, since its origin, made no progress toward knowledge and a better state? Are men still in their forests, destitute of everything, ignorant, stupid, and ferocious? Are all the nations still in that age when nothing was seen upon the globe but brutal robbers and brutal slaves? If at any time, in any place, individuals have ameliorated, why shall not the whole mass ameliorate? If partial societies have made improvements, what shall hinder the improvement of society in general? And if the first obstacles are overcome, why should the others be insurmountable?

Art thou disposed to think that the human race degenerates? Guard against the illusion and paradoxes of the misanthrope. Man, discontented with the present, imagines for the past a perfection which never existed, and which only serves to cover his chagrin. He praises the dead out of hatred to the living, and beats the children with the bones of their ancestors.

To prove this pretended retrograde progress from perfection we must contradict the testimony of reason and of fact; and if the facts of history are in any measure uncertain, we must contradict the living fact of the organization of man; we must prove that he is born with the enlightened use of his senses; that, without experience, he

can distinguish aliment from poison; that the child is wiser
than the old man; that the blind walks with more safety
than the clear-sighted; that the civilized man is more
miserable than the savage; and, indeed, that there is no
ascending scale in experience and instruction.

Believe, young man, the testimony of monuments, and
the voice of the tombs. Some countries have doubtless
fallen from what they were at certain epochs; but if we
weigh the wisdom and happiness of their inhabitants, even
in those times, we shall find more of splendor than of
reality in their glory; we shall find, in the most celebrated
of ancient states, enormous vices and cruel abuses, the true
causes of their decay; we shall find in general that the principles of government were atrocious; that insolent robberies,
barbarous wars, and implacable hatreds were raging from
nation to nation; that natural right was unknown; that
morality was perverted by senseless fanaticism and deplorable
superstition; that a dream, a vision, an oracle, were constantly the causes of vast commotions. Perhaps the nations
are not yet entirely cured of all these evils; but their intensity at least is diminished, and the experience of the past
has not been wholly lost. For the last three centuries, especially, knowledge has increased and been extended; civilization, favored by happy circumstances, has made a sensible
progress; inconveniences and abuses have even turned to its
advantage; for if states have been too much extended by
conquest, the people, by uniting under the same yoke, have
lost the spirit of estrangement and division which made
them all enemies one to the other. If the powers of government have been more concentrated, there has been more
system and harmony in their exercise. If wars have become
more extensive in the mass, they are less bloody in detail.
If men have gone to battle with less personality, less energy, their struggles have been less sanguinary and less
ferocious; they have been less free, but less turbulent;
more effeminate, but more pacific. Despotism itself has rendered them some service; for if governments have been
more absolute, they have been more quiet and less tempestuous. If thrones have become a property and hereditary,
they have excited less dissensions, and the people have

suffered fewer convulsions; finally, if the despots, jealous and mysterious, have interdicted all knowledge of their administration, all concurrences in the management of public affairs, the passions of men, drawn aside from politics, have fixed upon the arts, and the sciences of nature; and the sphere of ideas in every direction has been enlarged; man, devoted to abstract studies, has better understood his place in the system of nature, and his relations in society; principles have been better discussed, final causes better explained, knowledge more extended, individuals better instructed, manners more social, and life more happy. The species at large, especially in certain countries, has gained considerably; and this amelioration cannot but increase in future, because its two principal obstacles, those even which, till then, had rendered it slow and sometimes retrograde,— the difficulty of transmitting ideas and of communicating them rapidly,— have been at last removed.

Indeed, among the ancients, each canton, each city, being isolated from all others by the difference of its language, the consequence was favorable to ignorance and anarchy. There was no communication of ideas, no participation of discoveries, no harmony of interests or of wills, no unity of action or design; besides, the only means of transmitting and of propagating ideas being that of speech, fugitive and limited, and that of writing, tedious of execution, expensive, and scarce, the consequence was a hindrance of present instruction, loss of experience from one generation to another, instability, retrogression of knowledge, and a perpetuity of confusion and childhood.

But in the modern world, especially in Europe, great nations having allied themselves in language, and established vast communities of opinions, the minds of men are assimilated, and their affections extended; there is a sympathy of opinion and a unity of action; then that gift of heavenly Genius, the holy art of printing, having furnished the means of communicating in an instant the same idea to millions of men, and of fixing it in a durable manner, beyond the power of tyrants to arrest or annihilate, there arose a mass of progressive instruction, an expanding atmosphere of science, which assures to future ages a solid amelioration. This amelioration is a necessary effect of the laws of nature; for, by the law of sensibility, man as invincibly tends to render himself happy as the flame to mount, the stone to descend, or the water to find its level. His obstacle is his ignorance, which misleads him in the means, and deceives him in causes and effects. He will enlighten himself by experience; he will become right by dint of errors; he will grow wise and good because it is his interest so to be. Ideas being communicated through the nation, whole classes will gain instruction; science will become a common possession, and all men will know what are the principles of individual happiness and of public prosperity. They will know the relations they bear to society, their duties and their rights; they will learn to guard against the illusions of the lust of gain; they will perceive that the science of morals is a physical science, composed, indeed, of elements complicated in their operation, but simple and invariable in their nature, since they are only the elements of the organization of man. They will see the propriety of being moderate and just, because in that is found the advantage and security of each; they will perceive that the wish to enjoy at the expense of another is a false calculation of ignorance, because it gives rise to reprisal, hatred, and vengeance, and that dishonesty is the never-failing offspring of folly.

Individuals will feel that private happiness is allied to public good:

The weak, that instead of dividing their interests, they ought to unite them, because equality constitutes their force:

The rich, that the measure of enjoyment is bounded by the constitution of the organs, and that lassitude follows satiety:

The poor, that the employment of time, and the peace of the heart, compose the highest happiness of man. And public opinion, reaching kings on their thrones, will force them to confine themselves to the limits of regular authority.

Even chance itself, serving the cause of nations, will sometimes give them feeble chiefs, who, through weakness,

will suffer them to become free; and sometimes enlightened
chiefs, who, from a principle of virtue, will free them.

And when nations, free and enlightened, shall become
like great individuals, the whole species will have the same
facilities as particular portions now have; the communication of knowledge will extend from one to another, and
thus reach the whole. By the law of imitation, the example of one people will be followed by others, who will
adopt its spirit and its laws. Even despots, perceiving that
they can no longer maintain their authority without justice
and beneficence, will soften their sway from necessity
from rivalship; and civilization will become universal.

There will be established among the several nations an
equilibrium of force, which, restraining them all within the
bounds of the respect due to their reciprocal rights, shall
put an end to the barbarous practice of war, and submit
their disputes to civil arbitration.* The human race will
become one great society, one individual family, governed
by the same spirit, by common laws, and enjoying all the
happiness of which their nature is susceptible.

Doubtless this great work will be long accomplishing;
because the same movement must be given to an immense
body; the same leaven must assimilate an enormous mass
of heterogeneous parts. But this movement shall be
effected; its presages are already to be seen. Already the
great society, assuming in its course the same characters as
partial societies have done, is evidently tending to a like
result. At first disconnected in all its parts, it saw its
members for a long time without cohesion; and this general solitude of nations formed its first age of anarchy and
childhood; divided afterward by chance into irregular sections, called states and kingdoms, it has experienced the
fatal effects of an extreme inequality of wealth and rank;
and the aristocracy of great empires has formed its second

* What is a people? An individual of the society at large. What
a war? A duel between two individual people. In what manner
ought a society to act when two of its members fight? Interfere and
reconcile, or repress them. In the days of the Abbé de Saint Pierre
this was treated as a dream, but happily for the human race it begins to be realized.

age; then, these lordly states disputing for preëminence, have exhibited the period of the shock of factions.

At present the contending parties, wearied with discord, feel the want of laws, and sigh for the age of order and of peace. Let but a virtuous chief arise! a just, a powerful people appear! and the earth will raise them to supreme power. The world is waiting for a legislative people; it wishes and demands it; and my heart attends the cry.

Then turning toward the west: Yes, continued he, a hollow sound already strikes my ear; a cry of liberty, proceeding from far distant shores, resounds on the ancient continent. At this cry, a secret murmur against oppression is raised in a powerful nation; a salutary inquietude alarms her respecting her situation; she inquires what she is, and what she ought to be; while, surprised at her own weakness, she interrogates her rights, her resources, and what has been the conduct of her chiefs.

Yet another day — a little more reflection — and an immense agitation will begin; a new-born age will open! an age of astonishment to vulgar minds, of terror to tyrants, of freedom to a great nation, and of hope to the human race!

THE GREAT OBSTACLE TO IMPROVEMENT

THE Genius ceased. But preoccupied with melancholy thoughts, my mind resisted persuasion; fearing, however, to shock him by my resistance, I remained silent. After a while, turning to me with a look which pierced my soul, he said : —

Thou art silent, and thy heart is agitated with thoughts which it dares not utter.

At last, troubled and terrified, I replied : —

O Genius, pardon my weakness. Doubtless thy mouth can utter nothing but truth; but thy celestial intelligence can seize its rays, where my gross faculties can discern nothing but clouds. I confess it; conviction has not penetrated my soul, and I feared that my doubts might offend thee.

And what is doubt, replied he, that it should be a crime? Can man feel otherwise than as he is affected? If a truth be palpable, and of importance in practice, let us pity him that misconceives it. His punishment will arise from his blindness. If it be uncertain or equivocal, how is he to find in it what it has not? To believe without evidence or proof, is an act of ignorance and folly. The credulous man loses himself in a labyrinth of contradictions; the man of sense examines and discusses, that he may be consistent in his opinions. The honest man will bear contradiction; because it gives rise to evidence. Violence is the argument of falsehood; and to impose a creed by authority is the act and indication of a tyrant.

O Genius, said I, encouraged by these words, since my reason is free, I strive in vain to entertain the flattering hope with which you endeavor to console me. The sensible and virtuous soul is easily caught with dreams of happiness; but a cruel reality constantly awakens it to suffering and wretchedness. The more I meditate on the nature of man, the more I examine the present state of societies, the less possible it appears to realize a world of wisdom and felicity. I cast my eye over the whole of our hemisphere; I perceive in no place the germ, nor do I foresee the instinctive energy of a happy revolution. All Asia lies buried in profound darkness. The Chinese, governed by an insolent despotism,* by strokes of the bamboo and the cast of lots, restrained by an immutable code of gestures, and by the radical vices of an ill-constructed language,† appear to be in their abortive civilization nothing but a race of automatons. The Indian, borne down

---

*The emperor of China calls himself the son of heaven; that is, of God: for in the opinion of the Chinese, the material of heaven, the arbiter of fatality, is the Deity himself. « The emperor only shows himself once in ten months, lest the people, accustomed to see him, might lose their respect; for he holds it as a maxim that power can only be supported by force, that the people have no idea of justice, and are not to be governed but by coercion.» *Narrative of two Mahometan travelers in 851 and 877, translated by the Abbé Renaudot in 1718.*

Notwithstanding what is asserted by the missionaries, this situation has undergone no change. The bamboo still reigns in China, and

by prejudices, and enchained in the sacred fetters of his castes, vegetates in an incurable apathy. The Tartar, wandering or fixed, always ignorant and ferocious, lives in the savageness of his ancestors. The Arab, endowed with a happy genius, looses its force and the fruits of his virtue in the anarchy of his tribes and the jealousy of his families. The African, degraded from the rank of man, seems irrevocably doomed to servitude. In the North I see nothing but vilified serfs, herds of men with which landlords stock their estates. Ignorance, tyranny, and wretchedness have everywhere stupified the nations; and vicious habits, depraving the natural scenes, have destroyed the very instinct of happiness and of truth.

In some parts of Europe, indeed, reason has begun to dawn, but even there, do nations partake of the knowledge of individuals? Are the talents and genius of governors turned to the benefit of the people? And those nations which call themselves polished, are they not the same that for the last three centuries have filled the earth with their injustice? Are they not those who, under the pretext of commerce, have desolated India, depopulated a new continent, and, at present, subject Africa to the most barbarous slavery? Can liberty be born from the bosom of despots? and shall justice be rendered by the hands of piracy and and avarice? O Genius, I have seen the civilized countries; and the mockery of their wisdom has vanished before my sight. I saw wealth accumulated in the hands of a few, and the multitude poor and destitute. I have seen all

the son of heaven bastinades, for the most trivial fault, the Mandarin, who in his turn bastinades the people. The Jesuits may tell us that this is the best governed country in the world, and its inhabitants the happiest of men : but a single letter from Amyot has convinced me that China is a truly Turkish government, and the account of Sonnerat confirms it. See Vol. II. of *Voyage aux Indes*, in 4to.

† As long as the Chinese shall in writing make use of their present characters, they can be expected to make no progress in civilization. The necessary introductory step must be the giving them an alphabet like our own, or of substituting in the room of their language that of the Tartars. The improvement made in the latter by M. de Lengles, is calculated to introduce this change. See the Mantchou alphabet, the production of a mind truly learned in the formation of language.

rights, all powers concentred in certain classes, and the mass of the people passive and dependent. I have seen families of princes, but no families of the nation. I have seen government interests, but no public interests or spirit. I have seen that all the science of government was to oppress prudently; and the refined servitude of polished nations appeared to me only the more irremediable.

One obstacle above all has profoundly struck my mind. On looking over the world, I have seen it divided into twenty different systems of religion. Every nation has received, or formed, opposite opinions; and every one ascribing to itself the exclusive possession of the truth, must believe the other to be wrong. Now if, as must be the fact in this discordance of opinion, the greater part are in error, and are honest in it, then it follows that our mind embraces falsehood as it does truth; and if so, how is it to be enlightened? When prejudice has once seized the mind, how is it to be dissipated? How shall we remove the bandage from our eyes, when the first article in every creed, the first dogma in all religion, is the absolute proscription of doubt, the interdiction of examination, and the rejection of our own judgment? How is truth to make herself known? — If she resorts to arguments and proofs, the timid man stifles the voice of his own conscience; if she invokes the authority of celestial powers, he opposes it with another authority of the same origin, with which he is preoccupied; and he treats all innovation as blasphemy. Thus man in his blindness, has riveted his own chains, and surrendered himself forever, without defense, to the sport of his ignorance and his passions.

To dissolve such fatal chains, a miraculous concurrence of happy events would be necessary. A whole nation, cured of the delirium of superstition, must be inaccessible to the impulse of fanatacism. Freed from the yoke of false doctrine, a whole people must impose upon itself that of true morality and reason. This people should be courageous and prudent, wise and docile. Each individual, knowing his rights, should not trangress them. The poor should know how to resist seduction, and the rich the allurements of avarice. There should be found leaders disinterested and just, and their tyrants should be seized with a spirit of madness and folly. This people, recovering its rights, should feel its inability to exercise them in person, and should name its representatives. Creator of its magistrates, it should know at once to respect them and to judge them. In the sudden reform of a whole nation, accustomed to live by abuses, each individual displaced should bear with patience his privations, and submit to a change of habits. This nation should have the courage to conquer its liberty, the power to defend it, the wisdom to establish it, and the generosity to extend it to others. And can we ever expect the union of so many circumstances? But suppose that chance in its infinite combinations should produce them, shall I see those fortunate days? Will not my ashes long ere then be moldering in the tomb?

Here, sunk in sorrow, my oppressed heart no longer found utterance. The Genius answered not, but I heard him whisper to himself: —

Let us revive the hope of this man; for if he who loves his fellow creatures be suffered to despair, what will become of nations? The past is perhaps too discouraging; I must anticipate futurity, and disclose to the eye of virtue the astonishing age that is ready to begin; that, on viewing the object she desires, she may be animated with new ardor, and redouble her efforts to attain it.

THE NEW AGE

SCARCELY had he finished these words, when a great tumult arose in the west; and turning to that quarter, I perceived, at the extremity of the Mediterranean, in one of the nations of Europe, a prodigious movement — such as when a violent sedition arises in a vast city — a numberless people, rushing in all directions, pour through the streets and fluctuate like waves in the public places. My ear, struck with the cries which resounded to the heavens, distinguished these words: —

What is this new prodigy? What cruel and mysterious scourge is this? We are a numerous people and we want hands! We have an excellent soil, and we are in want of subsistence! We are active and laborious, and we live in indigence! We pay enormous tributes, and we are told they are not sufficient! We are at peace without, and our persons and property are not safe within. Who, then, is the secret enemy that devours us?

Some voices from the midst of the multitude replied: —

Raise a discriminating standard; and let all those who maintain and nourish mankind by useful labors gather round it; and you will discover the enemy that preys upon you.

The standard being raised, this nation divided itself at once into two bodies of unequal magnitude and contrasted appearance. The one, innumerable, and almost total, exhibited in the poverty of its clothing, in its emaciated appearance, and sun-burnt faces, the marks of misery and labor; the other, a little group, an insignificant faction, presented in its rich attire embroidered with gold and silver, and in its sleek and ruddy faces, the signs of leisure and abundance.

Considering these men more attentively, I found that the great body was composed of farmers, artificers, merchants, all professions useful to society; and that the little group was made up of priests of every order, of financiers, of nobles, of men in livery, of commanders of armies; in a word, of the civil, military, and religious agents of government.

These two bodies being assembled face to face, and regarding each other with astonishment, I saw indignation and rage arising in one side, and a sort of panic in the other. And the large body said to the little one : Why are you separated from us? Are you not of our number?

No, replied the group; you are the people; we are a privileged class, who have our laws, customs, and rights, peculiar to ourselves.

PEOPLE.—And what labor do you perform in our society?

PRIVILEGED CLASS.— None; we are not made to work.

PEOPLE.— How, then, have you acquired these riches?

PRIVILEGED CLASS.— By taking the pains to govern you.

PEOPLE.— What! is this what you call governing? We toil and you enjoy! we produce and you dissipate! Wealth proceeds from us, and you absorb it! Privileged men! class who are not the people; form a nation apart, and govern yourselves.*

Then the little group, deliberating on this new state of things, some of the most honorable among them said: We must join the people and partake of their labors and burdens, for they are men like us, and our riches come from them; but others arrogantly exclaimed: It would be a shame, an infamy, for us to mingle with the crowd; they are born to serve us. Are we not men of another race — the noble and pure descendants of the conquerors of this empire? This multitude must be reminded of our rights and its own origin.

THE NOBLES.— People! know you not that our ancestors conquered this land, and that your race was spared only on condition of serving us? This is our social compact! this the government constituted by custom and prescribed by time.

PEOPLE.— O conquerors, pure of blood! show us your genealogies! we shall then see if what in an individual is robbery and plunder, can be virtuous in a nation.

And forthwith, voices were heard in every quarter calling out the nobles by their names; and relating their origin and parentage, they told how the grandfather, great-grandfather, or even father, born traders and mechanics, after acquiring wealth in every way, had purchased their nobility for money: so that but very few families were really of the

---

* This dialogue between the people and the indolent classes, is applicable to every society; it contains the seeds of all the political vices and disorders that prevail, and which may thus be defined: Men who do nothing, and who devour the substance of others; and men who arrogate to themselves particular rights and exclusive privileges of wealth and indolence. Compare the Mamlouks of Egypt, the nobility of Europe, the Nairs of India, the Emirs of Arabia, the patricians of Rome, the beneficed clergy, the Imans, the Bramins, the Bonzes, the Lamas, etc., etc., and you will find in all the same characteristic feature— Men living in idleness at the expense of those who labor.

9

original stock. See, said these voices, see these purse-proud commoners who deny their parents ! see these plebeian recruits who look upon themselves as illustrious veterans ! and peals of laughter were heard.

And the civil governors said : these people are mild, and naturally servile ; speak to them of the king and of the law, and they will return to their duty. People ! the king wills, the sovereign ordains !

PEOPLE.— The king can will nothing but the good of the people ; the sovereign can only ordain according to law.

CIVIL GOVERNORS.— The law commands you to be submissive.

PEOPLE.— The law is the general will ; and we will a new order of things.

CIVIL GOVERNORS.— You are then a rebel people.

PEOPLE.— A nation cannot revolt ; tyrants only are rebels.

CIVIL GOVERNORS.— The king is on our side ; he commands you to submit.

PEOPLE.— Kings are inseparable from their nations. Our king cannot be with you ; you possess only his phantom.

And the military governors came forward. The people are timorous, said they ; we must threaten them ; they will submit only to force. Soldiers, chastise this insolent multitude.

PEOPLE.— Soldiers, you are of our blood ! Will you strike your brothers, your relatives? If the people perish who will nourish the army ?

And the soldiers, grounding their arms, said to the chiefs : We are likewise the people ; show us the enemy !

*　　*　　*　　*　　*　　*　　*

And the little group said : We are lost ! the mulitude are enlightened.

And the people answered : You are safe ; since we are enlightened we will commit no violence ; we only claim our rights. We feel resentments, but we will forget them. We were slaves, we might command ; but we only wish to be free, and liberty is but justice.

A FREE AND LEGISLATIVE PEOPLE

CONSIDERING that all public power was now suspended, and that the habitual restraint of the people had suddenly ceased, I shuddered with the apprehension that they would fall into the dissolution of anarchy. But, taking their affairs into immediate deliberation, they said :

It is not enough that we have freed ourselves from tyrants and parasites ; we must prevent their return. We are men, and experience has abundantly taught us that every man is fond of power, and wishes to enjoy it at the expense of others. It is necessary, then, to guard against a propensity which is the source of discord ; we must establish certain rules of duty and of right. But the knowledge of our rights, and the estimation of our duties, are so abstract and difficult as to require all the time and all the faculties of a man. Occupied in our own affairs, we have not leisure for these studies ; nor can we exercise these functions in our own persons. Let us choose, then, among ourselves, such persons as are capable of this employment. To them we will delegate our powers to institute our government and laws. They shall be the representatives of our wills and of our interests. And in order to attain the fairest representation possible of our wills and our interests, let it be numerous, and composed of men resembling ourselves.

Having made the election of a numerous body of delegates, the people thus addressed them :—

We have hitherto lived in a society formed by chance, without fixed agreements, without free conventions, without a stipulation of rights, without reciprocal engagements,— and a multitude of disorders and evils have arisen from this precarious state. We are now determined on forming a regular compact ; and we have chosen you to adjust the articles. Examine, then, with care what ought to be its basis and its conditions ; consider what is the end and the principles of every association ; recognize the rights which every member brings, the powers which he delegates, and those which he reserves to himself. Point out to us the rules of conduct — the basis of just and equitable laws. Prepare for us a new system of government; for we realize that the one which has hitherto guided us is corrupt. Our fathers have wandered in the paths of ignorance, and habit has taught us to follow in their footsteps. Everything has been done by fraud, violence, and delusion; and the true laws of morality and reason are still obscure. Clear up, then, their chaos; trace out their connection; publish their code, and we will adopt it.

And the people raised a large throne, in the form of a pyramid, and seating on it the men they had chosen, said to them :—

We raise you to-day above us, that you may better discover the whole of our relations, and be above the reach of our passions. But remember that you are our fellow-citizens; that the power we confer on you is our own; that we deposit it with you, but not as a property or a heritage; that you must be the first to obey the laws you make; that to-morrow you redescend among us, and that you will have acquired no other right but that of our esteem and gratitude. And consider what a tribute of glory the world, which reveres so many apostles of error, will bestow on the first assembly of rational men, who shall have declared the unchangeable principles of justice, and consecrated, in the face of tyrants, the rights of nations.

UNIVERSAL BASIS OF ALL RIGHT AND ALL LAW

THE men chosen by the people to investigate the true principles of morals and of reason then proceeded in the sacred object of their mission; and, after a long examination, having discovered a fundamental and universal principle, a legislator arose and said to the people :—

Here is the primordial basis, the physical origin of all justice and of all right.

Whatever be the active power, the moving cause, that governs the universe, since it has given to all men the same organs, the same sensations, and the same wants, it has thereby declared that it has given to all the same right to the use of its treasures, and that all men are equal in the order of nature.

And, since this power has given to each man the necessary means of preserving his own existence, it is evident that it has constituted them all independent one of another; that it has created them free; that no one is subject to another; that each one is absolute proprietor of his own person.

Equality and liberty are, therefore, two essential attributes of man, two laws of the Divinity, constitutional and unchangeable, like the physical properties of matter.

Now, every individual being absolute master of his own person, it follows that a full and free consent is a condition indispensable to all contracts and all engagements.

Again, since each individual is equal to another, it follows that the balance of what is received and of what is given, should be strictly in equilibrium; so that the idea of justice, of equity, necessarily imports that of equality.*

Equality and liberty are therefore the physical and unalterable basis of every union of men in society, and of course the necessary and generating principle of every law and of every system of regular government.†

A disregard of this basis has introduced in your nation, and in every other, those disorders which have finally roused you. It is by returning to this rule that you may reform them, and reorganize a happy order of society.

*The etymology of the words themselves trace out to us this connection: *equilibrium, equalitas, equitas*, are all of one family, and the physical idea of equality, in the scales of a balance, is the source and type of all the rest.

†In the Declaration of Rights, there is an inversion of ideas in the first article, liberty being placed before equality, from which it in reality springs. This defect is not to be wondered at; the science of the rights of man is a new science: it was invented yesterday by the Americans, to-day the French are perfecting it, but there yet remains a great deal to be done. In the ideas that constitute it there is a genealogical order which, from its basis, physical equality, to the minutest and most remote branches of government, ought to proceed in an uninterrupted series of inferences.

But observe, this reorganization will occasion a violent shock in your habits, your fortunes, and your prejudices. Vicious contracts and abusive claims must be dissolved, unjust distinctions and ill-founded property renounced; you must indeed recur for a moment to a state of nature. Consider whether you can consent to so many sacrifices.

Then, reflecting on the cupidity inherent in the heart of man, I thought that this people would renounce all ideas of amelioration.

But, in a moment, a great number of men, advancing toward the pyramid, made a solemn abjuration of all their distinctions and all their riches.

Establish for us, said they, the laws of equality and liberty; we will possess nothing in future but on the title of justice.

Equality, liberty, justice, — these shall be our code, and shall be written on our standards.

And the people immediately raised a great standard, inscribed with these three words, in three different colors. They displayed it over the pyramid of the legislators, and for the first time the flag of universal justice floated on the face of the earth.

And the people raised before the pyramid a new altar, on which they placed a golden balance, a sword, and a book with this inscription: —

TO EQUAL LAW, WHICH JUDGES AND PROTECTS.

And having surrounded the pyramid and the altar with a vast amphitheatre, all the people took their seats to hear the publication of the law. And millions of men, raising at once their hands to heaven, took the solemn oath to live equal, free, and just; to respect their reciprocal properties and rights; to obey the law and its regularly chosen representatives.

A spectacle so impressive and sublime, so replete with generous emotions, moved me to tears; and addressing myself to the Genius, I exclaimed: Let me now live, for in future I have everything to hope.

CONSTERNATION AND CONSPIRACY OF TYRANTS

BUT scarcely had the solemn voice of liberty and equality resounded through the earth, when a movement of confusion, of astonishment, arose in different nations. On the one hand, the people, warmed with desire, but wavering between hope and fear, between the sentiment of right and the habit of obedience, began to be in motion. The kings, on the other hand, suddenly awakened from the sleep of indolence and despotism, were alarmed for the safety of their thrones; while, on all sides, those clans of civil and religious tyrants, who deceive kings and oppress the people, where seized with rage and consternation; and, concerting their perfidious plans, they said: Woe to us, if this fatal cry of liberty comes to the ears of the multitude! Woe to us, if this pernicious spirit of justice be propagated!

And, pointing to the floating banner, they continued : —

Consider what a swarm of evils are included in these three words! If all men are equal, where is our exclusive right to honors and to power? If all men are to be free, what becomes of our slaves, our vassals, our property? If all are equal in the civil state, where is our prerogative of birth, of inheritance? and what becomes of nobility? If they are all equal in the sight of God, what need of mediators? — where is the priesthood? Let us hasten, then, to destroy a germ so prolific, and so contagious. We must employ all our cunning against this innovation. We must frighten the kings, that they may join us in the cause. We must divide the people by national jealousies, and occupy them with commotions, wars, and conquests. They must be alarmed at the power of this free nation. Let us form a league against the common enemy, demolish that sacrilegious standard, overturn that throne of rebellion, and stifle in its birth the flame of revolution.

And, indeed, the civil and religious tyrants of nations formed a general combination; and, multiplying their followers by force and seduction, they marched in hostile

array against the free nation; and surrounding the altar
and the pyramid of natural law, they demanded with loud
cries : —

What is this new and heretical doctrine? what this impious altar, this sacrilegious worship? True believers and
loyal subjects! can you suppose that truth has been first
discovered to-day, and that hitherto you have been walking
in error? that those men, more fortunate than you have the
sole privilege of wisdom? And you, rebel and mis-
guided nation, perceive you not that your new leaders are
misleading you? that they destroy the principles of your
faith, and overturn the religion of your ancestors? Ah,
tremble! lest the wrath of heaven should kindle against
you; and hasten by speedy repentance to retrieve your
error.

But, inaccessible to seduction as well as to fear, the free
nation kept silence, and rising universally in arms, assumed
an imposing attitude.

And the legislator said to the chiefs of nations: —

If while we walked with a bandage on our eyes the light
guided our steps, why, since we are no longer blindfold,
should it fly from our search? If guides, who teach mankind to see for themselves, mislead and deceive them, what
can be expected from those who profess to keep them in
darkness?

But hark, ye leaders of nations! If you possess the truth
show it to us, and we will receive it with gratitude, for
we seek it with ardor, and have a great interest in finding
it. We are men, and liable to be deceived; but you are
also men, and equally fallible. Aid us then in this labyrinth, where the human race has wandered for so many
ages; help us to dissipate the illusion of so many prejudices
and vicious habits. Amid the shock of so many opinions
which dispute for our acceptance, assist us in discovering
the proper and distinctive character of truth. Let us this
day terminate the long combat with error. Let us establish between it and truth a solemn contest, to which we
will invite the opinions of men of all nations. Let us con-
voke a general assembly of the nations. Let them be
judges in their own cause; and in the debate of all systems,

let no champion, no argument, be wanting, either on the
side of prejudice or of reason ; and let the sentiment of a
general and common mass of evidence give birth to a universal concord of opinions and of hearts.

GENERAL ASSEMBLY OF THE NATIONS

THUS spoke the legislator ; and the multitude, seized with
those emotions which a reasonable proposition always
inspires, expressed its applause ; while the tyrants,
left without support, were overwhelmed with confusion.

A scene of a new and astonishing nature then opened to
my view. All that the earth contains of people and of nations ; men of every race and of every region, converging
from their various climates, seemed to assemble in one allotted place; where, forming an immense congress, distinguished in groups by the vast variety of their dresses,
features, and complexion, the numberless multitude presented a most unusual and affecting sight.

On one side I saw the European, with his short close
coat, pointed triangular hat, smooth chin, and powdered
hair ; on the other side the Asiatic, with a flowing robe,
long beard, shaved head, and round turban. Here stood
the nations of Africa, with their ebony skins, their woolly
hair, their body girt with white and blue tissues of bark,
adorned with bracelets and necklaces of coral, shells, and
glass ; there the tribes of the north, enveloped in their
leathern bags ; the Laplander, with his pointed bonnet and
his snow-shoes ; the Samoyede, with his feverish body and
strong odor ; the Tongouse, with his horned cap, and carrying his idols pendant from his neck ; the Yakoute, with his
freckled face ; the Kalmuc, with his flat nose and little re-
torted eyes. Farther distant were the Chinese, attired in
silk, with their hair hanging in tresses ; the Japanese, of
mingled race ; the Malays, with wide-spreading ears, rings
in their noses, and palm-leaf hats of vast circumference;
and the tatooed races of the isles of the southern ocean and
of the continent of the antipodes. The view of so many
varieties of the same species, of so many extravagant inven-

tions of the same understanding, and of so many modifica-
tions of the same organization, affected me with a thousand
feelings and a thousand thoughts.* I contemplated with
astonishment this gradation of color, which, passing from a
bright carnation to a light brown, a deeper brown, dusky,
bronze, olive, leaden, copper, ends in the black of ebony
and of jet. And finding the Cassimerian, with his rosy
cheek, next to the sun-burnt Hindoo, and the Georgian by
the side of the Tartar, I reflected on the effects of climate
hot or cold, of soil high or low, marshy or dry, open or
shaded. I compared the dwarf of the pole with the giant
of the temperate zones, the slender body of the Arab with
the ample chest of the Hollander; the squat figure of the
Samoyede with the elegant form of the Greek and the
Sclavonian; the greasy black wool of the Negro with
the bright silken locks of the Dane; the broad face of the
Kalmuc, his little angular eyes and flattened nose, with the
oval prominent visage, large blue eyes, and aquiline nose
of the Circassian and Abazan. I contrasted the brilliant
calicoes of the Indian, the well-wrought stuffs of the European, the rich furs of the Siberian, with the tissues of bark,
of osiers, leaves, and feathers of savage nations; and the
blue figures of serpents, flowers, and stars, with which they
painted their bodies. Sometimes the variegated appearance
of this multitude reminded me of the enamelled meadows
of the Nile and the Euphrates, when, after rains or inun-
dations, millions of flowers are rising on every side. Sometimes their murmurs and their motions called to mind the

---

* A hall of costumes in one of the galleries of the Louvre would,
in every point of view, be an interesting establishment. It would
furnish an admirable treat to the curiosity of a great number of persons, excellent models to the artist, and useful subjects of meditation
to the physician, the philosopher, and the legislator.

Picture to yourself a collection of the various faces and figures of
every country and nation, exhibiting accurately, color, features, and
form; what a field for investigation and inquiry as to the influence of
climate, customs, food, etc. It might truly be called the science of
man! Buffon has attempted a chapter of this nature, but it only
serves to exhibit more strikingly our actual ignorance. Such a collection is said to have been begun at St. Petersburg, but it is also said
at the same time to be as imperfect as the vocabulary of the three hundred languages. The enterprise would be worthy of the French nation.

numberless swarms of locusts which, issuing from the desert, cover in the spring the plains of Hauran.

At the sight of so many rational beings, considering on the one hand the immensity of thoughts and sensations assembled in this place, and on the other hand, reflecting on the opposition of so many opinions, and the shock of so many passions of men so capricious, I struggled between astonishment, admiration, and secret dread — when the legislator commanded silence, and attracted all my attention.

Inhabitants of earth! a free and powerful nation addresses you with words of justice and peace, and she offers you the sure pledges of her intentions in her own conviction and experience. Long afflicted with the same evils as yourselves, we sought for their source, and found them all derived from violence and injustice, erected into law by the inexperience of past ages, and maintained by the prejudices of the present. Then abolishing our artificial and arbitrary institutions, and recurring to the origin of all right and reason, we have found that there existed in the very order of nature and in the physical constitution of man, eternal and immutable laws, which only waited his observance to render him happy.

O men! cast your eyes on the heavens that give you light, and on the earth that gives you bread! Since they offer the same bounties to you all — since from the power that gives them motion you have all received the same life, the same organs, have you not likewise all received the same right to enjoy its benefits? Has it not hereby declared you all equal and free? What mortal shall dare refuse to his fellow that which nature gives him?

O nations! let us banish all tyranny and all discord; let us form but one society, one great family; and, since human nature has but one constitution, let there exist in future but one law, that of nature — but one code, that of reason — but one throne, that of justice — but one altar, that of union.

He ceased; and an immense acclamation resounded to the skies. Ten thousand benedictions announced the transports of the multitude; and they made the earth re-echo JUSTICE, EQUALITY, and UNION.

But different emotions soon succeeded; soon the doctors and the chiefs of nations exciting a spirit of dispute, there was heard a sullen murmur, which growing louder, and spreading from group to group, became a vast disorder; and each nation setting up exclusive pretensions, claimed a preference for its own code and opinion.

You are in error, said the parties, pointing one to the other. We alone are in possession of reason and truth. We alone have the true law, the real rule of right and justice, the only means of happiness and perfection. All other men are either blind or rebellious.

And great agitation prevailed.

Then the legislator, after enforcing silence, loudly exclaimed: —

What, O people! is this passionate emotion? Whither will this quarrel conduct you? What can you expect from this dissension? The earth has been for ages a field of disputation, and you have shed torrents of blood in your controversies, What have you gained by so many battles and tears? When the strong has subjected the weak to his opinion, has he thereby aided the cause of truth?

O nations! take counsel of your own wisdom. When among yourselves disputes arise between families and individuals, how do you reconcile them? Do you not give them arbitrators?

Yes, cried the whole multitude.

Do so then to the authors of your present dissensions. Order those who call themselves your instructors, and who force their creeds upon you, to discuss before you their reasons. Since they appeal to your interests, inform yourselves how they support them.

And you, chiefs and governors of the people! before dragging the masses into the quarrels resulting from your diverse opinions, let the reasons for and against your views be given. Let us establish one solemn controversy, one public scrutiny of truth — not before the tribunal of a corruptible individual, or of a prejudiced party, but in the grand forum of mankind — guarded by all their information and all their interests. Let the natural sense of the whole human race be our arbiter and judge.

MÉRIMÉE

LETTERS TO ANONYMA

PROSPER MÉRIMÉE

PROSPER MÉRIMÉE was born in Paris in 1803 and died in 1870. Though a writer of exceptional gifts and range, he will perhaps be best known to posterity by his *Lettres à Une Inconnue*, only published after the author's death. He knew the languages and literatures of England, Spain, Italy, Germany, and Russia, besides the classics, and was an enthusiastic archæologist. In early life he published translations of plays, and original works in history and fiction. His novel "Columba" is still popular. He became an Academician in 1844 and a Senator in 1853. He had cultivated an austere manner which mystified his friends. They believed him incapable of any tender emotion. A cynic of cynics, he was supposed to be a stranger to love. The greater, therefore, was the surprise when these "Letters" revealed Mérimée as the clandestine lover, not the slave of love, indeed, but still entangled in its web, which he did not seriously try to break. Who the Anonyma was we do not know, nor does it matter. Whether a French or English woman, her power is confessed in these strangest of genuine love letters. They sparkle with wit and a hundred charms - not commonly found in epistles acceptable to the average feminine heart as substitutes for the poetical. The correspondence lasted from 1842 until 1870.

(143)

LETTERS TO ANONYMA

PARIS, *Thursday.* — Everything about you is mysterious; and the causes inducing in others a certain line of conduct, impel you always to opposite action. I am becoming accustomed to your ways, and nothing any longer surprises me. Spare me, I beg of you; do not put to too harsh a test the unfortunate habit I have contracted of finding good in all that you do. I was perhaps a little too frank in my last letter, in speaking of my character. An old diplomatist, a shrewd man of the world, has often advised me, "Never say any ill of yourself; your dear friends will say quite enough." Do not, however, take literally my self-depreciation; believe, rather, that my chief virtue is modesty, which I carry to excess, and I tremble lest it injure me in your estimation. I may at another time, when inspired, supply you with an exact catalogue of my qualities; for the list will be long, and being to-day slightly indisposed I dare not project myself into this "progression of the infinite." You cannot guess where I was on Saturday evening, and in what engaged at midnight. I was on the platform of one of the towers of Notre Dame, drinking orangeade and eating ices in the society of four friends and a magnificent moon, with the accompaniment of a great owl flapping his wings. Paris at this hour, and by moonlight, is a superb spectacle, resembling a city of the "Thousand and One Nights," the inhabitants of which have been enchanted during their sleep; but Parisians usually go to bed at midnight, and are most stupid in so doing. Our party was a curious one, four nations being represented, each of us with a different way of thinking; but the bore of it was, that some of us, inspired by the moon and the owl, thought it necessary to assume a poetic tone and indulge in platitudes — in fact, little by little every one began to utter nonsense.

10

I do not know by what chain of ideas this semi-poetic evening leads me to think of one that was not in the least so ; a ball given by some young men, to which all the opera dancers were invited. These women are usually very stupid ; but I have observed how superior they are in moral delicacy to the men of their class. Only one vice separates them from other women — that of poverty.

PARIS.— Frankness and truth toward women are not desirable — indeed quite the reverse ; for see, you regard me as a Sardanapalus because I have been to a ball of *figurantes*. You reproach me as for a crime, and reprove as a still greater crime my praise of these poor girls. Make them rich, I repeat, and only their good qualities will remain ; but insurmountable barriers have been raised by the aristocracy between the different classes of society, so that few persons understand how entirely what passes beyond the wall resembles what passes within. I will tell you a story that I heard in this perverse society. In the Rue Saint Honoré lived a poor woman who never left her miserable attic, and who had a little girl twelve years old, neat, reserved, well behaved, who never spoke to any one. Three times a week this child left home in the afternoon, returning alone at midnight, being a supernumerary at the opera. One night she came down to ask for a lighted candle, which being given to her, the porter's wife followed her after a while to the garret, where she found the woman dead on her wretched pallet, and the child occupied in burning a quantity of letters which she drew from a battered trunk. She said, " My mother died to-night, and charged me to burn these papers without reading them." The child knows the name neither of father nor mother, is entirely alone in the world, having no other resource than that of personating monkeys, vultures and devils on the stage. Her mother's last counsel to her was, to remain a *figurante* and to be very good ; which she certainly is, even very pious, and does not care to relate her history. Will you be good enough to tell me if there is not infinitely greater merit in this child leading such a life, than belongs to you who enjoy the singular happiness of irreproachable surroundings, and are endowed with a nature so refined as to picture for me, in a measure, the bloom of civilization? I will tell you the truth. I can only endure low society at rare intervals, and through an inexhaustible curiosity respecting all varieties of the human species, seldom entering that of men, there being to me something inexpressibly repulsive in it, especially with us; but in Spain, muleteers and bull-fighters were my friends. I have more than once eaten from the platter of people at whom an Englishman would not look for fear of compromising his self-respect; and I have even drunk from the same leathern bottle with a galley-slave; there was, however, but one bottle, and one must drink when thirsty. Do not believe that I have a predilection for the *canaille*. I simply like to study different manners, different faces, and to hear a different language. Ideas are the same everywhere, and aside from the merely conventional, I do not find good breeding limited to the Faubourg Saint-Germain. All this is Arabic to you, and I know not why I say it. My mother has been very ill, exciting in me great uneasiness, but is now out of danger, and will be in a few days entirely restored to health. I cannot endure anxiety, and during the period of danger I have been in a state of distraction.

As a rule, never select a woman for a confidante; soon or late you would repent of it. Learn also, that there is nothing more common than to do evil for the very pleasure of it. Shake off your ideas of optimism, and be convinced that we are in this world simply to fight against each other. In this connection, I remember that a learned friend who reads hieroglyphics told me that on the Egyptian sarcophagi are often engraved these two words: LIFE, WAR; which proves that I did not originate the maxim just given you. The characters are represented by one of those vases called *canopes*, and a shield with an arm holding a lance.

PARIS.— Your reproaches afford me great pleasure. As to your over-moral relative who says so much evil of me, he recalls Thwackum, who asks: CAN ANY VIRTUE EXIST WITHOUT RELIGION? Have you read "Tom Jones," a book as immoral as all of mine put together? If it was prohibited, of course you read it. What a droll education you receive in England! And what avails it! Breath is wasted for years in preaching to a young girl, with the certain result that she will desire to know precisely that immoral person for whom it was hoped to inspire her with a holy aversion. What an admirable story is that of the serpent!

All that I know of you pleases me prodigiously. I study you with ardent curiosity. I have certain theories respecting the veriest trifles,— gloves, boots, buckles, to which I attach much importance, having discovered that a certain relation exists between the character of women and the caprice,— or rather, the connection of ideas and the ratiocination,— that dictates the choice of such or such stuffs. I could show, for instance, that a woman who wears blue gowns is a coquette and affects sentiment.

I went the other day on a boating excursion, a number of sailing vessels being on the river, in one of which were several women of a vulgar class. As the vessels reached the shore, from one of them stepped a man about forty years of age who was persistently beating a drum for his own amusement; and while I was admiring the musical organization of this animal a young woman approached him, called him a monster, saying that she had followed him from Paris, and if he declined to admit her to his society he should dearly rue it. The man continued to pound his drum vigorously during this appeal, replying phlegmatically that he would not have her in his boat, whereupon she ran to the vessel moored farthest from the shore and within twenty feet of our own, and sprang into the river, splashing us infamously; but although she had put out my cigar my indignation did not hinder me, aided by my friends, from dragging her out before she had swallowed two glasses of the muddy water. The noble object of such despair had not budged, and grumbled between his teeth: "Why did you pull her out if she wished to drown herself?" Why is it that these cold, indifferent men are the most beloved? I asked myself this question as we sailed home; I ask it still, and I beg you to tell me if you know.

PARIS.— *Mariquita de mi alma*— it is thus I should begin were we at Granada. I believe, notwithstanding my anger, that I love you better in your fits of pouting than I do in any other mood. One sentence of your letter made me laugh like one of the blessed. Without hostile preliminaries for the blow, you tell me SHORT AND SWEET : " My love is promised." You say that you are engaged for life as if it were simply for a quadrille ! Very good ! My time, it seems, has been profitably employed in discussing love, marriage, and the rest of it ! You still say and believe, that when told to "love Monsieur," you at once love. Has your engagement been signed before a notary ? When I was a school-boy I received a love-letter with two flaming hearts pierced with a dart, from a seamstress, which precious effusion was captured by the school-master, and I locked up ; and, as a denouement of the drama, the object of this budding passion consoled herself with the cruel schoolmaster. Engagements are fatal to the happiness of those who subscribe to them. It is a primal law of nature to hold in aversion whatever savors of the obligatory. All bonds are inherently irksome ; and if so trammeled, I seriously believe that you would love ME ; me, to whom you have promised nothing.

To me you appear very devout, superstitious even. This reminds me of a pretty little girl from Granada, who when mounting her mule to cross the Ronda Pass, a route famous for robbers, devoutly kissed her thumb and struck her breast three times, assured by this pious action that the robbers would not dare to show themselves, provided that the *Ingles*—that is myself ; with these people all travelers are English—would not swear by the Blessed Virgin and the saints : but only this wicked mode of speech will make these horses move among such roads. See "Tristram Shandy." You are weak and jealous, two qualities not objectionable in a woman, but defects in a man, and I possess them both. Let us cease quarreling and be friends. I kiss the hand that you offer me in pledge of peace.

September.— You allude to special reasons that prevent you from seeking to be with me. I respect secrets and

will not pry into your motives. Some kind busybody may
have taken me for the text of a sermon that sways you;
nevertheless, in fearing me you would be doing me an infinite wrong. Be reassured I shall never be in love with
you; I am now too old and have been too unhappy. I
once felt myself falling in love and fled to Spain, one of
the finest actions of my life, the cause of the journey never
being suspected by the lady. To remain, would have been
to commit a great folly — that of offering to a woman in
exchange for all that was dear to her, a tenderness that I
was conscious of being inadequate to the sacrifice I should
have tempted her to make. " Love excuses all, but we
must be quite sure that it IS love; " and this precept, be
assured, is more inflexible than those of your Methodistical
friends. In me you will acquire a true friend, while I may
find a woman with whom I am not in love and in whom I
can confide. Should I die this year, you will feel regret
at having hardly known me.

The remembrance of your splendid black eyes is no in-
considerable element of my admiration for you. I am old,
and nearly insensible to beauty, yet on hearing a fastidious
man say that you are very handsome I could not repress a
feeling of sadness, and for this reason: that I am horribly
jealous (I am not the least in love with you) of my
friends, and distressed at the thought that your beauty exposes you to the attentions of men who only appreciate in
you that which attracts me the least. The truth is, I am in
a frightful humor; nothing makes me so melancholy as a
marriage. The Turks who buy a woman after examining
her like a fat sheep, are more honest than we who cover
our shameful bargain with the transparent varnish of
hypocrisy. I have often asked myself what I could say to
my wife on my wedding day, and have found nothing possible unless it be a compliment to her nightcap. The devil
would be very cunning to entrap me to such a *fête*. The
woman's rôle is easier than that of the man. On that day
she models herself after the Iphigenia of Racine; but if
she observe at all keenly, what droll things she must see!
Of course at this *fête* love will be made to you, and you
will be regaled with allusions to domestic happiness. When

angry, the Andalusians say: "I would stab the sun but for the fear of leaving the world in darkness."

You jest in saying so charmingly that you are afraid of me. You know that I am ugly, capricious in temper, always abstracted, and often tormenting when suffering. Do you not find all this reassuring? You are no python-ess; you will never be in love with me. You are a combination of the angel and the devil, but the latter predominates. You call me a tempter! Dare to say that this word does not apply more strongly to yourself! Have you not thrown a bait to me, poor little fish that I am? And holding me at the end of your line you keep me dancing between heaven and earth, until weary of the sport it may please you to cut me loose, and I shall swim about with the hook in my gills, but never again to find the angler. Adieu, *niña de mi ojos*.

Lady M—— announced to me yesterday that you are going to be married. This being so, burn my letters: I burn yours, and adieu. You know my principle that does not permit me to maintain an intimacy with a married woman whom I have known as demoiselle, with a widow whom I have known as wife. The change in a woman's legal status affects also her various social relations, and always for the worse. In a word, I cannot bear my female friends to marry, therefore, should you marry, let us forget each other. I still love you and commend myself to your prayers.

PARIS. — We are becoming very tender. You say to me, *Amigo de mi alma*, which is very pretty on a woman's lips. It is needless to say that the answer to my question has greatly pleased me. You say, perhaps involuntarily, to my delight, that the husband of a woman who should resemble you would inspire you with true compassion. I believe this readily, and I add that no one would be more unhappy, unless it be the man who should love you. You must be cold and mocking in your fits of ill humor, with an invincible pride that prevents you from saying, "I am in the wrong." Add to this an energy of character causing you to despise complaints and tears. When by the

lapse of time and force of events we shall become friends,
it will be seen which of the two can more skillfully torment the other. The mere thought of it makes my hair
stand on end. Cannot we meet without mystery and as
good friends? I am ill and terribly weary. Come to Paris,
dear Mariquita, and excite my love anew. I shall never
be weary then.

PARIS. — What is your malady? Some heart sorrow?
Some mysterious phrases of yours would seem to imply as
much. You both suffer and enjoy through the head, but
entre nous, I do not believe that you are yet in the enjoyment of that viscus (*viscère*) called heart, which is only
developed toward twenty-five years of age, in the forty-
sixth degree of latitude. Now you are knitting your beautiful black eyebrows and saying: "The insolent fellow,
to doubt that I have a heart!" This is, indeed, the great
pretension of the day; since the manufacture of such numbers of so-called passionate romances and poems, all women
pretend to have a heart. Wait yet a while; when you
have a heart in earnest, send me the tidings. You will
then regret the happy time in which you only lived by
the head, and the ills you now suffer will seem only pin-
pricks in comparison with the stabs that will rain upon
you with the birth of passion. Your gracious promise to
give me your portrait is a double pleasure, as a proof of
your increased confidence in me. I am thinking at this
moment of the expression of your countenance, which is a
little hard : A LIONESS, THOUGH TAME. I kiss your mysterious feet a thousand times. Adieu.

LONDON, *December.*—Tell me, in the name of God, if
you be of God, *querida Mariquita*, why have you not answered my letter? Your last one put me into such a flutter that my reply, on the impulse of the moment, was
hardly common sense. Why will you not see me? Your
chief motive appears to be the dread of doing something
IMPROPER, as they say here. I do not accept as serious
your fear that a more intimate knowledge of me may destroy your illusions. Were this indeed your motive, you

would be the first woman, the first human being even, the gratification of whose desires or curiosity had been hindered by a similar consideration. The thing can be IMPROPER only as regards society. You know in advance that I shall not eat you. Note in passing, that this word SOCIETY makes us unhappy from the moment of donning inconvenient garments at its behests, until the day of our death. A man's discretion, and mine exceptionally, is the greater in proportion that it is trusted. There is, and there will be throughout your life, a conflict between your intuitions and your conventual discipline; thence arises the whole difficulty.

The sea always makes me excessively ill, and THE GLAD WATERS OF THE DARK BLUE SEA are only agreeable to me when seen from the shore; after my first voyage to England it required a fortnight to restore my usual color, that of the pale horse of the Apocalypse. One day at dinner I was seated opposite to Madame V——, who suddenly exclaimed, "Until to-day I thought you were an Indian!"

PARIS, *March*, 1842.—Since you do not refuse my gifts, I send you conserves of rose, bergamot, and jasmine. I offered you Turkish slippers, but have been plundered. Will you have this Turkish mirror in exchange? It may be more acceptable, for you strike me as being even more COQUETTE than in the year of grace 1840. It was in December, and you wore ribbed silk stockings.

You are now rich — rich, that is to say free. A capital idea this of your friend, who is another Auld Robin Gray. He must have been in love with you, which you will never confess, for you too dearly love mystery. Why not go to Rome and Naples to see the sun? You are worthy of comprehending Italy, and would return richer in ideas and sensations. I do not advise Greece; your skin is not sufficiently tough to resist all the villainous insects that devour one in that classic land. Speaking of Greece, I send you a blade of grass gathered on the hill of Anthela at Thermopylæ, on the spot where fell the last of the "three hundred." It is not improbable that particles of the dead Leonidas mingle with the constituent atoms of this little flower. It was, I remember, at this very spot, while lying on heaped-up straw and talking to my friend Ampère, that I told him that among the tender memories remaining to me there was only one unmixed with bitterness. I thought of our beautiful youth. PRAY KEEP MY FOOLISH FLOWER.

I revisited my dear Spain in 1840, passing two months at Madrid where I saw a droll revolution, admirable bull-fights, and the triumphal entry of Espartero, the most comical show possible. I stayed at the country-house of a friend, who in her devotion to me is a sister, and went every morning to Madrid, returning to dine with six charming women, of whom the eldest was thirty-six years old. Owing to the revolution I was the only man permitted to go and come freely, so these six unfortunates had no other *cortejo*. They spoiled me prodigiously. I was not in love with any of them, in which perhaps I was wrong ; and though not deceived by these privileges conferred by the revolution, I found it very sweet to be Sultan, even *ad honores*. On my return I indulged in the innocent pleasure of having a book printed, not published, magnificent in binding and engravings. I would offer you this rarity, but it is historic and pedantic, and so bristling with Greek, Latin, and even Osque (do you know in the least what Osque is?), as to be beyond your mark. Last summer, finding myself with money in my pocket, I roved between Malta, Athens, and Constantinople for five months, during which there were not five tedious minutes. I saw the Sultan in varnished boots and a black frock coat, afterward, covered with diamonds, in the procession of Baïram ; on which occasion a very handsome dame, on whose slipper I trod inadvertently, gave me a tremendous blow with her fist, calling me a *giaour*, and this was my sole association with Turkish beauties. At Athens and in Asia I saw the finest monuments in the world, and the loveliest landscapes. The drawback consisted in fleas, and gnats the size of larks. With all this I have grown very old. My firman gives me turtle-dove hair, which is a pretty Oriental metaphor for expressing an ugly truth. Imagine your friend quite gray ! Your claim to rival Ionic

and Corinthian capitals in my heart, made me laugh. In
the first place, I like only the Doric, and there are no
capitals, not even those of the Parthenon, which are worth
to me the memory of a friendship.

PARIS, *May*, 1842. — If I must be frank, and you know
that I cannot correct myself of this defect, I will confess
that you struck me as much improved physically, not at
all so morally; that you have a very fine complexion, and
beautiful hair which I looked at more than your cap,
which probably was worthy of admiration, as you seem
to be provoked that I did not appreciate it; but I have
never been able to distinguish lace from calico. You
have still the figure of a sylph, and though rather *blasé*
as to black eyes, I never saw finer ones at Constantinople
nor at Smyrna.

Now for the reverse of the medal. You have continued
a child in many things, and have acquired into the bargain
a nice little dash of selfishness and hypocrisy, which may
be serviceable, only it is nothing of which one need boast.
You do not know how to conceal your first impulses, but
think to make amends by a host of puerile evasions. What
do you gain by it? Remember Jonathan Swift's fine
maxim : A LIE IS TOO GOOD A THING TO BE WASTED.
This magnanimous idea of being hard to yourself, will, assuredly, lead you very far, and a few years hence you will
find yourself as happy as the Trappist, who, after having
perseveringly scourged himself should one day discover that
there is no Paradise. It is your Satanic pride that has
hindered you from seeing me. You believe, at least, that
you have pride, but it is only a petty vanity well worthy
of a devotee. The fashion of the day tends to sermons—
do you frequent them? This alone is lacking in you! As
respects myself, I am not more of a hypocrite, in which
perhaps I am wrong : certain it is that I am not therefore
the better liked. Ah! great news! The first Academician
out of the forty who shall die will be the cause of my
paying thirty-nine visits. I shall pay them as awkwardly
as possible, and shall gain thirty-nine enemies. It would

be tedious to explain to you this 'fit of ambition. Suffice it that the Academy is now my blue cashmere. Be happy, but remember this maxim : Never to commit other follies than those agreeable to you. Perhaps you prefer M. de Talleyrand's apothegm, that one must guard against good impulses, because they are nearly always honest.

PARIS, *June*, 1842. — I have received your purse, which exhales a charmingly aristocratic perfume, and if embroidered by yourself does you honor ; in it also I recognize your recent taste for the positive. It would have been poetical to value it at one or two stars ; and I should prize it even more had you deigned to add to it some lines from your white hands. No, I will not accept your pheasants which you offer in a detestable way, saying, moreover, disagreeable things about my Turkish sweetmeats. It is you who have the palate of a *giaour* in not appreciating the food of houris. Your conscience, I am sure, is often less lenient than I, whom you accuse of hardness and indifference. The hypocrisy that you now cleverly practice, merely as a game, will, in the end, play you a trick — that of becoming a reality. As to coquetry, the inseparable companion of the deplorable vice that you affect, you have long been duly convicted of it, and it became you when tempered by frankness, by heart and imagination. Is it your friendship that you designate as an ESSENCE ? a word I like. Since all that you wish for comes to pass, I humbly pray you to intercede with Destiny that I may be an Academician ; but the plague must supervene among these gentlemen to favor my chances, to improve which I must also borrow a little of your talent for hypocrisy. I am too old to reform, and in making the effort I should perhaps become even worse than I am. Formerly I had no high opinion of my precious self, but my self-esteem has increased, simply because the world has degenerated. I pass my evenings in re-reading my books which are being republished, and find myself very immoral and sometimes stupid. The question now is to diminish the immorality and stupidity with the least trouble ; but at the cost of BLUE DEVILS to myself.

CHALON-SUR-SAONE, *June*, 1842.—Thanks for your prayers, if they are not a mere rhetorical figure. I am aware of your devoutness, which is now the fashion, like blue cashmeres. Our French devotion displeases me, being a species of shallow philosophy proceeding from the head and not the heart. When you have seen the Italians you will agree with me that their devotion is alone genuine: only one cannot have it at will, and one must be born beyond the Alps or Pyrenees to possess such faith. You cannot imagine the disgust with which our present society inspires me, and one would say that it had sought by every possible combination to augment the mass of *ennui* apparently necessary in the order of the world; while in Italy everything tends to render existence easy and endurable.

AVIGNON, *July*, 1842.—Since you assume this tone *ma foi*, I yield. Give me brown bread, which is better than none at all, only permit me to say that it IS brown, and write to me again. You see that I am humble and submissive. The figure of rhetoric of which you believe yourself to be the inventor has been long in use, and might be clothed with an uncouth Greek name, but in French it is known under the less lofty term of lying. Make use of it with me as little as possible, and do not lavish it on others: it must be kept for great occasions. Do not seek to find the world foolish and ridiculous; it is only too much so in reality. It is better to cherish illusions, and I hold several which are perhaps rather transparent, but I exert myself to retain them. I am sorry that you read Homer in Pope, and recommend as preferable Dugas-Montbel's translation, which is the only readable one. If you had the courage to brave ridicule and the time to spare, you would read Planché's "Greek Grammar" a month to make you sleep, which would not fail of this effect; at the end of two months you would amuse yourself by comparing M. Montbel's translation with the Greek; and two months afterward you would easily perceive from the ambiguity of phrase, that the Greek has a meaning other than that given by the translator. At the end of a year

you would read Homer as you do a melody and the accompaniment ; the melody being the Greek, the accompaniment the translation.   It is possible that this would incite
the wish to study Greek in earnest ; but such assiduity is
also to presuppose you with neither dresses to occupy you,
nor people to whom they may be displayed.   Everything
in Homer is remarkable.   His epithets, so seemingly
strange in French, are singularly appropriate.   I remember
that he calls the sea " purple," and I never understood its
application until last year.   I was in a little *caïque* on the
Gulf of Lepanto, going to Delphi.   The sun was setting,
and as it disappeared the sea wore for ten minutes a magnificent tint of dark violet — but this requires the air, the
sea, the sun of Greece.   I hope that you will never become
sufficiently an artist to discover that Homer was a great
painter.   I hope that you find me this time passably resigned and decorous, *Signora Fornarina!*

PARIS, *August*, 1842. — I congratulate you on your Greek
studies, and to begin with something that may interest you
will tell you the word by which in Greek persons possessing like yourself hair of which they are justly proud are
described : *efplokamos*.   *Ef*, much ; *plokamos*, curl.   Homer,
somewhere says : —

> « *Nimfi efplokamouça Calypso.* »
> (Curly-tressed nymph Calypso.)

I am sorry that you should set out so late in the season
for Italy, which you will see only through atrocious rains
that obscure half the charm of the loveliest mountains in
the world, and you will be obliged to accept on faith my
eulogies on the exquisite skies of Naples.   Moreover, you
will have no good fruit, but in compensation, *becaficos*, so
called because they live on grapes.

While packing my trunk at Avignon, two venerable figures
entered, announcing themselves as members of the Municipal Council.   I supposed them emissaries from some church,
when they informed me with much pomposity and prolixity
that they wished to commend to my loyalty and virtue a
lady about to travel with me.   I replied very crossly that
I should be very loyal and virtuous but that I detested

traveling with women, whose presence precluded smoking. The mail coach arrived, within which I found a large, handsome woman, simply and coquettishly attired, who declared herself to be always very ill in a carriage, and despaired of reaching Paris alive. Our *tête-à-tête* began, and I was as polite and amiable as I find it possible to be while remaining in a cramped position. My companion talked well, without any Marseillaise accent, was an ardent Bonapartist, very enthusiastic, believed in the immortality of the soul, not too much in the Catechism, and saw things generally *en beau;* nevertheless, I was conscious that she felt a certain fear of me. We were some fifty odd hours alone; but though we chatted immensely I found it impossible to come to any conclusion respecting my neighbor except that she was married, and a person of good society. On arriving at Paris she precipitated herself into the arms of an excessively ugly man, no doubt her father, and raising my hat I was about entering a cab, when my unknown, leaving the gentleman, said in an agitated voice: "Monsieur, I am much moved by the respectful consideration shown me by you, for which I cannot sufficiently express my gratitude; and I shall never forget my good fortune in traveling with so ILLUSTRIOUS a man." And this word explains the Municipal Councilors, and the terror of the lady. They had evidently seen my name on the register, and the lady, having read my books, expected to be swallowed alive, which opinion no doubt is shared by many of my feminine readers. This incident put me into a bad humor for two days. It is a singular thing, that having at one period of my life become a very worthless fellow, I lived during two years on my former good reputation; and since resuming my very moral life, I now am considered a scamp. . . . If you are surprised that the goddesses are blondes, you will be still more astonished at Naples at seeing statues whose hair is painted red. It seems that beautiful women formerly used red, even gold powder; but on the other hand you will see in the pictures of the *Studii,* a number of goddesses with black hair, descriptive of which there is in Greek a terrible word: *mélankhétis:* the $\chi\alpha$ being a diabolical aspirate.

It distresses me to perceive your rapid progress in Satan-
ism, that you are becoming ironical, sarcastic, and even
diabolical, all which words are drawn from the Greek, the
meaning of the last being calumniator. You jest at my
finest qualities, and even your praise is impaired by a reti-
cence and cautiousness that deprive the commendation of
all merit. As for good company, I have often found it
mortally tedious. I am vain enough to believe myself not
out of place with unpretending persons whom I have long
known, and at a Spanish inn with muleteers and Andalusian
peasant women. Write that in my funeral oration and you
will have told the truth. And if I speak of this, it is that
I believe the time approaches for you to prepare it; for I
suffer excessively from confused sight, spasms, and frightful
headaches, which would indicate some serious affection of
the brain, and I may soon become, as Homer says, a guest
of gloomy Proserpine. I should be delighted were it to
sadden you for a fortnight.

I believe the ancients to have been more amusing than
ourselves : they had not such paltry aims, were not preoccupied by such inanities. Julius Cæsar at fifty-three was
guilty of follies for Cleopatra, and forgot all for her, nearly
to the point of drowning himself actually and figuratively.
What statesman of our generation is not callous, completely
insensible at the age at which he can aspire to be a
Deputy?

The little that I have seen of Greece has enlarged my
comprehension of Homer. Throughout the " Odyssey " one
sees the incredible love of the Greeks for their own country. To dwell in a foreign land is to them the greatest of
misfortunes ; but to die in exile is to them beyond all imagination frightful. You jest at my gastronomy ; do you
appreciate the entrails so greedily devoured by ancient
heroes? They are still eaten, and are truly delicious, being
composed of spiced and appetizing little crusts skewered by
perfumed mastic wood, which at once explains why the
priests reserved for themselves this tempting morsel of the
victims.

You ask if there are any Greek novels — there are many,
but very tedious in my opinion. " Daphnis and Chloe,"

translated by Courier is pretentionsly *naïf* and not over exemplary. An admirable novel, but very immoral, is " L'Ane de Lucius ; " one does not boast, however, of reading it though a masterpiece. The worst of the Greeks is, that their ideas of morality and decency differ so essentially from our own. If you have the courage to attempt history you will be charmed with Herodotus, who enchants me. Begin with "Anabasis or the Retreat of the Ten Thousand ; " take a map of Asia and follow these ten thousand rascals in their journey ; it is Froissard *gigantesque*. Lucian is the Greek with the most wit, or rather OUR wit : but he is a libertine and I dare not commend him.

I gratefully appreciate your condecension at the opera in permitting me to look at your face during two hours, and I owe it to truth to say that I admired it greatly, as also your hair, which I had never seen so near. As to your assertion of having refused nothing that I have asked of you, several millions of years in purgatory will be your penance for this fine falsehood. I do not remember comparing you to Cerberus, but you certainly bear him a resemblance, not only in your love for cakes, but in possessing three heads, or rather brains — one of a frightful coquette, the other of an old diplomatist ; the third I will not name, as to-day I wish to tell you nothing agreeable. I have returned from seeing " Frédégonde," which was excessively tedious, notwithstanding Mademoiselle Rachel, who has very handsome black eyes without white, as it is said has the devil. You tell me amiably that you do not wish to see me for fear of becoming wearied of me. If I am not mistaken, we have met six or seven times in six years, and adding up the minutes, we may have passed three or four hours together, the half of which was in silence. Admit that it is little flattering to my self-love to be treated thus after an intimacy of six years, and in face of the proofs of regard that you have vouchsafed me ; moreover, pardon the word, I think it somewhat silly. If you believe yourself to be doing wrong in meeting me, do you commit no fault in writing to me ? As I am not well versed in your catechism, this remains a perplexing question. I speak harshly perhaps, but you wound me, and I cannot imitate you in

11

ridding myself of a weight on the heart by eating cakes. But I will ask nothing more of you,— for you become every day more imperious, and develop a scandalous refinement in coquetry. You are careful to recall your eyes to me, which I have not forgotten though so seldom seen. You should see me were it only to escape from the atmosphere of flattery surrounding you. When I met you at the house of our friend, your extreme elegance greatly surprised me, and the quantity of cakes necessary to restore you after the fatigue of the opera astonished me still more ; not that I do not place coquetry and *gourmandise* in the first rank of your faults, but I thought the form of these defects a moral one ; believing that you bestowed little thought on your toilette, that you were a woman who eat merely through abstraction, and preferred to make an impression on men by your eyes and clever sayings rather than by your dresses. See how deceived I have been.

December, 1842.— Formerly the absurdities of others amused me, but now I prefer to conceal them from the world. I have also become more humane, and when witnessing lately the bull-fights at Madrid, the pleasurable sensations of ten years previous were not renewed. I have a horror of all suffering, and for some time past have believed in moral suffering. In short, I strive as much as possible to forget my ME ; and this in a few words is a list of my perfections. No, I have no *Vanagloria*. I see things too practically, perhaps, having been *escarmentado* through regarding them too poetically. I have passed my life in being praised for qualities that I do not possess, and calumniated for defects that are not mine.

Your letter does not surprise me in the least : for I now know you well enough to be certain that when a good thought strikes you it is at once repented of, and you strive to have it speedily forgotten — but this justice I will do you : that you understand admirably how to gild the most bitter pill. You compare me to the devil. I was quite conscious on Tuesday of not thinking enough about my old books and too much of your gloves and *bottines*. But in spite of all that you say with such diabolical coquetry, I cannot believe that you have the slightest fear of renewing at the Museum our former follies. It pleases you to have some vague mark for your coquetry, and you find it in me; but you do not wish it to be too near, for should you miss the target your vanity would suffer, and perhaps in approaching it closely you would discover it to be not worth your shaft. Have I read you aright?

I suffer terribly and cough incessantly, nevertheless I shall go to hear Rachel declaim tirades from "Phèdre" before several great men, and she will believe my cough to be a cabal against her. This evening I heard Madame Persiani sing, and she has reconciled me to human nature; were I King Saul I should choose her in place of David.

I am told that M. de Pongerville, the Academician, is about to die, which throws me into despair, for I shall not be chosen to replace him, and I wish he could wait until my time shall arrive. He has translated into verse a Latin named Lucretius, who died at the age of forty-three from having taken a philtre to make himself beloved, previous to which he wrote a great poem, atheistic, impious, abominable, on "The Nature of Things." You appear to me to grow more handsome, which I had thought impossible; but one always improves in beauty when in good health; and that comes with a hard heart and good digestion.

December, 1842.—I have been exceedingly ill with my throat, and all the fires of hell in my breast, and have passed several days in bed meditating on the strangeness of this world. I find myself on the declivity of a mountain whose summit, with much fatigue and little pleasure, I have hardly attained, the descent being so steep and tedious that perhaps it would be rather an advantage to fall into a crevice before reaching the bottom; while the only ray of consolation along the whole route has been a little distant sunshine, a few months passed in Italy, Spain, or in Greece while forgetting the whole world, the present, and especially the future. All this is far from gay: but some one brings me four volumes by Doctor Strauss, "The Life of Jesus," which in Germany is called *exegesis*, a pure Greek word they have found by which to express discussion on the point of a needle, but it is very amusing. I have remarked that the more closely a thing is shorn of any useful conclusion, the more amusing it becomes.

There are people who buy furniture of a color to suit their taste, but for fear of spoiling it shroud it in linen covers that are only removed when the furniture is worn out. In all that you do and say, you substitute a factitious for a true sentiment — this perhaps is DECORUM. You say in your letter, "I believe that I have never loved you so well as yesterday" — you should have added, "I love you less to-day." I often repent of being too loyal in my rôle of statue. You gave me your soul yesterday : I would have given you mine in return but you did not wish it. Always the linen cover !

Yesterday on returning from a dinner I discovered that I knew by heart the speech of Tecmessa that you admired, and being in a somewhat pensive mood I translated it into English verse, as I abhor French verse.

PARIS, *January*, 1843. — I heartily forgive your jest about the Academy, of which I think less than you believe. Should I ever be an Academician, I shall not be hard as a rock, though perchance a little case-hardened and mummified ; but rather a good fellow at heart.

I am reminded of an incident that occurred a fortnight ago at a dinner given by an Academician for the purpose of presenting Béranger to Mademoiselle Rachel. A number of celebrities were assembled. Rachel came late and her manner of entering displeased me ; while the men said so many silly things to her, and the women did so many on seeing her, that I remained in my corner ; besides, it is a year since I have spoken to her. After dinner, Béranger with his candor and usual good sense told her that she was wrong to fritter away her talent in salons, there being for her only one true public, that of the Théâtre Français. Rachel appeared to appreciate the advice, and to prove that she benefited by it, at once declaimed the first act of "Esther." Some one was needed to give her the cue, and by her direction a Racine was formally brought to me by an Academician who was officiating as *cicisbeo;* but I replied rudely that I knew nothing about verses and that there were persons present who being in that line would scan them much better. Hugo excused himself on account of his eyes; another for some other reason, the master of the house being finally victimized. Picture to yourself Rachel costumed in black, standing between the piano and tea-table, with a door behind her, assuming a theatrical pose and expression, the transformation being very fine and vastly amusing. This lasted about two minutes, then she began: —

"Est-ce toi, chère Elise?"

The confidante in the middle of his reply lets fall both book and spectacles, ten minutes passing before he can recover his page and his eyes. The audience perceive that Esther is getting into a rage. She resumes. The door behind opens, a servant enters, who is signed to withdraw. He hurriedly retreats but does not succeed in shutting the door, which remaining ajar swings to and fro, accompanying Rachel with a melodious and most comical creak. This not ceasing, Rachel puts her hand to her heart and grows faint, but, like a person accustomed to die on the stage, giving one time to come to her assistance. During this interlude Hugo and M. Thiers fall to quarreling on the subject of Racine, Hugo asserting that Racine had a narrow mind (*un petit esprit*) and Corneille a master intellect (*un grand*). "You say that," replied Thiers "because you are *un grand esprit;* you are the Corneille"— here Hugo's head assumed an air of great modesty —"of an epoch of which Casimir Delavigne is the Racine." Meanwhile the swoon passes off and the act is finished, but *fiascheggiando.* One of the guests who knows Rachel well, remarked: "How she must have sworn this evening on going away." This is my story; do not compromise me with the Academicians.

I deeply regret having exposed you through my persistency to such a frightful drenching. It rarely happens to me to sacrifice others to myself, and when it occurs I am filled with all possible remorse. Happiness only gives me strength, while it diminishes yours. *Wer besser liebt?* You laughed at me and received as a jest what I said as to the wish to sleep, or rather the torpor that sometimes steals over one when in a state of happiness so great as to preclude its utterance in words. I observed yesterday that you were under the influence of this sleep, which is worth many vigils, and I was too content to wish to disturb my happiness. It is in exaggerating facts by brooding on them that you have succeeded in making a star-chamber matter of what you have yourself termed FRIVOLITIES; and allow me to say, that the very obstinacy and rabid ferocity with which you thwart me as to these frivolities render them more dear to me, and endue them with a fresh importance. If I must see you only to resist the most innocent temptations, it is the rôle of a saint surpassing my strength, and the condition exacted by you that I transform myself into a statue, like the king in the "Arabian Nights," is simply insupportable. The only hypocrisy of which I am capable is that of concealing from those whom I love all the ill they do me; I might sustain the effort for a season; but forever, no. As to our walk, I am like a cat that continues to lick his moustache after lapping milk. Acknowledge that repose, even the *kef*, which is superior to all that is best of this nature, is nothing in comparison with the happiness "that is almost a pain." You claim to have spoiled me, but you do not understand the art; your triumph is to put me in a fury. Adieu, DEAREST!

PARIS, *February*, 1843.— Since seeing you I have been much in society, committing a multitude of academic meannesses which cost me a painful effort, having lost the habit, but doubtless I shall quickly pick it up again. To-day I saw five illustrious poets and writers of prose, and had night not overtaken me the thirty-six visits might possibly have been achieved at a dash. The drollery of it is the meeting one's rivals, several of whom glared as if they wished to eat me alive. Truth to say, I am worn out with this odious drudgery and should be glad to forget it all in an hour with you.

I have been this evening to the Italians, where, thanks to the *claquers*, my enemy Madame Viardot had a success.

I find that I have omitted to attend the Opera House Ball —where, alas! is the happy time in which I so enjoyed it? now it bores me horribly. Do I not seem to you very old? Theodore Hook is dead. Have you read Bulwer's "Ernest Maltravers," and "Alice," which contain charming pictures of old love and young love? You may reflect with pride on the strange influence you have exercised over my ideas and resolutions; you have read my thought as quickly as it was conceived — and yet yesterday, on the strength of a Greek verse, I went to Saint-Germain-l'Auxerrois, full of hope, but fruitlessly. Do you remember when we always divined each other's wishes? The other evening at the opera your rainbow costume inspired me with various fancies, but you have no need of coquetry with me. I do not love you better as a rainbow than in black. I have long suspected something diabolical in you, but am somewhat reassured in thinking that I have seen your feet, neither of which is cloven; nevertheless it may be that beneath these *bottines* you have a little claw concealed. I have passed a wretched night of suffering, and as a diversion shall think of your feet and hands.

I have received the sad news of the death by paralysis of poor Sharp,* one of my most intimate friends whom I was about to visit in London. I cannot yet accustom myself to the thought of seeing him no more.

My fate will be decided at the Academy on the fourteenth, which corresponds with the ides of March, the day of the death of my hero, Cæsar. Ominous, is it not? Reason encourages me to hope, but a depressing intuition whispers of failure. Meanwhile I conscientiously pay my visits. I find people very polite, quite accustomed to their parts and enacting them very much in earnest, while I strive to play mine with equal gravity, though I find it difficult. Does it not strike you as comical to say to a man, "Monsieur, I believe myself to be one of the forty cleverest men of France; I am worthy of you," and similar *facetiæ*. This must, moreover, be translated into civil and fitting phrase to suit the various persons; an occupation to weary me beyond endurance if prolonged. I envy the fate of women

* Mr. Sutton Sharp, a very distinguished English barrister.

who have no employment but to make themselves beautiful, and to rehearse the effect to be produced on others. I return your *cravate*, which was found in the anteroom of His Royal Highness the Duke de Nemours, but no one has asked any explanation of its presence in my pocket.

I am full of remorse for my fury, my only excuse being that the transition from our delicious halt in a strange species of oasis, to our walk, was too abrupt — it was falling from heaven to hell. You reproach me with being indifferent to every one; I suppose you simply mean that I am undemonstrative — when untrue to my nature I suffer. Admit also that it is sad, after becoming all that we are to each other, to find you still distrustful of me. Two personalities exist in you: the one all heart and soul; the other a beautiful statue, polished by society, draped in silk and cashmere, a charming automaton with most skillfully adjusted springs. We speak to the first, and find only the statue; but why need it be so lovely! You ask if I believe in the soul — not over much; nevertheless, on reflection I find an argument in favor of the hypothesis, namely: how could two inanimate substances give and receive a sensation by a union that would be simply insipid but for the idea that we associate with it? This is rather a pedantic mode of saying that when two persons who love, embrace each other, they experience a sensation quite different from that communicated by kissing the softest satin. But the argument has its value, and we will discuss metaphysics at our next meeting — a subject of which I am fond, for it is inexhaustible.

You shall have your portrait *en Turquesse*, and I have placed a *narghilé* in your hand to add a local coloring; but I must have my pay, or prepare for a terrible vengeance. I have been asked to-day to contribute a sketch for an album to be sold for the benefit of sufferers by an earthquake, and I shall give them your portrait!

PARIS, *April*, 1843. — You do well not to speak of Catullus. He is not an author to be read during Holy Week, and there are passages in his writings quite impossible to translate into French. We clearly see what love was at

Rome toward the year 50 before J. C. ; it was, however, a little better than love at Athens in the time of Pericles. Women were already a recognized force : they made men commit follies. Their power arose, not, as is commonly said, through Christianity, but I think through the influence that the barbarians of the North exercised over Roman society. The Germans were capable of exaltation. They loved the soul ; the Romans loved little save the body. It is true that for a long period women were without souls : they have none as yet in the East, and it is a pity. You comprehend how two souls speak to one another, but yours seldom responds to mine. I am glad that you value the verses of Musset, and you are right in comparing him with Catullus, who, however, wrote his native tongue better, while Musset has the defect of not believing more in the soul than Catullus, whom his time excused. Would you believe that a Roman could say pretty things, and could be tender? I will show you some verses that will fit in like wax *à propos* of our usual disputes. You will see that the ancients are worth more than your *Wilhelm Meister*.

Our walks have become a part of my life, and I hardly understand how I previously existed. In what mood shall I find you? Each time that we meet you are mailed in a fresh panoply of ice that only melts at the end of a quarter of an hour. By the time of my return you will have accumulated a veritable iceberg.

AVALLON, *August*, 1843. — I came here to visit an old uncle whom I have seldom seen. I dislike relations ; one is obliged to be familiar with persons whom one has rarely met because they happen to be the son of the same father as one's mother. My uncle, however, is a good fellow, not too provincial, and whom I should find agreeable if we possessed two ideas in common. The women here are as ugly as those of Paris, having, moreover, ankles as thick as posts. In addition to our moral perfections we have the advantage of being the ugliest and most stunted people in Europe. At Vezelay I found myself in a horrible little town perched on a high mountain, bored to death by the country people, and preoccupied by a speech I was to deliver.

I am a Representative, and you know me well enough to judge how odious to me is the rôle of a public man. While I sketched, a crowd gathered about me, emulating each other in conjectures as to the nature of my occupation. To console me there was an admirable church which owes to me its escape from demolition, and which I first saw soon after meeting you ; and I asked myself to-day if we were more mad then than now. There was also a natural terrace that a poet might well call a precipice, where I philosophized on the ME, on Providence, in the hypothesis that it exists ; and finished with the despairing thought that you are far away. I send you an owl's feather that I found in the abbatical church, having read in some book of magic that when a woman places it beneath her pillow she dreams of her friend.

SAINT-LUPICIN, *August*, 1843, 600 *metres above the level of the sea — in the midst of an ocean of very active and famished fleas.* — This village is in the Jura Mountains, is ugly to the last degree, filthy, and populous with fleas. I shall pass a night like those at Ephesus, but at my awaking, unfortunately, I shall find neither laurels nor Greek ruins. There are immense quantities of colossal flowers, a singularly keen and pure air, and the human voice can be heard at a league's distance. I have had leaden skies, a broken wheel, and a poulticed eye, all tolerably remedied : but I cannot become habituated to solitude — solitude in motion, than which there is nothing more sad ; and were I in prison, I should be more at my ease than thus roving alone about the country.

AVIGNON, 1843. — The district that I am now traversing is very fine, but the natives are stupid beyond measure. No one opens his mouth but to praise the country, and this from the priest to the porter. There is no appearance of that tact constituting the gentleman, which I found among the common people of Spain ; but with that exception it is impossible to find a country more nearly resembling Spain. There is the same aspect of town and landscape ; the workmen lie in the shade and drop their cloaks with a tragic air that is Andalusian; the odor of garlic and oil is mingled with that of oranges and jasmine; the streets are shaded with linen during the day, and the women have small, well-shod feet; there is nothing, even to the *patois*, that has not a flavor of Spain. A still closer relation exists in its abundance of gnats, fleas, and other insects, and I have yet two months of this life to pass before seeing human beings!

I have sent my sketches to Paris; besides, a Roman capital would not interest you,— devils, dragons, and saints forming the decoration. The devils of the first centuries of Christianity are not very seductive, and I am sure that you would not value dragons and saints. I have sketched a Maçon costume for you, the only graceful one I have seen, though the sash is so drolly placed as to afford no advantage in a slender over a thick waist,— the dress would seem to require a special physical organization. The cheapness of cotton stuffs and the facility of communication with Paris have wrought the disappearance of our national costumes. Avignon is filled with churches and palaces, all provided with battlemented and machicolated towers. The palace of the Pope is a model of a fortification for the Middle Ages, which proves what amiable security reigned toward the fourteenth century. There are subterranean chambers used by the Inquisition, with the remains of an infernal complicated machine, and furnaces for heating the irons with which heretics were tortured. The natives are as proud of their Inquisition as the English of their Magna Charta. "We also," say they, "have had *auto-da-fé*, and the Spaniards had none until after us!"

Toulon, *October.*— It is impossible to find a place dirtier or prettier than Marseilles; and these words are especially appropriate to its women. They have expressive countenances, fine black eyes, beautiful teeth, very small feet, and imperceptible ankles; but the pretty feet are shod in thick, cinnamon-colored stockings the color of Marseilles mud, and darned with cotton of twenty different tints. Their dresses are badly made, untidy and covered with stains, while their fine hair owes its lustre mainly to candle-grease. Add to this an atmosphere redolent of garlic mixed with fumes of rancid oil, and you have a picture of the Marseilles beauty. What a pity that nothing can be perfect in this world! Yet, in spite of all, they are ravishing — a positive triumph.

Your letter is admirably diplomatic; you practice the axiom that language has been given to man to conceal his thought: and yet I see between the lines the tenderest things in the world. I think unceasingly of my return to Paris, and my imagination paints I know not how many delicious moments passed at your side.

PARIS, 1843.— I WEARY FOR YOU, to make use of an ellipsis that you affect. I did not clearly realize that we were about to part for so long a time. Shall we really see each other no more? We separated without a word, almost without a look. I was sensible of a calm happiness not usual with me, and for a few moments I seemed to wish for nothing more. How ingenious you are in depriving others and yourself of an enchantment that comes so near! Doubtless I am wrong to use the word enchantment, as marmots probably never experience the sensation, and you were one of those pretty animals before Brahma transferred your soul to the body of a woman. But notwithstanding my ill-humor I love better to see you with your grand air of indifference than not at all. The affection you bear me is merely an emanation of the intellect. You are all mind, one of those chilly women of the North who live only through the head. Our characters are as opposite as our STAMINA, and though you may divine my thoughts, you can never comprehend them. Yet, with all these conflicting characteristics a great affinity exists between us; it is Goethe's *Walverwandschaft.* Throw away your faded flowers and come with me to seek fresh ones. You say that sunshine exercises a cheering influence over you,— and for myself, though I love you at all seasons, in all weather, the happiness of seeing you in sunshine is a more exquisite happiness still. Is it possible that you cannot SAY to me all that you write? What is this *bizarre* timidity that hinders frankness, prompts you to wrap your thoughts in words more perplexing than the Apocalypse, and to assert the most extraordinary falsehood rather than allow a word of truth to escape which would give me such pleasure? Do you believe in the devil? In my opinion the pith of the matter lies there. If he terrifies you, contrive that he do not carry you off. I do not guaranty my catechism, which, however, I believe to be the best. I have never sought to make converts, but, up to the present time, neither has my conversion been accomplished by others.

Yesterday evening I went to the opera, where they proposed to close the doors, Ronconi being drunk or in prison for debt; but yielding to our clamor they gave us " L'Elisir d'Amore " ; after which I corrected proofs until three o'clock in the morning. I do not concern myself so much about the Academy as you suppose. I have hardly a chance of success. Do you think any magic that will conjure my name from the deal-box called Urn?

PARIS, *March*, 1844.* — Many thanks for your congratulations, but I wish for something better; to see and walk with you. I think you take the matter too tragically. Why do you weep? The " forty chairs " were not worth one little tear. I am very heartily gratified, the more that I expected defeat; and my mother who was suffering from acute rheumatism was suddenly cured. I am worn out, demoralized, and completely "out of my wits." Then my novel, " Arsène Guillot," makes a signal *fiasco* and rouses the indignation of all the self-styled virtuous people, especially the women of fashion who dance the polka and throng to the sermons of Père Ravignan, and who go so far as to liken me to a monkey who climbs to the top of the tree and makes grimaces at the world below. I believe that some votes have been lost by this scandal; on the other hand, some have been gained. Now, to show my greatness of soul, I must rush about thanking friends and enemies. I had the good fortune to be blackballed seven times by persons whom I detest, yet who tell me that they were my warmest partisans; but it is a happiness not to

* His election to the French Academy.

be burdened with gratitude toward those whom we hold in slight esteem. My Homer deceived me, or rather it was M. Vatout to whom the threatening vatication was addressed.

March, 1844.— I fear that the address may have seemed too long. I am still shivering from the cold, and you may have perceived my terrible cough, which might have been mistaken for a cabal. Did you prefer the full dress to the frock coat? I had some difficulty in discovering you hidden beneath your neighbor's bonnet — another bit of childishness. Did you see what I sent you, in full view of the Academy? But of course you never wish to see anything. Why will you dispute on this text: "Which loves the best?" A desirable preliminary would be to come to an agreement as to the meaning of the verb, and this we shall never do ; we are both too ignorant, and above all too ignorant of each other. More than once I have fancied you to be clearly revealed, but you always escape me. I was right in calling you Cerberus, "three gentlemen in one." Our mutual concessions only result in making us more unhappy ; and, more clear-sighted than you, I greatly blame myself, for I have made you suffer in prolonging an illusion that I should never have conceived. For you I have no reproaches. You wished to reconcile two incompatible things, but in vain. Should I not be grateful that you essayed the impossible for my sake? On the whole, perhaps you will one day come to regard our folly only in its fairest light, will remember only the happy moments we have passed together.

Consider if it be not sad for me to find myself always in conflict with your pride, my great enemy, or rather rival in your heart, and which triumphs over your tenderness, in comparison with which it is a Colossus to a pigmy. This premeditated pleasure, or, I prefer to believe, instinct that leads you to excite in me a desire for what you obstinately refuse, is in reality a species of selfishness. All that wounds your pride stirs you to rebellion ; and unconsciously this colors the most trivial details. You are happy, you tell me, when I kiss your hand, and you yield yourself to the feeling because your pride is satisfied by this demonstration of humility. You wish me to be a statue that you may be my life, my soul-awakener; but you wish for no reciprocity in the happiness to which I aspire, as that would imply an equality that displeases you. I shall never place my pride and happiness in the same scale, therefore if you will kindly suggest new formulas of humility, I will adopt them without hesitation. Is not the friendship which so strangely unites us, a sweeter, more living force than all the victories gained by your demon pride?

PARIS, 1844.— It is decided that I go to Algeria next month; and while you are learning Greek I am studying Arabic, a diabolical language of which I shall never acquire two words. I passed a day at Strasbourg, exhorting the authorities with sublime eloquence to restore an ancient church; their reply being that they were in greater need of tobacco than monuments, and that they should convert the church into a storehouse. The cathedral that formerly I liked so much appears absolutely ugly, and even the wise and foolish virgins of Steinbach hardly found grace in my eyes. You are right in liking Paris so well; it is, after all, the only city in which one can truly live.

I dined yesterday with General Narvaez — an entertainment in honor of his wife's birthday. Few ladies except Spanish were present. One was pointed out to me who is starving herself to death through love, and is gently fading away. This species of suicide must seem very cruel to you. There was another demoiselle, whom General Serrano has deserted for her fat Catholic Majesty; but she is not dying of it, and seems even to be in excellent health. There was also Madame Gonzalez Bravo, sister of the actor Romea, and sister-in-law of the same Majesty, who, it is said, gives herself a large number of sisters-in-law. This one is very pretty and very clever.

PARIS, 1844.— We separated yesterday mutually discontented, and both were in the wrong. It is evident that we can no longer meet without quarreling horribly. We both desire the impossible. You — that I should be a statue; I

—that you should cease to be one. Every fresh proof of this impossibility, which at heart we have never doubted, is cruel for both. For my part I regret all the pain I have caused you. I too often give way to impulses of absurd anger; it would be as reasonable to feel angry against ice for being cold. I hope that you will forgive me; no resentment remains, only a heavy sadness. Adieu, since only at a distance can we be friends. When both shall be old, we may perhaps meet again with pleasure; meanwhile, in misfortune or in happiness, remember me. Once more, while I have the courage, adieu.

PARIS, 1844.— My occupation at this moment is tedious and low beyond measure; I am soliciting votes for the Academy of Inscriptions. The most absurd scenes occur, and I am often seized with a wish to laugh, which must be repressed for fear of shocking the gravity of the Academicians. I embarked somewhat blindly in the affair, but my chances are not bad. You are wrong to be jealous of Inscriptions. I have a little *amour propre* is the matter; just as in a game of chess with a skillful adversary, but neither loss nor gain will affect me a quarter so much as one of our quarrels. But what a vile calling is this of solicitor! Did you ever see dogs enter the hole of a badger? When experienced in the game they have an appalled look on entering, and often come out more quickly than they go in, for it is an ugly brute to visit, is the badger. I always think of the badger when about to ring the bell of an Academician, and "in the mind's eye" I see myself an exact likeness of that dog. However, I have not yet been bitten.

POITIERS, 1844.— No doubt you have amused yourself exceedingly, which I cannot but believe to be synonymous with an indulgence in coquetry. Since leaving Paris my life has been unspeakably disagreeable. Like Ulysses, I have seen much of manners, men, and cities, and find them all very ugly. I have had several attacks of fever that astonished and grieved me as proving that I am growing old. I find the country the flattest and most insignificant

in France, but fine forests, great trees, and vast solitudes
abound, wherein I should like to meet you. I pass my
time in meditating on our walks. I applaud Scribe for
having made a virtuous and neo-catholic public laugh with
the prizes for virtue; and I am equally surprised as to
what you say of his elocution, as formerly he read abominably. It must be the academic robe that bestows this self-
command; and this restored a little hope for me.

PERPIGNAN, 1844.—I have been tormented by an absurd
idea which I hardly dare to tell you. While visiting the
arena of Nîmes with the architect of the department, who
was explaining some repairs under his direction, I observed
ten paces from me a charming bird a little larger than a
titmouse, gray body, with white, red, and black wings,
which, perching itself on a cornice, looked fixedly at me.
The architect, a great sportsman, had never seen one resembling it. As I approached it flew off, poising itself
again a few steps distant, still regarding me closely; and
wherever I went, in every story of the amphitheatre, it followed me, its flight being noiseless, like that of a night
bird. The next day the scene was repeated. I brought
bread, it would not touch it; I then threw it a grasshop-
per, which it equally disregarded, still watching me. The
most learned ornithologist of the town tells me that no bird
of this species exists in this region. Finally, at my last
visit to the amphitheatre, my bird still followed my steps
so far as to enter a dark and narrow corridor where a day
bird would seldom venture. I then remembered that the
Duchess of Buckingham saw her husband under the form
of a bird the day of his assassination, and the idea flashed
upon me that you were dead and had assumed this shape
to visit me. In spite of myself this nonsense distressed
me, and I was enchanted to find your letter dated the day
on which I first saw my marvelous bird.

A fair is in progress here, and the town additionally
thronged with Spaniards flying from the epidemic, so that
I was unable to obtain lodging at an inn, and should have
been reduced to a bed in the street but for the commisera-
tion of a hatter. I write in a cold little room with a

12

smoking chimney, cursing the rain that dashes against my window ; the woman who serves me speaks Catalan, and only understands me when I speak Spanish ; while, worst of all, the flood threatens to carry away the bridge and detain me here, a wretched prisoner. An admirable situation for the expression of ideas.

I have been to the Fountain of Vaucluse, where I wished to inscribe your name, but there were so many atrocious verses, so many Sophies and Carolines, that I would not profane it by such bad company. Parthenay I found a horrible town of *chouans*, with an abominable tavern where they made an infernal noise, and mixed so much stable with my dinner as to make it impossible for me to eat. At Saint-Maixent I saw women with headgear of the fourteenth century, and the waist of the dress of nearly the same period, allowing the chemise to be seen, which is of coarse house-cloth, buttoned under the chin, and open like men's shirts ; and in spite of the gingerbread beneath I thought it very pretty.

Paris, *February*, 1845. — Everything passed off better than I had hoped.* I was perfectly self-possessed, and am well content with the public, though I know not if it be so with me. All is well since you did not find me ridiculous. I should have lost my confidence had I known you to be present, in view especially of my tarragon-colored coat and my face *idem*.

Toulouse. — Fortunately I find here your letter, for I was furious at your silence. You are never so near forgetting me as when persuading me that I am in your thought. You ask me to pet you, but I am in too bad a humor, havin been in a continuous rage this past fortnight against you, against myself, the weather, and the architects. I passed four-and-twenty hours at the house of a Deputy and if I were ambitious of being a politician this visit would have completely quenched my aspirations. What a calling ! what people one must see, conciliate, flatter ! I say with

* His reception at the French Academy.

Hotspur: "I had rather be a kitten and cry mew." Slavery for slavery, I prefer the court of a despot; at least the greater part of despots wash their hands. In England, no doubt, Lady M—— will beset you again with her fine theories "about the baseness of being in love." God knows if you will not return three-quarters English. While you are luxuriating in melting peaches, I am eating yellow, acid ones of a singular but not unpleasant flavor, and figs of every color. I am immeasurably bored in the evening, and begin to wish for the society of bipeds of my own species. I count the provincials as naught, being fatiguing to my eyes and entirely foreign to my circle of thought.

BARCELONA, 1845.— I have reached the goal of my long journey, and have been admirably received by my archivist, who had already prepared my tables and the ancient books in which I shall lose what remains of my sight. To find his *despacho*, a gothic hall of the fourteenth century must be traversed, and a marble court planted with orange-trees as tall as our lime-trees, and covered with ripe fruit. This is very poetical, and as regards comfort and luxury recalls, as does my chamber, the Asiatic caravanserai. However, it is better than Andalusia, though the natives are inferior and have a fatal defect in my eyes, or rather ears, in that I understand nothing of their gibberish. At Perpignan, I met two gypsies who were cropping mules, and I spoke *caló* to them to the great horror of my companion, a colonel of artillery; while they, finding me even more skilled than themselves in the *patois*, offered a striking testimony to my attainments of which I was not a little proud. In summing up the results of my journey, my conviction is, that it was unnecessary to come so far, and that my history could have been satisfactorily accomplished without disturbing the venerable dust of Aragonese archives.

MADRID, *November*, 1845.— I have been installed here a week in the midst of intense cold, rain, and a climate quite similar to that of Paris; only, I look on snow-capped mountains and live familiarly with very fine Velasquez. Thanks to the ineffable slowness of these people, I have only to-day begun to ferret among the manuscripts, as an academic council was necessary to permit me to examine them, and I know not how many intrigues to enable me to obtain information as to their existence.

I find this country much changed, and less agreeable since my last visit. Persons whom I left friends are now mortal enemies; many of my former acquaintances have become grandees, and very insolent. Every one thinks aloud, with but slight consideration for others, and a frankness prevails that amazes us Frenchmen, and me the more, inasmuch as you have lately accustomed me to something very different. You should make a tour beyond the Pyrenées to take a lesson in frankness. You can form no conception of the expression of the swain's face when the beloved object does not arrive at the appointed hour, nor of the noise of the escaping sighs; but such scenes are so common as to create no scandal nor tittle-tattle. I see happy lovers, and find that they take advantage of the confidence and intimacy accorded by their *innamoratas*. The most romantic do not comprehend in the least what we term gallantry: the lovers here, truth to say, are merely husbands non-authorized by the church. They are the *souffre douleur* of the legal husband, execute commissions, and nurse Madame when she takes medicine. Notwithstanding your infernal coquetry, and your aversion for the truth, I love you far more than all these over-frank people. Do not take advantage of this avowal. It is so cold that we shall have no bull-fight; but a number of balls are announced, the tedium of which is inexpressible.

August, 1846, on board a steamboat.—I have been among the mountains seeking some spot remote from electors and candidates, but I found such quantities of flies and fleas that I am not sure if the elections be not preferable. Yesterday evening I spent with peasant men and women, making their hair stand on end with ghost stories. There was a magnificent moon that lighted up their regular features and showed the fine black eyes of these damsels, while idealizing the condition of their hands and stockings.

I went to bed very proud of my success with this, to me, novel audience; but in the morning on seeing my *Ardé-choises* by sunlight *con villanos manos y pies*, I almost regretted my eloquence.

PARIS, 1846. — I find the provinces more stupid and unendurable each year. I could not well describe the tedium and various annoyances of this little tour. It recalls Clarence's dream: —

> «I would not spend another such a night,
> Though 't were to buy a world of happy days.»

Paris is absolutely empty of intelligent inhabitants, only cap-makers and Deputies remaining, which is nearly the same thing. I am even more isolated here than usual, depressed by something of the feeling of an *emigré* who on returning to his country finds a new generation. It will strike you that I have grown horribly old — all of which simply means that I am sad, very cross, and that it is you, our walks, which I need. Perhaps when the sea air shall have tarnished your dresses, or fresh ones arrive from Paris, you will send me a thought. There is nothing on earth half so charming to a woman, it is said, as to display pretty toilets. I can offer you no equivalent for these joys; but I should suffer too much in believing you to be so constituted. I learn, with pleasure, that you are so heartily wearied at ——, which I predicted. After living in Paris, the provinces are insupportable; one says and does numberless enormities that are overlooked in Paris, but which in a village are magnified to the size of a house.

BONN, 1846. — When once launched on a journey I have the utmost difficulty in coming to a halt; and very seductive promises will be needed to prevent me from pushing on to Lapland. I have been six days in this admirable country, I mean Rhenish Prussia, where civilization is very advanced, with the exception of the beds, which are still four feet long, the sheets three. I lead an altogether German life. I rise at five o'clock and go to bed at nine, after

partaking of four meals, which routine suits me quite well ;
and I am not yet ill with doing nothing save opening my
mouth and eyes. Only, the German women have become
horribly ugly since my last visit.

With respect to monuments, I am by no means satisfied
with those I have seen, the German architects appearing
to me even worse then our own. They have denuded the
Minister at Bonn, and painted the Abbey at Lahr in a way
to make one grind one's teeth. The scenery of the Moselle
is very much overpraised, and I have seen nothing really
striking since passing the Tmolus. My admiration is exclusively reserved for the umbrageous foliage and for their
fine conception of the *cuisine ;* here the most important
occupation is *zu speisen.* All honest people after dining at
one o'clock take tea and cakes at four, go to a garden at
six to eat a roll and stuffed tongue, which enables them
to sustain nature until eight, when they go to a hotel to
have their supper. What becomes of the women during
this period I do not know, but it is certain that from eight
to ten o'clock not a man remains in the house, each one
being at his favorite hotel, eating, drinking, and smoking ;
and the reason of this may, I think, be found in the large
feet of these ladies and the excellence of Rhenish wine.

PARIS, *March*, 1848.—I have never been more sadly
shocked by the stupidity of the Northern people, and also
by their inferiority to those of the South, than during my
recent tour, the average native of Picardy striking me as
much below the lowest class of Provence ; in addition to
which I nearly perished with cold in all the inns to which
my evil destiny led me.

I am tormented by the failure of the —— firm, in
which I fear your interests also are at stake ; and each day
will bring us fresh disturbance. We must sustain each
other and share the little courage remaining to us. You
are too much alarmed ; but it is difficult to give advice and
to see clearly through the fog that stretches over our
future. Many persons believe Paris, all things considered,
to be safer than the country, and I am also of this
opinion. I have no fear of a street battle, first, because no

sufficient motive exists; then that strength and audacity are on the one side, while I see only dullness and cowardice on the other. If civil war should break out, it will be first declared in the country, as great irritation has been aroused against the dictatorship of the capital, and perhaps measures, now impossible to foresee, may lead to this result in the West. As to the consequence of the riots, contrast those of the first revolution in Paris with the one two years ago at Buzançais,— more deplorable than all those of '93. Everything passed off quietly yesterday, and we shall have numerous similar processions before any shot will be fired, if indeed that should ever happen in this timid country.

PARIS, *May*, 1848.— All has passed off well, for the reason that they are such fools that the Chamber, notwithstanding all its faults, has proved to be stronger than they. There are neither killed nor wounded, everything is quiet, and an excellent feeling prevails between the people and the National Guard. The leading insurgents have been arrested, and so many troops are under arms that for some time to come there will be nothing to fear. I have witnessed some highly dramatic scenes. I am worn out with a night's service with the Guards, but, after all, fatigue has its advantage at this time. The happiness of seeing you is as great under the Republic as under the Monarchy, and you must not be avaricious in its bestowal. But the most important, pressing thing to tell you is, that each day I love you more and more, and I should be glad could you summon courage to say the same to me.

June, 1848.— I returned this morning from a little campaign of four days, during which I ran no danger and was enabled to see the horrors of the day and of this country. In the midst of my distress I grieve above all for the folly of France: it is unequaled. I cannot see that it will ever be possible to turn her aside from the savage barbarism in which she shows so strong an inclination to wallow. I hope that your brother is safe: I do not think that his legion was seriously in action. I will hastily relate a

curious incident or two before going to bed. The La
Force prison was protected for several hours by the National Guard and surrounded by the insurgents, who said
to the soldiers : " Do not fire on us and we will not fire on
you — take care of the prisoners." To watch the battle I
entered a house that had just been rescued from the rebels
and asked the occupants, " Did they take much from
you ? " " They stole nothing." Add to this, that I led a
woman to the abbey who had employed herself in cutting
off the heads of the Guards with her kitchen knife ; and
that I saw a man whose two arms were red with the
blood of a dying soldier whose belly he had ripped up,
laving his hands in the gaping wound. Do you begin to
understand somewhat of this great nation? What is quite
certain is, that we are going headlong to the devil.

July, 1848.— Paris is, and will be quiet for some time to
come. I do not think that the civil, or rather the social
war is at an end, but another battle so frightful as the
recent one seems impossible, the recurrence of the infinity
of circumstances necessary to bring it about not being
probable. Of its hideous results which your imagination
doubtless paints, you will find but few traces, the glazier
and house-painter having already effected their removal ;
but you will see many long faces. What can one do? the
régime is *de facto*, and we must accustom ourselves to it.
By and by we shall cease to think of the morrow, and on
awaking in the morning shall be happy in the certainty of
an undisturbed evening. The days are long and warm, and
as tranquil as could be wished, or rather hoped for under
the Republic. All the signs foretell a prolonged truce. The
disarming is effected with vigor, and produces good results.
One curious symptom is remarked ; namely, that in the
insurgent *faubourgs* any number of informers can be found
to point out the hiding-places and even the leaders of the
barricades. It is a good sign, you know, when wolves fall
to fighting among themselves. The 14th of July passed by
very quietly, notwithstanding the sinister predictions with
which we were favored. The truth — if it can be discovered under the government under which we have the good

fortune to live—the truth is, that our chances for tranquillity have been singularly increased. To bring about the events of June, several years of organization and four months of arming were requisite. A second representation of this bloody tragedy appears to me impossible ; nevertheless, some little plot, several assassinations, and a few riots are still probable. We shall have perhaps a half century in which to perfect ourselves, the one party in the construction of barricades, the other in their destruction. Paris is now being filled with mortars and howitzers, both transportable and efficacious — a novel argument, and said to be excellent.

I went yesterday to Saint-Germain to order a dinner for the Society of Bibliophiles, where I found a cook not only capable, but eloquent, who comprehended at once the most fantastic dishes that I proposed. This great man resides in the portion of the palace in which Henry IV. was born, which commands one of the loveliest views in the world, while a few steps bring one to a wood with great trees and magnificent undergrowth. And not a soul to enjoy all this !

You resemble Antæus, who renewed his strength in touching the earth. You no sooner touch your native soil than you relapse into your old defects. Your letter does not tell me how long I am to suffer the purgatory of your absence. It was redolent of a perfume so much the more delicious from being familiar to me, and which brings to me so many charming associations. I think of you unceasingly; even while looking at the fighting at the Bastille my thoughts were of you.

August, 1848.—This evening while my friend M. Mignet was strolling with Mademoiselle Dosne in the little garden fronting the residence of M. Thiers, a ball came down without the least noise, struck the house very near Madame Thiers's window and glancing thence wounded a little girl seated beyond the garden railing. The ball was quickly extracted, and no ill will ensue save a slight scar: but for whom was it intended? Mignet? that is impossible. Mademoiselle Dosne? still more so. Neither Madame nor M. Thiers was at home. No one heard the explosion, the ball was of regulation size, and air-guns are of a much smaller calibre. I believe it to have been a republican attempt at intimidation, as foolish as all else that is done in this our day. Cavaignac says: " They will kill me, Lamoricière will succeed me, then Bedeau ; after whom will come the Duc d'Isly, who will sweep everything clean." Does this not strike you as prophetic? No one believes in an intervention in Italy. The Republic will be even rather more cowardly than the Monarchy ; they may, however, make a pretense of allowing it to be supposed that intervention is probable, hoping by this ruse to obtain a congress, protocols, and a compromise. One of my friends, just returned from Italy, was plundered by the Roman volunteers, who find that travelers are made of better stuff than the Croats. He asserts that it is impossible to make the Italians fight, with the exception of the Piedmontese. Throw aside your Romaic ; it will be love's labor lost. In vainly trying to learn it I forgot my Greek, and it will play you the same trick. I am surprised at your facile comprehension of this gibberish, which as a language, morever, will soon disappear, for Greek is already spoken at Athens, and Romaic will only be used by the lower orders. Since 1841, not a single Turkish word, formerly so frequent, has been heard in the Greece of King Otho.

Yesterday, at the general competition for prizes, one was awarded to an urchin named LEROY, whereupon his comrades exclaimed " *Vive le roi !* "

General Cavaignac who assisted at the ceremony laughed with a very good grace : but the same boy receiving yet another prize, the applause became so uproarious that the general lost countenance and twisted his beard as if he would pluck it out by the roots.

August, 1848. — We hear rumors of fresh riots ; and now the cholera is coming to complicate matters. M. Ledru is thought to be inciting a disturbance by way of protest against the administrative inquiry. The situation closely resembles that of Rome during Catiline's conspiracy, only there is no Cicero. A most grievous symptom is that Citizen Proudhon has a great number of adherents, his little sheets being sold in the *faubourgs* by thousands — all of which is sad, but to me the *ennui* of the approaching rain and cold is more serious and much more certain than the riot. I suffer much, and should be excessively vexed to die before our breakfast at Saint-Germain.

LONDON, *June*, 1850. — The most decided impression received from this journey is that the English are individually stupid (*bêtes*), but an admirable people *en masse*. Everything that can be done by the aid of money, good sense, and patience, they do ; but of the arts they have no more notion than my cat.

The Nepaulese princes are here, with whom you would fall in love. They wear flat turbans bordered with enormous pear-shaped emeralds, and are a mass of satin, cashmere, and gold. They are of a deep milk and coffee color, have a good air, and appear to be intelligent.

We are going to Hampton Court to avoid the chances for suicide that the LORD'S DAY in this city would not fail to offer. I dined yesterday with a bishop and a dean, who have made me even still more a socialist. The bishop belongs to what the Germans call the rationalist school ; he does not even believe what he preaches, and on the strength of his black silk apron enjoys five or six thousand pounds a year and passes his time in reading Greek. The women all look as if made of wax ; and wear such expansive bustles that the pavement of Regent Street is only wide enough to hold one woman at a time. I passed yesterday morning in the new House of Commons, which is a frightful monstrosity ; I had previously no conception of what could be accomplished with an utter want of taste and two millions sterling. I have strong fears of becoming a thorough socialist by dint of eating admirable dinners from silver gilt plates, and seeing persons who win forty thousand pounds sterling at the Epsom races. There is as yet no probability of a revolutionary outbreak here. The servility of the lower orders, of which we see each day some fresh example, conflicts with our democratic ideas : it is a question of moment to know if they are more happy.

SALISBURY, *June*, 1850. — I begin to have enough of this region. I am worn out with the perpendicular architecture, and the manners, equally perpendicular, of the natives. I have passed two days at Cambridge and Oxford with the reverends, and, all things considered, I prefer the Capuchins. I am especially furious against Oxford. A Fellow had the insolence to invite me to dinner. There was a fish four inches long, in a great silver dish, and a lamb cutlet in another: all this served in magnificent style, with potatoes in a dish of carved wood. But never was I so hungry. This is the result of the hypocrisy of these people. They like to show their abstinence to foreigners, and, eating luncheon, they do not dine. Were it not broad day at eight o'clock in the evening, one might believe it to be December, which does not hinder the women from going out with open parasol. It is impossible to see anything more ridiculous than an Englishwoman in the hoop that is worn here.

I have just committed a blunder. I gave half a crown to a man in black who showed me over the cathedral, and then I asked him for the address of a gentleman for whom I had a letter from the dean. He proved to be the very person to whom the letter was addressed. He looked very foolish, and so did I : but he kept the money.

Who is a Miss Jewsbury, rather red-haired, who writes novels? I met her recently and she told me that she had dreamed all her life of a pleasure that she believed impossible, that of seeing me — *verbatim*. She has written a novel entitled " Zoe. " Will you, who read so much, tell me who is this person for whom I am a romance?

PARIS, *June*, 1851. — Yesterday I accepted an invitation from the Princess Mathilde to see the Spanish dancers, who are very *médiocre*. The dance at the Mabille has killed the *bolero*, and these dames wore such a quantity of crinoline as to prove clearly the encroachment of civilization. A girl and her old duenna amused me by their intense surprise at finding themselves beyond the *tierra* of Jesus; they were as perfect barbarians as could be desired.

PARIS, *December*, 1851.— The last battle, I believe, is now being fought; but who will win? Should the President lose, it seems to me that the heroic Deputies should give way to Ledru-Rollin. I have returned home horribly fatigued, and have met none but madmen. The look of Paris recalls that of February, except that now the soldiers are very fierce and terrify the citizens. The military are sure of success, but we understand their almanac. However this may be, we have just escaped a reef and are sailing toward the unknown.

PARIS, 1852.— I am threatened with a lawsuit for contempt of court and attack upon the final judgment; while the School of Charts is also sharpening its claws to tear me to pieces, I shall be compelled to undergo an examination and to engage in desperate polemics. In case I fail, try to keep well and come to see me in prison. I do not know whether they will hang me, but I am very FIDGETTY at the thought of a public ceremony in presence of the very cream of the rabble, and three imbeciles in black gowns as stiff as pickets and convinced of their own importance, to whom one cannot dream of expressing one's contempt for their gowns, their person, and their mind.

May, 1851.— Four days in prison and a thousand francs fine? My lawyer argued well, the judges were civil, and I not at all nervous. I shall not appeal. I pass my time in reading Beyle's correspondence. It has rejuvenated me twenty years. It is as if I were making the autopsy of the thoughts of a man whom I have known intimately and whose ideas respecting men and things had grown singularly colorless by the side of my experience. This renders me sad and gay twenty times within the hour, and makes me regret having burned Beyle's letters to me.

CARABANCHEL, 1853.— On arriving here I found preparations for a *fête* at which a comedy was to be played and a *loa* (a dithyrambic dialogue) recited in honor of the lady of the house and her daughter. My services were called into requisition to paint skies, repair decorations, and design costumes, not to enumerate the rehearsals of five mythological goddesses, who on the fatal day looked exceedingly pretty but were overcome with terror. The audience applauded warmly, without understanding in the least the nonsensical rigmarole of the poet author of the *loa*. The comedy was better, and I admire the facility with which the young girls of society transform themselves into passable actresses. During supper a *protégé* of the Countess improvised some pretty verses that moved the heroine to tears and disposed every one else to drink rather too generously. As there are nine ladies here without a gentleman, I am called at Madrid, "Apollo." Of the nine Muses five unfortunately are mothers, but the remaining four are true born Andalusians with little ferocious airs that are ravishing, especially when in their Olympian costume with peplum, which through love of euphony they persist in calling *peplo*.

MADRID, *October*, 1853.— I went yesterday to see Cucharès, the best matador since Montès. The bulls were so indifferent that it was necessary to excite them by little fiery darts. Two men were thrown into the air, and for a moment we thought them dead, which imparted some slight interest to the spectacle ; otherwise everything was detestable. The bulls no longer have any spirit, and the men are not much better than the bulls. The ugly convent of the Escurial is as sad as when I saw it twenty years ago, but civilization has penetrated its walls and one finds iron bedsteads and cutlets, but no longer fleas and monks. The absence of the latter distinctive element renders Herrera's heavy architecture still more ridiculous.

I will bring you the garters, which I had difficulty in finding. Civilization makes such rapid progress that on nearly every leg the ELASTIC has replaced the classic *ligas* of former days ; and when I asked the chamber-maids to show me a shop where they were sold they indignantly crossed themselves, saying that they no longer wore such obsolete fashions, which were only in use by the common people. Mantillas are nearly as rare ; they are superseded by bonnets ; and such bonnets !

Last week the *fête* of SAINT EUGÉNIE was celebrated at the French embassy by a ball, at which Madame ——, wife of the United States Minister, appeared in a costume so designed as to make one split with laughter — black velvet bordered with gold lace and tinsel, and a tawdry diadem. Her son, who looks like a boor, made inquiries respecting the position of the persons present and having obtained satisfactory information sent a challenge to a very noble, very rich duke, a great simpleton, and desirous of living yet a long time. The parley still continues, but no one will be killed.

I am re-reading " Wilhelm Meister," a strange book, in which the finest possible things alternate with the most absurd childishness. In all that Goethe wrote there is a singular mingling of genius and German silliness (*niaiserie*): was he laughing at others or at himself? On my return remind me to give you " The Elective Affinities," the oddest, most anti-French of all his works. No one reads at Madrid. I have asked myself how the women pass their time when not making love, and I find no plausible reply. They are all thinking of being empresses. A demoiselle of Granada was at the play when it was announced in her box that the Countess de Teba was to marry the Emperor. She rose with impetuosity, exclaiming: *"En ese pueblo no hay parvenir."* *

The absorbing question here is, whether the Ministry will remain in, or whether there will be a *coup d'état*. The house in which I reside is neutral ground, where the Ministers and leaders of the Opposition meet, which is agreeable for lovers of news. What is called here society is composed of so small a number of persons, that to break up into factions would be fatal. In all public places one is sure of meeting the same three hundred faces, from which results a more amusing and infinitely less hypocritical society than elsewhere.

It is the custom here to offer in return everything that is praised. At a recent dinner I sat next the Prime Minister's fair friend, who is as stupid as a cabbage and excessively stout. She displayed somewhat handsome shoulders,

* In this country there is no chance of rising.

on which rested a garland with glass or metal acorns, and not knowing what to say to her, I praised both beads and shoulders, to which she replied: "*Todo ese a la disposicion de V.*"

PARIS, 1854.— You will find the Sydenham Crystal Palace a vast Noah's Ark, marvelous as to its collection of curious objects, but regarded from an artistic standpoint, perfectly ridiculous; yet there is something at once so grand and so simple in its construction that one must go to England to form a conception of it. It is a toy costing twenty-five millions; a cage in which several churches might waltz; and to you who are *gourmande*, I recommend its dinners. The last days I passed in London interested me. I met socially all the eminent politicians, and was present at the debates on the Supplies in the Houses of Lords and Commons, in which the most renowned orators spoke, but in my opinion very abominably. I have brought a pair of garters from London. I do not know with what Englishwomen keep up their stockings, nor how they procure this indispensable article, but I believe it to be a very difficult matter and very trying to their virtue. The shopman who gave me these garters blushed up to the eyes. All the charming things you say to me would be a delight if experience had not taught me to distrust you. I dare not hope for what I desire so ardently. There is something very painful in conforming to your protocols, which, in point of contempt of logic and probability, are worthy of Nesselrode. I returned this morning from Caen. On my arrival there I proceeded to the hall of the Law School, where I found about two hundred men and a dozen ladies. I delivered my little discourse without the slightest emotion, being very civilly applauded. The ceremonies' terminated with the reading of some rather good verses by a humpbacked dwarf, immediately after which I was conducted by the authorities to the *hôtel de ville*, where a banquet was given in my honor, at which excellent fish and delicious lobsters were enjoyed. At last the hoped-for moment of release came, when to my dismay the President of the Antiquaries arose, every one standing, and proposing

my health, referred to me as remarkable in the three qualities of senator, a man of letters, and a scientist. Only the
table separated us, and I was much inclined to throw a
dish of rum jelly at his head. When he spoke I was meditating my reply, with no apparent possibility of finding a
word. I returned thanks, however, in a speech of five
minutes, with but a slight idea of what I was saying,
which, however, I was assured was very eloquent. But my
sufferings were not over. I was seized by the mayor and
led to a concert of the Philharmonic Society, where I was
exhibited to a large number of well dressed people, the
women very fair and very pretty, attired much like Parisians except in a less lavish display of shoulders, and in
wearing maroon colored half boots with their ball dress.

INNSPRUCK, *August*, 1854.— I am intoxicated with magnificent landscapes and panoramas. From Basle to Schaff-
hausen, on the right hand and left, are enchanting mountains, far finer than those of the lower Rhine so much
admired by Englishwomen. At Constance we had capital
trout and heard Tyroleans play on the ZITTHER. Thence
to this place we have traversed a region of forests, lakes,
and mountains of increasing beauty and grandeur, but are
overcome with fatigue such as one experiences after examining a fine picture gallery. I am recruiting here with delicious woodcock and extraordinary soups. The drawback
of the journey lies in an ignorance of the manners and
ideas of the people, far more interesting to me than all the
landscapes. In the Tyrol the women seem to be treated
according to their merit. They are harnessed to wagons
and easily draw heavy loads, are excessively ugly, with
enormous feet; and the ladies whom I met on the railway
and boats are not much better. They wear indecent bonnets, sky-blue boots with apple-green gloves. It is in great
part the above peculiarities that constitute what the natives
call *gemüth*, and of which they are exceedingly vain. It
strikes me that the radical deficiency in the works of
art of this country is that of imagination, upon which,
nevertheless, they pique themselves, falling consequently
into the most pretentious extravagances.

13

PRAGUE, *September*, 1854.—This city is exceedingly picturesque and there is admirable music. Yesterday I strolled through several gardens and public concerts, and saw the national dances performed decently and soberly; while nothing can be more captivating than a Bohemian orchestra. The physique here differs much from that of Germany; very large heads, broad shoulders, very small hips, and no legs whatever—that is a picture of Bohemian beauty. We have exhausted our knowledge of anatomy in striving to understand how these women walk. They have, however, fine black eyes, very long and fine black hair, but feet of a length, thickness, and breadth to surprise travelers accustomed to the most extraordinary sights. Crinoline is unknown. At the public gardens in the evening they drink a bottle of beer, after which they take a cup of coffee, which disposes them to partake of three veal cutlets with ham, the interstices being filled up with some light pastry cakes resembling our buns. The blanket of my bed of various pretty colors, is one metre long, to which is buttoned a napkin that serves me for sheet, and when I have arranged that in equilibrium, my servant places over the whole an eider down coverlet which I pass the night in throwing down and replacing.

VIENNA, *October*, 1854.—Really, this good city is an agreeable place of sojourn, and it requires a certain degree of courage to leave it, now that I have learned to enjoy sauntering about its pleasant places, and have made many friends. We are agitated by news from the Crimea. Is Sebastopol taken? It is believed so here; and the Austrians, with the exception of a few ancient families who are Russian at heart, congratulate us. God grant that the news may not be an invention such as the telegraph delights in when at leisure. However it may be, I think it a fine thing that our troops, six days after landing, should have pommeled the Russians so vigorously. We enjoy the looks of the Russians now here. Prince Gortschakoff says that it is an "incident" that will effect no change as to the principles. The Belgian Minister, the wit of Vienna, says that Gortschakoff is right to intrench himself behind principles, because they are never taken with the bayonet. *À propos* of wit, willing or unwilling, I have been made a LION. Society here being so *gemüthlich*, everything that a Frenchman says is accepted as wit. I am thought very amiable. I write sublime thoughts in albums, I make drawings, in a word I have been perfectly ridiculous. I passed three days at Pesth, where my modesty suffered in being shown a public bath, in which Hungarian men and women were together in the hot mineral water. I saw one beautiful Hungarian who hid her face with her hands; in this unlike the Turkish women, who wear the chemise for that purpose. I have heard Bohemian musicians play very original Hungarian airs that intoxicate the natives. The music begins lugubriously and ends with a mad gayety that quickly spreads to the audience, who stamp, break the glasses, and dance on the table; but foreigners are not affected by these phenomena. Magnificent furs are obtained here for a trifle — the only bargains in the country. I am ruined by hack hire and dinner parties. The custom is to pay the domestics who serve the dinner, and the hall porter; in fact one pays at every turn.

LONDON, *July*, 1856. — I am about to visit a real Scotch chieftain, who has never worn any breeches, has no staircase in his house, but maintains a bard and a seer. I find the people here so amiable, so pressing, so monopolizing, that my arrival is evidently a relief to their *ennui*. Yesterday I saw two of my former beauties; the one has become asthmatic, the other a Methodist. I have also made the acquaintance of eight or ten poets, who struck me as rather more ridiculous even than our own.

EDINBURGH. — I have passed three days at the Duke of Hamilton's, in an immense castle, and a very fine country. At no great distance is a herd of wild oxen, said to be the only ones now remaining in Europe, but which appeared to me as tame as the deer at Paris. Throughout this castle are pictures by the great masters, magnificent Greek and Chinese vases, and richly bound books from the greatest collections of the last century. All this is arranged without taste, and one sees that it affords the proprietor but small enjoyment. I now understand why the French are so much in request in foreign countries ; they take pains to be amused, and in so doing amuse others. I found myself the most entertaining person of the very numerous society assembled, and was at the same time conscious of being rather the reverse. I find Edinburgh altogether to my taste with the exception of the execrable architecture of the monuments, the claim of which to be Greek is about as well founded as an Englishwoman's pretension to be a Parisian because her toilets are prepared by Madame Vignon. The accent of the natives is odious to me. The women, as a rule, are very ugly. The country necessitates short skirts, and they conform to the fashion and to the exigencies of the climate, by holding up their gown with both hands, a foot above the petticoat, displaying sinewy legs and half-boots of rhinoceros leather, with feet to match. I am shocked at the proportion of red-haired women whom I meet.

August, 1856, *at a country house near Glasgow.*— I lead a pleasant life, going from *château* to *château*, and everywhere entertained with a hospitality for which I despair of finding adequate expression, and which is only practicable in this aristocratic country. I am contracting bad habits. The guest here of poor people who have little more than thirty thousand pounds a year, I have thought myself not sufficiently honored because of dining without wind instruments and a piper in grand costume.

At the Marquis of Breadalbane's I passed three days in driving about the park. There are about two thousand deer, besides eight or ten thousand in his forests not adjacent to the castle. There are also, for the sake of singularity, at which every one aims here, a herd of American buffaloes, very fierce, inclosed in a peninsula, and which one goes to look at through the palings. Every one there, Marquis and buffalo, had the air of being bored. I believe that their pleasure consists in making people envious, and I doubt whether this compensates for the pother of playing innkeeper to all sorts of people. Amid all this luxury, I observe, from time to time, bits of stinginess which amuse me.

KINLOCH-LINCHARD, *August*, 1856.— I begin to be satiated with grouse and venison. The truly remarkable scenery has still a charm for me, but my curiosity is satisfied. What I am not weary of admiring is, the bristling attitude the people here maintain : being chained together at the galleys even would not make them more sociable. This arises from their fear of being "caught in the act of being stupid," as Beyle says, or rather an organization that inclines them to prefer selfish pleasures. We arrived here at the same time with two gentlemen and a middle-aged woman accustomed to high society, and who had traveled. At dinner the thick ice necessarily thawed ; but in the evening the husband took up a newspaper, the wife a book, the other gentleman began to write letters, while I was left to play a single-handed game against my hosts. I am told that the Celtic race (who live in frightful holes near the palace in which I am a guest) know how to talk. The fact is, I fancy, that on market day a continual noise of animated voices, laughter and shouts, is heard. Gælic is very soft. In England and the Lowlands, complete silence.

CARABACEL, *December*, 1856.— I have been besieged by Russian and English cards, and have been offered a presentation to the Grand Duchess Helen, an honor that I pointedly declined. To furnish us with gossip we have a Countess Apraxine, who smokes, wears round hats, and keeps a goat in her salon, which she has strewn with grass. But the most amusing person is Lady Shelley who commits some fresh drollery every day. Yesterday she wrote to the French Consul : "Lady S—— informs M. P—— that she has a charming dinner party of English people to-day, and she will be delighted to see him afterward, at five minutes past nine o'clock." She wrote to Madame Vigier, ex-Mademoiselle Cruvelli : "Lady Shelley would be charmed to see Madame Vigier if she would be good enough to bring her music with her." To which the ex-Cruvelli immediately replied : "Madame Vigier would be charmed to see Lady Shelley, if she would be good enough to come to her house and behave as a lady."

LONDON, *British Museum*, 1858.— You can form no conception of the beauty of the Museum on Sunday when there is no one present except M. Panizzi and myself; it seems to be permeated by a marvelous atmosphere of thought. Last Wednesday I fell into rather a droll scrape. I was invited to the Literary Fund dinner presided over by Lord Palmerston, and at the moment of setting out was notified that I should be expected to make a speech, as my name would be associated with a toast to the literature of Continental Europe. I was victimized with a satisfaction that you may imagine, and during fifteen minutes uttered nonsense in bad English before an assemblage of three hundred literary men, and a hundred women admitted to the honor of seeing us eat stringy chickens and tough tongue. I have never been so saturated with foolishness, as Pourceaugnac says.

Yesterday I received a visit from a gentleman and wife who brought me a number of autograph letters from Napoleon to Josephine, which they wished to sell. They are exceedingly curious in the fact of touching on nothing but love, and are doubtless authentic; but it is difficult to understand why Josephine did not burn them as soon as read.

PALACE OF FONTAINEBLEAU, *May*, 1858.— I am excessively annoyed and half poisoned from having taken too much laudanum; in addition to which I have written verses for His Majesty of the Netherlands, played charades, and « made a fool of myself » generally. Shall I describe the life we lead here? Yesterday we took a stag and dined on the grass; the other day we were all drenched with rain; every day we eat too much, and I am completely exhausted. Destiny did not fashion me for a courtier. I shall try to snatch a little sleep while awaiting the fatal hour of getting under arms, which is to say, donning tights. How much I should prefer to stroll through this fine forest with you, chatting of fairy-land. I am exceedingly vexed with your ridiculous prudery. The book in question has the misfortune to be badly written, that is to say, in an enthusiastic tone that Sainte-Beuve extols as poetic, so much do tastes differ. One does not, when possessed of your taste, exclaim that it is frightful, immoral, but finds all that is good in the volume very good. You allow your prejudice to sway your judgment, and each day you grow more prudish, more in consonance with the affectation of the age. Your crinoline I overlook, but not your prudery.

VENICE, *August*, 1858.— Venice filled me with sadness. I have been moved to indignation by all the commonplaces uttered of the architecture of the palaces, which is effective, but destitute of taste and imagination. The canals resemble the Bièvre, and the gondola an inconvenient hearse. The pictures of the second-rate masters at the Academy pleased me; but there is not a Paul Veronese worth " The Marriage of Cana," not a Titian to be compared with " Christ with the Tribute Money" at Dresden, or even " The Crown of Thorns" at Paris. On the other hand, I am pleased with the physiognomy of the people. The streets swarm with charming girls with bare feet and head, who, if bathed and scrubbed, would serve as models for the Venus Anadyomene. I was present at an amusing *funzione* in honor of the Archduke. A serenade was given, six hundred gondolas following the colossal boat that carried the music, all bearing lanterns and burning red and blue Bengal lights, which touched the palaces on the grand canal with a magical tint. In passing the Rialto no gondola would draw back, nor give way, so that the mass formed a solid bridge, and at every moment was heard the crash of collision and breaking oars; but an observable feature was, that amid all the excitement of the throng, which in France would have led to a general battle, no abusive language was heard, not even a cross word. These people are made of milk and maize. To-day I saw a monk, in the middle of St. Mark's Square, fall on his knees before an Austrian corporal about to arrest him. There was never anything more pitiable, and in front of the lion of St. Mark !

In a pretty villa on the banks of Lake Como I saw Madame Pasta, whom I had not met since her palmy days at the Italian Opera. She has singularly increased in size, cultivates cabbages, and says that she is as happy as

when crowns and sonnets showered on her. We discussed
the theatre, music, and she remarked, justly, that since
Rossini, no opera had been composed in which there was
unity of thought and treatment.

CHÂTEAU DE COMPIÈGNE, *November*, 1858. — This morning I saw my friend Sandeau in the frame of mind natural
to one who has appeared in knee-breeches the first time.
He asked me a hundred questions with a *naiveté* that
alarmed me. We have had great men from over the Channel, Russians and the Ministers, but the greater part of the
guests took their departure yesterday, and we are left *en
petit comité*, that is to say, we are but thirty or forty at
table. One cannot sleep in this place. The time is passed
in being frozen or roasting, and this has given me an irritation of the chest that exhausts me. But it is impossible
to imagine a more amiable host or a more gracious hostess.
When I think that I could have seen you to-day in Paris,
I am tempted to fly from here ; and also to hang myself
at your resignation : a virtue that I do not possess, and
which enrages me in others. Nothing is easier here than
to absent one's self from breakfast, or the morning walk,
but dinner is the momentous ceremony ; and when I spoke
to the old courtiers of my intention to dine in town, they
frowned in such evident consternation that I saw it must
not be thought of.

CANNES, *January*, 1859. — There are great numbers of
English here. I dined yesterday with Lord Brougham and
I know not how many Misses freshly arrived from Scotland, whom the sight of the sun appeared greatly to surprise.
Had I the talent to describe costumes, I could amuse you
with those of these ladies ; you have never seen anything
to parallel it since the invention of crinoline.

I have just read the " Memoirs of Catherine II.," which
presents a strange picture of the people and courts of that
period. Catherine on her marriage with the Grand Duke,
afterward Peter III., had a quantity of diamonds and
superb brocaded robes, and for her lodgings a chamber that
served as a passageway for her women, who, to the num-

ber of seventeen, slept in a single room next that of the queen. There is not to-day a grocer's wife who does not live more comfortably than the empresses of a hundred years ago. Catherine gives us sufficient strong reasons for believing Paul I. to be the son of Prince Soltikoff ; and the curious thing is, that the manuscript in which she narrates these fine histories was addressed to her son, this same Paul, an animal for whom strangling was the best mode of suppression. I am glad that my critique on Mr. Prescott has pleased you. I am not altogether satisfied with it as I only expressed half of what I should like to say, acting on the aphorism of Philip II.: that one must say only good of the dead. In fact, the work is only of slight interest, and not above mediocrity. It strikes me that had the author been less Yankee, he could have done something better. We have marvelous moonlight, the sea like glass, and the heat of June. I am more and more convinced that heat is my great restorative. When it rains I have horrible spasms : as soon as the sun returns Richard is himself again. Cannes is becoming too civilized : one of the loveliest walks is to be destroyed for the railway ; we shall become the prey of Marseilles, and the picturesque will be lost.

PARIS, *April*, 1859. — The war in Italy will be sharp, but not long ; the financial state of the world could not allow it ; and after the first shock I hope that England will intervene. Austria has no money, and many persons believe her motive to be simply a pretext for declaring her bankruptcy. Our people are warlike and confident, the soldiers gay and sanguine. There is an enthusiasm, a buoyancy in our army, in which the Austrians are totally deficient. Little of an optimist as I may be, I have full faith in our success. Our reputation is so well established that those who fight against us enter into it with little heart. A Russian alliance is still spoken of, in which I have no faith, for Russia has nothing to lose in the quarrel, and however it may terminate she will find it to be to her advantage : meanwhile she amuses herself with panslavist intrigues among the Austrian subjects, who regard the

Emperor Alexander as their Pope. The Austrians are said to
wear a modest, somewhat shamefaced air. The mass of our
people are intensely interested and offer vows for success.
The salons, especially those of the Orleanists, are perfectly
anti-French and arch fools, who imagine that they will
float back with the tide, and that their burgraves will resume the thread of their discourse that was snapped in
1848. Poor people! who do not understand that after this
will come division, a republic, and anarchy. Germany is
bawling against us; a mere jet of underlying red liberalism
which just now assumes the Teutonic form. Russia is a
terrible ally who would devour Germany, but who would
gain for us England's ill-will, and perhaps hostility. We
have so long led a sybaritic life as to ignore the emotions
of our fathers ; but we must now return to their philosophy.
Our troops, rest assured, will be well taken care of, and
will eat *macaroni stupendi* while the Austrians will sometimes find verdigris in their soup. Were I a young man,
an Italian campaign would be to me the most attractive
way of seeing a spectacle always noble — the awaking of an
oppressed people.

PARIS, *May*, 1859. — Germany is still fermenting, which
will result, aparently, rather in beer drinking than in blood
shedding. Prussia resists to her utmost the pressure of the
Franzosenfresser, and proclaims her intention to retake not
only Alsace, but also the German provinces of Russia. This
last jest would indicate that this Teutonic enthusiasm is neither serious nor well-considered. M. Yvan Tourguenieff,
who comes direct from Moscow, says that all Russia is
offering prayers for us, and that the army would be delighted to have a brush with the Austrians, whom, the
priests are preaching, God will punish for their persecution
of the orthodox Greeks of Sclavonic race ; and subscriptions
are open to send Sclavonic Bibles and tracts to the Croats
to preserve them from papal heresy. This looks very like
a political propaganda of panslavism.

A strong attack is now being organized against the Derby
Ministry. Lord Palmerston and Lord John would be reconciled — rather an improbable event — or still more unlikely

would unite for the destruction of the present Cabinet. The radicals will support them. Whatever may be the issue, we shall gain little by the change. Lord Palmerston, though the main promoter of the Italian agitation, would no more uphold it than would Lord Derby, only he would treat Austria with less consideration and would not seek to embarrass us. The wiseacres announce that all Europe will intervene : not improbable ; but after the famous phrase *Sin all' Adriatico*, how can we leave Italy only half-delivered? How hope that a young emperor, suckled and governed by the Jesuits, beaten and in a bad humor, should confess his folly and ask pardon! Would not the Italians, who until now have been circumspect, be goaded into every imaginable imprudence pending the negotiations?

PARIS, *July*, 1859. — You alone reconcile me to the Peace. Perhaps it was necessary ; but on the whole what matters to us the liberty of a parcel of smokers and musicians? We heard this evening the Emperor's speech, which was well delivered, with a grand air, an air of frankness and good faith : there is sense and truth in it. The returning officers say that the Italians are brawlers and cowards ; that only the Piedmontese can fight, who, however, pretend that we were in their way, and that without us they could have done better. The Empress asked me in Spanish what I thought of the speech ; to which I replied, combining candor with courtesy : "*Muy necesario.*"

PARIS, 1859. — I am reading the "Letters of Madame du Deffand." They are very amusing, giving an excellent picture of the society of her day, which was very amiable and somewhat frivolous. A striking contrast to the present era is manifest in their general and earnest endeavor to please ; as also in the sincerity and fidelity of their affections. They were more obliging people than ourselves, and especially than you, whom I no longer love.

PARIS, *September*, 1859. — The other day I met Edmond About, who is always charming. He resides at Saverne

and passes his life in the woods, where a month ago he
encountered a singular animal walking on all fours, wearing a black coat and varnished boots without soles. It
proved to be a professor from Angoulême, who had been
driven to the Baden gambling table by conjugal unhappiness, where he lost everything. Returning to France through
the forests he missed his way and had eaten nothing for
eight days. About carried and dragged him to a village
where he was supplied with linen and food, but he survived only a short time. When the man-animal lives in
solitude for a certain period, and reaches a certain state of
physical dilapidation, it appears that he walks on all fours.
About assures me that this *chef-d'œuvre* makes a very ugly
animal.

You are growing stout and brown with the sun : but
however you may be, fat or thin, I shall love you always
tenderly. I have frightful spasms, am still ill, and suspect
that I am on the great railway leading beyond the tomb.
At some moments this thought is painful, at others I find
the consolation that one experiences on the railway — the
absence of responsibility in the presence of a superior and
irresistible power.

PARIS, *September* 15, 1859.— I was summoned from
Tarbes by letter to Saint-Sauveur to pass the day, my
visit being returned by their majesties ; which occasioned a
great disturbance in M. Fould's household, Madame Fould
improvising a dinner and breakfast, taxing to the utmost
the resources of the little village. Their majesties were in
excellent health and capital spirits at Saint-Sauveur, and I
admired the natives, who had the good taste to leave them
entirely to themselves. The Emperor has bought a dog
rather larger than a donkey, of the ancient Pyrenean breed :
a magnificent brute which climbs rocks like a chamois.

MADRID, *October*, 1859.— Everything here is changed.
The ladies whom I left as thin as spindles have become
elephants, the climate of Madrid having a very fattening
quality. Not only the manners, but the picturesque aspect
of old Spain are notably altered by politics and a parlia-

mentary government. At this moment nothing is discussed but war, the question of avenging the national honor exciting a general enthusiasm that recalls the Crusades. It is imagined that the English view the African expedition with displeasure and even wish to prevent it, which redoubles the warlike ardor. The army wish to lay siege to Gibraltar, after taking Tangiers!

CANNES, 1860.—Baron Bunsen is here with his two daughters, both mounted on crane's feet, with ankles resembling the club of Hercules; one of the young ladies, however, sings very well. Bunsen is clever enough and knows the news, of which you keep me but ill-informed. I have read the pamphlet by Abbé ——, which strikes me as even more clumsy than violent. He must be thought an *enfant terrible* at Rome, where neither good sense nor finesse is lacking, and where the priests are skillful intriguers. Ours have the national blustering instinct, and are devoid of tact.

Here is a nice little incident characteristic of this region. A farmer in the neighborhood of Grasse is found dead in a ravine where he had fallen or been thrown during the night. Another farmer comes to see a friend and tells him that he has killed the man. " How? and why? " " Because he cast a spell over my sheep; then I asked the advice of my shepherd, who gave me three needles to boil in a pot, over which I pronounced the words he taught me. The same night that I put the pot on the fire the man died." Do not be surprised should my books be burned in the church square at Grasse.

The recent *brochure* by my colleague Villemain, is singularly vapid. When one has attempted to write a book against the Jesuits, and has boasted of being the defender of liberty of conscience against the omnipotence of the Church, it is droll to hurl forth a recantation and to support it by such feeble argument. I believe that every one has gone mad, except the Emperor, who reminds one of the shepherds of the Middle Ages whose magic flute inspired the wolves to dance. I am seriously told that the French Academy, which has been markedly Voltairean these

few years past, wishes to nominate Abbé Lacordaire as a
protest against the violence to which the Pope is subjected.
The matter is really one of perfect indifference to me.   So
long as I shall not be compelled to listen to their sermons,
all the members of the Sacred College may be nominated
to the Academy.

I have been on a little excursion in the region of eternal
snow, where I saw fine rocks, cascades, and precipices, and
a great subterranean cavern of unknown extent, supposed
to be inhabited by all the gnomes and devils of the Alps.
In fact, I passed a week in the enjoyment of pure nature
and lumbago. We have here a Siberian wind, and this
morning some snow-flakes fell before my window; an un-
heard-of scandal in the memory of the oldest inhabitant of
Cannes.   I am ill, melancholy, wearied.   My sight is fail-
ing and I can no longer sketch.   What a sad thing is this
growing old ! Bulwer's novel, " What will He do with It? "
appears to me senile to the last degree ; nevertheless it
contains some pretty scenes and has a very good moral.
As to the hero and heroine, they transcend in silliness
the limits of romance.   A book that has amused me is a
work by M. de Bunsen on the origin of Christianity and
on EVERYTHING, to speak more exactly ; but it styles itself : " Christianity and Mankind. "   M. de Bunsen, though
calling himself a Christian, has little respect for the Old
and New Testaments.

PARIS, *May*, 1860.— The ball at the Hôtel d'Albe was
superb ; the costumes were very fine, many of the women
very pretty, and typifying the audacity of the age being
décolletées in the most outrageous fashion both as to skirt
and waist.   During the waltz I saw a number of charming
feet and many garters. Crinoline is declining.   Be assured
that within two years dresses will be worn very short, and
the natural advantages of those so fortunate as to possess
them will be distinguished from artificial charms.   Some of
the Englishwomen passed belief.   The captivating daughter
of Lord —— represented a Dryad, or some mythological
personage, in a dress that would have left the entire bust
exposed but for the semi-veil of a sort of swaddling band.

It was nearly as conspicuous as the scanty drapery of the Mamma. The *ballet* of the Elements was danced by sixteen quite pretty women in short petticoats and covered with diamonds. The Naiads were powdered with silver, which, falling on their shoulders, resembled drops of water.

The Salamanders were powdered with gold; one among them, Mademoiselle Errazu, being wondrously beautiful. The Princess Mathilde, painted a deep *bistre*, personated a Nubian, and was much too exact in costume. In the midst of the ball, a domino embraced Madame S——, who uttered loud screams. The dining-room with its surrounding gallery, the servants in their dresses as pages of the sixteenth century, and the electric light, recalled Martin's picture of Belshazzar's Feast. The Emperor changed his domino in vain; he would have been recognized at a league distant. The Empress wore a white bournous and black velvet mask, which did not disguise her in the least. There were many foolish dominos; the Duc de —— walking about as a tree,—an excellent imitation. At the ball given by M. Aligre, a wife was pinched black and blue by her ferocious husband. The wife screamed and fainted; general tableau! The jealous idiot was not thrown out of the window, which would have been the only sensible thing to do. At a recent masked ball a lady had the temerity to appear in a costume of 1806, without crinoline, which produced a great sensation. These are fine commentaries on the times and women.

An amusing incident occurred lately. M. Boitelle, Prefect of Police, who should certainly be the best informed man in Paris, learned through the reports of faithful agents that M. Fould, the Minister of State, had gone to sleep in his newly-built house in the Faubourg Saint-Honoré. Very early in the morning the Prefect appeared, pressed the Minister's hand very demonstratively, explaining the important part he had taken in what had just occurred. M. Fould thought that he referred to his son, who is committing follies in England. This *quid pro quo* lasted until the Prefect asked permission to know the name of his successor in the Cabinet, to which M. Fould replied, that he had come to his new residence merely as a housewarming, and had found it more convenient to sleep there than at the Ministerial palace.

It appears that Lamoricière is already somewhat weary of the imbroglio that greets him in the papal territory. Cardinal Antonelli remarked a short time ago to a foreign minister, that he had never met a man of more comprehensive mind than Lamoricière. "I have discussed the intricate situation of affairs with him, for which he immediately suggested five or six remedies; and he talks so well, that within the hour he gave me four different opinions on the same question, all so strongly fortified that I am perplexed as to a choice." Every one here is preoccupied by Garibaldi's expedition, which will, it is feared, result in a general complication. Should he break his back in Sicily, I think that perhaps M. de Cavour would not be too much distressed, but if he succeed, he will become ten times more dangerous.

Read Granier de Cassagnac's book on the Girondins. Portions of it are exceedingly curious, and it presents a horrible picture of the massacres and revolutionary atrocities: all written with much fire and vigor. Three days ago I received a visit from M. Feydeau, who is a very fine fellow, but artlessly betrays an extreme vanity. He is going to Spain to complement what Cervantes and Lesage have merely outlined! He has still thirty romances to write, the scene of which will be laid in thirty different countries; this is why he travels. I think of you incessantly in spite of your faults.

PARIS, *July*, 1860.—The funeral of Prince Jerome was a terrible ceremony. I do not know how many vacancies it has created in our ranks, but fear that only the undertakers have profited by it. More than thirty thousand persons came to sprinkle holy water, which shows the flunkyism of this high-minded nation! It is even more senseless than is supposed, and that is saying much. You lost a fine spectacle, that of seeing me *in fiocchi* and black gloves, pass through the Rue de Rivoli amid the admiring populace. We were one hour and three quarters in defiling between the Palais Royal and the Invalides, then came the mass, then the funeral oration by Abbé Cœur, who praised the principles of '89, while declaring our soldiers to be ready to die in defense of the Pope. He also said that the first Napoleon had no love for war, but was always forced to the defensive. The finest part of the ceremony was a *De profundis* chanted in the vault, and which we heard through black crape that separated us from the grave. Were I a musician I would profit in opera by the admirable effect of this crape in modifying sound.

The Orleanists pretend that M. Brénier has been knocked in the head by an uncivil husband; but the more credible rumor is that the lazzaroni have thus sought to avenge the violence offered to their king. The liberals, in retaliation, have assassinated the police, which has been of much benefit to M. Brénier. The northern Italians have not the quick sensibility of the Neapolitans. They have logic and common sense, as Stendhal said, while the Neapolitans are merely badly trained children.

In the evening every one goes to the Champs-Elysées to hear Musard's music; fine ladies and *lorettes* mingled pell-mell, and are difficult to distinguish one from the other. And people go to the circus to see the learned dogs roll a ball up an inclined plane by leaping on it! This generation is losing all taste for intellectual pleasures.

SOUTH PARADE, BATH, *August*, 1860.— Such a life as mine here would make a thorough-bred horse broken-winded: in the morning, walks, shopping, and visiting; in the evening, dinners with the aristocrats, where I always find the same dishes and nearly the same faces. I could hardly remember the names of my hosts, for in their white cravats and black coats, all Englishmen look very much alike. We are extremely detested here, and still more dreaded. Nothing is more droll than the fear they have of us, which they are at no pains to disguise. The volunteers are even more stupid than the National Guard was with us in 1830; for in this country everything is invested with an air of gravity not to be seen elsewhere. I know a very honest fellow sixty years of age, who drills every day in Zouave breeches. The Ministry is very weak and does

not know its own mind, and the Opposition is not more
wise. But great and small agree in believing that we covet
general annexation. At the same time, there is no one
who supposes a war to be possible, unless the question of
annexing the three kingdoms should be agitated. I am not
very well pleased with the Emperor's letter to M. de Persigny. It would have been much better in my opinion, to
say nothing at all, or simply to tell them what I repeat
every evening : that they are great fools.

LONDON, 18 *Arlington Street*, 1860.— Only after some
time in London do I accustom myself to its singular light,
which seems to pass through brown gauze, the effect being
that of an eclipse. This atmospheric peculiarity and the
curtainless windows will annoy me for some days to come ;
but on the other hand I am regaling on all manner of
good things, breakfasting and dining like an ogre.

It is evident that the affairs of the East are becoming
more complicated every moment. The disembarking of the
French in Syria would be followed by a general explosion
of massacre and pillage throughout the East ; very probably,
also, the Turkish provinces of Greece — that is to say,
Thessaly, Macedonia, and Christian Albania — would be excited to retaliation. Everything will be on fire this winter
in the East, and to visit Algeria at such a moment seems
to me perfect madness. The " Times " to-day announces
four feet of snow at Inverness. Shall I find enough char-
coal and plaids in Scotland to remedy this evil?

GLENQUOICH, *August*, 1860.— The weather here is always
detestable, but it does not hinder people from going out.
They are so accustomed to rain, that unless it be of extraordinary violence they are not deterred from walking.
The paths are sometimes torrents, and the mountains are
invisible within a hundred paces ; but these people return,
saying " Beautiful walk. " One of the greatest annoyances
of this region is a little fly called midge, which is exceedingly venomous ; and though there are two young ladies
here, the one blonde, the other red-haired, and both with
skin of satin, these horrible insects prefer to attack me.

Our chief amusement is fishing, and fortunately the insects do not venture on the lake. There are fourteen persons here. During the day each one goes his own way; in the evening, after dinner, each one takes a book or writes letters. To chat and seek to amuse each other is a thing unknown to the English. The Highland air has benefited me, and I breathe more easily. Our hunters kill deer and grouse; and every day we have excellent birds; but I cannot eat, the main pleasure amid this rain and fog; and I sigh for a *soupe maigre*, or for a solitary dinner at home, or with you at Saint-Cheron: this last wish will never be realized, I fear.

PARIS, *September*, 1860.— Panizzi has been with me for ten days, and I am acting *cicerone*, showing him everything, from cedar to hyssop. I understand nothing of the disorders that have begun. My guest thinks that the Pope and the Austrians will be driven out. For the first, appearances are unfavorable; as to the others, I believe that if Garibaldi meddles with them he will burn his fingers. From Naples comes a royal philosophical witticism. Previous to embarking, His Majesty received, every five minutes, the resignation of a general or an admiral: "Now they are too thoroughly Italians to fight against Garibaldi; a month hence they will be too much of royalists to fight against the Austrians." It would be impossible for you to imagine the fury of the Orleanists and Carlists. A rather sensible Italian tells me that M. de Cavour caused the Sardinian army to enter the States of the Church, because Mazzini was about to incite a revolution there.

I hear that the *fêtes* at Marseilles in the Imperial honor were very fine: that the enthusiasm was at once deliberate and clamorous, and that perfect order was maintained notwithstanding the immense, overexcited Southern multitude. The spectacle of the Marseillaise, in their ordinary state, is always sufficiently amusing, but, when under excitement, they must be still more absurd. But they not only lost their heads on the occasion of the Emperor's visit, but also two barrels of Spanish wine that I have been expecting. The merchant who should have received them writes to me very naïvely, that he was too much occupied with the *fêtes* to think of my wine, and could only attend to it after taking a little rest.

I lately passed a few days at Saintonge, where I found every one discomfited, weeping their eyes away for the misfortunes of the Holy Father and General Lamoricière. It is said that General Changarnier is writing a narrative of his colleague's campaign, in which, after bestowing the highest eulogies, he proves that Lamoricière committed the most enormous follies. In my opinion, the only one of the martyr heroes at whom one cannot laugh, is Pimodan, who died like a brave soldier. Those who exclaim against the martyrs because they have been taken, move me to no pity. Moreover, the present time is perfectly comic; and it is comfortable to learn every morning, through one's paper, of a catastrophe, to read Cavour's notes and the encyclicals. I see that they have shot Walker, in America, which surprises me, for his case is precisely that of Garibaldi whom we all admire.

Two evenings ago, wishing for some music, I went to the Italians, where they gave the "Barber of Seville." This music, the gayest ever written, was executed by people with the air of having just returned from a funeral. Alboni, who played Rosina, sang admirably, with the expression of a bird organ. Gardoni sang like a gentleman who fears to be mistaken for an actor. Had I been Rossini I should have beaten them every one. Only Basilio, whose name I do not recall, sang as if he understood the words.

I am told that the Empress, whom I have not yet seen, is still terribly afflicted. She sent me a fine photograph of the Duchesse d'Albe, taken twenty-four hours after death, which was very calm; she looks as if in a quiet sleep. Five minutes before her death she laughed at her waiting-maid's Valencian *patois*. I have no direct news of Madame de Montijo since her departure, but I fear that the poor lady will not bear up under this dreadful blow.

I am in the midst of academical intrigues; the question not one touching the French Academy, but that of the fine arts. An intimate friend of mine is the favored candi-

date, but he has received an intimation from His Majesty
to give place to M. Haussmann, the Prefect. The Academy
is annoyed, and wishes to nominate my friend in spite of
himself, which I encourage to the utmost ; and I should
like to tell the Emperor the wrong he does himself in mingling with matters that do not concern him. I hope for
success, and that the Colossus will be finely blackballed.

Italian affairs are very amusing, and what is said of
them by the few honest people here is still more droll.
The martyrs of Castelfidardo are beginning to arrive,
among them a young man of eighteen years who allowed
himself to be taken, and whose aunt I saw a few days
ago. She said : "The Piedmontese behaved in an atrocious manner to my nephew." I awaited some appalling
revelation. "Only imagine, Monsieur, five minutes after
being made prisoner the poor fellow's watch was gone. A
gold hunting watch that I had given him !"

October, 1860. — I quite understand that the first view of
Oriental life should dazzle you. One sees things both droll
and to be admired at every step ; in fact, there is always something droll in Orientals as in certain strange, pompous
beasts that we formerly saw at the Jardin des Plantes.
Decamps has caught this ludicrous phase, but not the very
fine, noble side of their character.

Thanks to your sex you are privileged to enter the
harems and chat with the women. Do they in Algeria, as
in Turkey, make a display of their charms? Tell me how
they dress, what they say, and what they think of you.
What is the character of the dances that you saw? Were
they modest, and did you comprehend their sentiment? I
imagine that they are more interesting than those of Parisian balls ; and they probably resemble the dances of the
gypsy women of Granada. I do not doubt that an Arab,
from Sahara, in witnessing a waltz in Paris, would con-
clude, and naturally, that the French women were enacting
pantomime. In going to the root of things we always find
the same primal ideas. Have you seen the women at the
Moorish baths? I am inclined to believe that the habit of
living with crossed legs must give them horrible knees. I

suppose you will adopt kohl for your eyes, which is very pretty, being also, it is said, an excellent preservative against ophthalmia, an affection common and dangerous for European eyes in hot climates. I grant you my permission to try the effect. You give me sketches; I wish for details. There is nothing that you cannot say to me, and besides, you are renowned for your euphuisms. You have the art of academical expression. I congratulate you on your courage in learning Arabic. I once glanced through M. de Sacy's grammar and recoiled in terror, but I remember that there are lunar and solar letters, and I know not how many conjugations. My cousin, one of the most learned Arabists, who had passed twenty-five years at Djeddah, told me that he never opened a book without learning some new word, of which there were, for instance, five hundred for the one word lion.

PARIS, *October*, 1860.— I went to Saint-Cloud yesterday, where I breakfasted almost *tête-à-tête* with the Emperor, the Empress, and "Monsieur fils," as they say at Lyons. I talked a long while with the Emperor, principally of ancient history and Cæsar. He surprises me by the ease with which he comprehends erudite subjects, for which he has only recently acquired the taste. The Empress related some curious anecdotes of her journey in Corsica. The Bishop spoke to her of a bandit named Bosio, a thoroughly honest youth, whom the counsels of a woman had driven to commit several little murders. He is pursued for some months, but uselessly ; women and children suspected of carrying him food are thrown into prison, but to lay hands on him is impossible. Her Majesty, who has read a certain romance,* became interested in this man, and said she should be very glad if he could be enabled to leave the island and go to Africa or elsewhere, where he might become a good soldier and an honest man. "Ah! Madame," said the Bishop, "will you allow me to have this told to him?" "How, Monseigneur, you know where he is?" General rule : the most worthless fellow in Corsica is always related to the most honest man. It greatly surprised the Imperial party

* Mérimée's novel of *Colomba*.

that they should have been asked for a prodigious number of favors (*grâces*), but not for a sou; so the Empress returns full of enthusiasm.

The meeting at Warsaw is a failure. The Emperor of Austria invited himself, and was received with the politeness that is accorded to the indiscreet. Nothing of importance was accomplished. The Emperor of Austria essayed to prove that if Hungary was a source of danger to Austria, Russia had Poland; to which Gortschakoff replies: "You have eleven millions of Hungarians, and you are three millions of Germans. We are forty millions of Russians, and have no need of assistance in bringing six thousand Poles to their senses. Consequently, there is no necessity for mutual guaranties." England is calming down, and it is possible that she may make us overtures to adopt a joint policy with regard to Italy. In that event war would be impossible unless Garibaldi should attack Venice. They write me from Naples that the muddle is at its height, and the Piedmontese are expected there with the same impatience with which we in Paris in 1848 looked for the arrival of the troops of the line. They sigh for order and rest their hopes for its restoration on Victor Emmanuel alone. Moreover, Garibaldi and Alexandre Dumas have prepared their minds for peace, much in the same way as a freezing rain disposes one to a hot dinner.

PARIS, *November*, 1860. — Affairs are still complicated by the condition of the East, which is such that our Ambassador at Constantinople expects the old machine to crack from top to bottom at any moment. The Sultan is selling his cashmeres, and does not know if he will be able to buy a dinner next month. Do you know the Emperor Francis Joseph's greeting to the Emperor Alexander? "I bring you my guilty head!" The serf's formula on approaching his master in the fear of being beaten. This he said in good Russian, for he knows all languages. His servile meanness did not profit him much; Alexander preserved a most discouraging coldness, and the Prince Regent of Prussia, following his example, put on airs. After the departure of the Emperor Alexander, the Austrian emperor remained four hours alone at Warsaw, where there was no great

Russian or Polish noblemen so poor to do him reverence. All this has been a great triumph to the old Russians, who detest the Austrians still more than the English or ourselves.

You have heard of our victory over these poor Chinese. What an absurdity to go so far for the purpose of killing people who have done us no harm. True, being a species of ourang-outang, the Grammont law alone can be invoked in their favor. I am preparing for our Chinese conquests by reading a new romance just translated by Stanislas Julien. It is the story of Mademoiselle Cân and Mademoiselle Ling who are very witty, making verses and crambo on every occasion. They meet with two students possessing the same poetic facility, and a never-ending combat of quatrains ensues, the prominent idea of which is the blue lotus and white doves. It is impossible to conceive of any imaginative effort more uncouth and more barren of passion. The people who can be amused by this style of literature are evidently abominable pedants, who well deserve to be beaten and conquered by us, who are disciples of the noble Greek literature.

I dined to-day with Prince Napoléon. The Princess Clotilde admired my wrist buttons, and asked the address of my jeweler.

MARSEILLES, *November*, 1860.— My friend Mr. Ellice, of Glenquoich, will be my neighbor this winter. He has just purchased a Scotch estate next his own ; or rather lakes, rocks, and heaths several leagues in extent. I cannot conceive what it will produce, unless it be grouse and deer.

I have brought with me a new edition of Pouschkine's works, and have promised to write a notice of him. I find magnificent things in his lyric poems, entirely after my own heart ; that is to say, Greek in their truth and simplicity. I should like to translate several that are marked by great sprightliness, in which, as in precision and clearness, he strikes me as pre-eminent. One in the style of Sappho's ode reminds me that I am writing in the chamber of an inn, dreaming of happy moments in the past. I am ill and suffering ; but of all petty miseries the worst for me is sleeplessness, when thoughts are gloomy, and one takes a dislike to one's self. The journey of the Empress to Scotland creates much gossip, and every one is mystified.

CANNES, *December*, 1860. — The political disturbance has somewhat agitated me, however unprejudiced in the premises I may be. You know how intimate I have been with the chief victim, M. Fould. As yet I know nothing positive respecting the reasons for his disgrace. It is evident, however, that a beautiful woman is somewhat implicated, who is anxious to dislodge him, and who has long sought to accomplish this end. M. Fould is less philosophical than I should have thought, or than I should have been in his place ; but he has been wounded by certain proceedings. As to the liberal measures, we must wait to see the result. As a principle, it is better to take the initiative in giving than to grant what has been long and impatiently demanded. On the other hand, the Emperor may be seeking support in the Chambers to enable him to withdraw from our false position in Italy,— protecting a Pope who excommunicated us *in petto*, while we risk a quarrel with our friends out of tenderness for the vanity of a puppet (the Emperor of Austria) who has never wished us well. Here, throughout France, the people who wear black coats and claim to be powerful are in favor of the Pope and the King of Naples, as if they had incited no 'revolution in France, but their love for the papacy and legitimacy does not stretch to the point of expending a crown for them. What will be the effect of the recrudescent eloquence with which the new concessions threaten us ? The old Parliamentarians begin to prick up their ears. M. Thiers, it is said, will enter the lists as a candidate for the Deputies, and this example will be followed by many others. I can hardly imagine what will become of the Ministers without portfolio commissioned to represent the eloquence of the Legislative Body and the Senate ; but it will be diverting to see orators like Messieurs Magne and Billault, with the Jules Favres and *tutti quanti*.

My friend Mr. Ellice is at Nice, whence he occasionally comes to visit me ; he complains of finding no intellectual associates. I see that you have had a visit from Mr. Cobden, a man of talent and very interesting, the opposite of an Englishman, in that he never utters commonplaces and has few prejudices. I can give you no political news, for my correspondents tell me nothing, except that nothing is done. It is a characteristic of our generation to set out with a great hubbub that ends in loitering and amusing ourselves on the road.

CANNES, *February*, 1861. — I have been to Nice on a visit to my friend Mr. Ellice who is cruelly tortured by the gout. I confess to an involuntary sentiment of satisfaction in passing the bridge of the Var free from custom-house officers, gensdarmes, and passports. It is a fine annexation and makes one feel several millimetres taller.

M. Fould has been on a visit to me, and related many curious stories touching both men and women who intermeddled in his affairs. I doubt if he will have the courage to persevere in sulking. It appears that when one has carried a red portfolio under the arm for some time, the loss of it reduces him to the state of an Englishman without his umbrella.

If you find some pretty silk stuff that washes, and not too much like a woman's gown, order me a *robe de chambre* the longest possible, and buttoned down the left side, and in the Oriental fashion. Bring it with you, for I have no wish to wear silk gowns when the ice of the Seine is two feet thick. The cold reported at Paris makes my hair stand on end ; nevertheless I am summoned there by the President. Do not be alarmed to see my illness announced. A dignity has been conferred on me which I could very well have dispensed with, but which compels me to be punctual ; and they also write me that our Senate is papistical and legitimist, and that my vote will not be one too many for the ballot.

The poor Duchess of Malakof is an excellent person, not very bright, especially as to French. She appears to be entirely domineered over by her frightful monster of a husband, who is rough by habit and perhaps through policy. It is said, however, that she accommodates herself to the inevitable. Should you see her, speak of me and of our theatrical performances in Spain. I am told that her brother is an amiable fellow, very handsome, and a poet into the bargain. Thanks for the tobacco pouch, the gold and colored embroidery of which is exquisite. Only barbarians can do these things, our workmen having too much acquired art and not enough sentiment to equal them. Thanks also for the bananas, to my taste the most delicious fruit in the world.

PARIS, *March*, 1861.—Since my return to Paris I have been in a condition of utter stultification; first, as regards our exhibition at the Senate, where, I may say with M. Jourdain, I have been surfeited with nonsense. Every one had a speech prepared, that it was necessary to display, and so contagious was the example of dullness that I delivered my own like an idiot. I was cruelly frightened, but overcame it by reminding myself that I was in the presence of two hundred imbeciles, and with no reason for agitation. The joke of it was that M. Walewski, for whom I wished to obtain a satisfactory budget, was offended by my praise of his predecessor, and honestly declared that he would vote against my resolution M Troplong, near whom in virtue of my office as Secretary I was seated, condoled with me in a low tone; to which I replied that it was impossible to make a Minister drink who was not thirsty. This was repeated piping hot to M. Walewski, who took it for an epigram, and has frowned at me ever since.

The second *ennui* of the day is the official and private dinners, where one sees the same turbot, fillet, and lobster, and the same tiresome persons as on the preceding occasion. But the most irksome of all is Catholicism. You can hardly imagine the degree of exasperation to which Catholics are moved, flying in one's face for a mere nothing; for example, if one does not show the whites of one's eyes in hearing them discourse of the sainted martyr; and still more if one innocently inquires, as I have done, who has been martyrized. I have also got into a scrape in expressing astonishment that the Queen of

Naples should be photographed in boots!— an exaggeration
of my words and a surpassing stupidity. The other evening a lady asked me if I had seen the Empress of Austria.
I said that I thought her very pretty. "Ah! she is
ideal!"—No, it is an irregular face, more agreeable perhaps than if perfectly classical.—"Ah! Monsieur, she is beauty
itself! Tears of admiration come to one's eyes!" And this
is the society of to-day! I fly from it as from the plague.
What has become of the French society of former years!

The latest, but a colossal bore, has been "Tannhauser."
Some persons say that its representation at Paris was one
of the secret clauses of the treaty of Villafranca; others,
that Wagner has been given to us to compel our admiration of Berlioz. The fact is, it is prodigious. I am convinced that I could write something similar if inspired by
the scampering of my cat over the piano keys. The Princess de Metternich bestirred herself enormously in feigning
to understand it and to lead the applause, which, however,
never came. Every one yawned; but at first the audience
assumed the air of comprehending this keyless enigma.
Beneath Madame de Metternich's box, it was said by the
wits that the Austrians were taking their revenge for
Solferino. It was also said that one wearies of the recita-
tives, and tires of the airs (*se tanne aux airs*). Try to
catch the pun. Your Arabic music, I fancy, would be a
capital preparation for this infernal uproar. The failure is
stupendous! Auber says that it is Berlioz without melody.

I am satisfied that within two months the Pope will
either be off, or that we shall leave him to his own de-
vices, or that he will come to some arrangement with
Piedmont; but matters cannot remain in their present
status. The bigots are raising a horrible outcry, but the
Gallic *bourgeois* and the people are anti-papists.

You tell me nothing of your health, which appears to be
good, nor of your complexion, which must be, I fear, somewhat browned.

PARIS, *May*, 1861.—You must have been sadly impressed with the aspect of winter in Central France, coming as you do from Africa. Whenever I return from

Cannes I am horrified at the sight of the leafless trees and damp, dead earth.

The Catholics have rendered our salons insupportable. Not only have the former devotees become acid as verjuice, but all of the ex-Voltaireans of the political opposition have turned papists. What consoles me, is, that some among them believe themselves obliged to attend mass, which must bore them sufficiently. My old Professor, M. Cousin, who formerly never spoke of the Pope but as the Bishop of Rome, is converted and never misses a mass. It is even said that M. Thiers is becoming devout, but I find some difficulty in believing it, for I have always had a weakness for him.

I am, at this very moment, a prey to the herrings that the sea-calves of Boulogne have raised up to torment us, and I await the Maronites as a finishing stroke — that is to say, we are disputing in the Senate, and very sharply, à propos to herrings, and we are menaced with daily sittings. Is it true that all the Boulogne herring fishers are thieves who buy the herrings taken by the English, and which they pretend to have caught themselves? Is it also true that the herrings have been seduced by the English, and pass no more along our coasts?

CHÂTEAU DE FONTAINEBLEAU, *June*, 1861.—I am resting under the trees with great happiness after my tribulations. Never have I seen men so enraged, so out of their senses as the magistrates. I console myself in thinking that if twenty years hence some antiquary shall burrow in the "Moniteur" of this week, he will say that one philosopher of moderation and calmness was found among an assembly of lunatics. This philosopher, without vanity, is myself. In this country magistrates are selected from men too stupid to gain their living as lawyers; they are badly paid, and are allowed to be crabbed and insolent. I have done my duty, and all is at an end. I was well received here, with no raillery on my defeat. I very clearly gave my opinion of the matter, and they do not appear to think me in the wrong. It is magnificent weather and the air of the forest is delicious. There are rocks and heather which would have their charms could I walk with you among them, chatting of all manner of things; but we go in a long file of *chars à bancs*, where one is not always well matched in point of capacity for amusing. There is not a republic, however, where one can have more freedom or find a host and hostess more amiable and kind to their guests. There are few people here. We have the Princess de Metternich, who is very animated after the German fashion, that is to say, she affects a species of originality composed of two parts *lorette*, one part great lady. I suspect that in reality there is not too much wit to sustain the rôle that she has adopted. One accomplishes nothing here. Sometimes I am summoned for a stroll in the woods; sometimes to make verses; but time is especially wasted in waiting. The great philosophy of the day is to know how to wait, and I have some difficulty in educating myself in the art. Thanks to Cæsar, doubt-less, I shall be here until the end of the month. I am working for the *bourgeois* (the Emperor), with whom I am more pleased every day. I went last week to Alise with the Emperor, who is becoming an accomplished archæolo-gist. He passed three hours and a half on the mountain, under the most terrific sun, examining the vestiges of Cæsar's siege, and reading the "Commentaries." We re-turned with the skin pealed from our ears, and the color of chimney-sweeps.

CHÂTEAU DE FONTAINEBLEAU, *June*, 1861.—We have had a capital ceremony here, reminding me of that in the "Bourgeois Gentilhomme." It was the most diverting spec-tacle possible, that of twenty black men exceedingly like monkeys, dressed in gold brocade with white stockings and varnished shoes, and swords at their side, all flat on their face and crawling on hands and knees the whole length of the Henri II. gallery, each one with his nose level with the back of the crawler preceding him. The hardest task fell to the first ambassador, who wore a felt hat embroid-ered in gold that danced on his head with each motion, and who held a bowl of gold filagree work within which were two boxes containing each a letter from their Siamese Majesties. The letters were inclosed in purses of gold-

woven silk, the whole being very pretty. After delivering
the letters to the Emperor, it became necessary to retire
backward, and confusion fell upon the embassy. A succession of blows on the face of those behind them by the
first rank, whose swords pierced the eyes of the second
rank, who in turn made blind of one eye the third rank,
was the result of this masterly retreat. They presented
the appearance of a swarm of black beetles on the carpet.
The Minister of Foreign Affairs had arranged the ceremony
and exacted that the ambassadors should crawl, the effect
of which moreover failed for the Emperor at length lost all
patience, rose, made the beetles rise, and spoke in English
with one of them. The Empress kissed a little monkey whom
they had brought, said to be the son of one of the ambassadors, who ran about on all fours like a little rat, but had
an intelligent expression. The temporal king of Siam sent
his portrait to the Emperor, and that of his wife, who is
hideously ugly. You would be charmed by the beauty
and variety of the stuffs they brought ; gold and silver tissues so light and transparent as to resemble the clouds of
a fine sunset. They gave the Emperor trowsers embroidered with ornaments in enamel and gold, and a vest of
gold brocade as flexible as foulard, the designs, gold on
gold, being really exquisite ; while the buttons are of a
filagree gold, diamonds, and emeralds. They have a red
gold and a white gold which produce an admirable effect
when blended. In short, I have never seen anything at
once so bewitching and splendid. The tastes of these sav-
ages is singular, in that their fabrics are not glaring, although they use only brilliant silks, gold, and silver. All
this is marvelously combined, producing on the whole a
quiet and harmonious effect.

LONDON, *British Museum, July*, 1861.—You know, or you
do not know, that there is a new Lord Chancellor, Lord
B——, who is old, but his morals by no means so. A
lawyer named Stevens sends his clerk with a card for the
Chancellor ; the clerk makes inquiries, and is told that my
lord has no house in London, but that he often comes
from the country to Oxford Terrace, where he has a tem-

porary lodging. Thither the clerk proceeds and asks for my lord. "He is not here." "Do you think he will return for dinner?" "No, but to sleep, certainly; he sleeps here every Monday." The clerk leaves the letter, and Mr. Stevens is greatly astonished that the Chancellor should look frightfully black at him. The gist of the story is, that my lord maintains a clandestine *ménage*.

I have not had a moment's rest since my arrival; dinner parties, balls, and concerts without cessation. Yesterday I attended a concert at the Marquis of Lansdowne's where there was not a single pretty woman, a remarkable circumstance here; but, on the other hand, they were all dressed as if the first *modiste* of Brionde had composed their toilet. I have never seen anything to parallel their head-dresses; one ancient dame, who wore a diamond crown composed of small stars with a huge sun in the centre, being an absolute counterpart of the wax figures that one sees at fairs.

Yesterday I dined at Greenwich with some great personages who exerted themselves to be lively, not like the Germans by throwing themselves from the windows, but by making an excessive noise. The dinner was abominably long, but the white bait excellent. We have unpacked two cases of antiquities just arrived from Cyrene. There are two statues and several remarkable busts, one of a good period and quite Greek; a Bacchus, that is especially captivating though with rather a mincing expression, the head being in an extraordinary state of preservation.

M. de Vidil is committed and will be tried at the next assizes. He is not admitted to bail, and the worst that can happen to him will be a sentence of imprisonment for two years; for where death does not supervene the English law does not recognize murder.

Lord Lyndhurst said to me that one must be extremely MALADROIT to be hung in England. I went the other evening to the House of Commons and heard the debate on Sardinia. Anything more verbose, more pointless (*gobe-mouche*), and fuller of braggadocio than the majority of the speakers it is impossible to imagine, and notably so Lord John Russell, now Earl Russell.

I have been interrupted by a visit to the bank. They placed in my hand four small packages amounting to four million pounds sterling, but I was not allowed to bring them away. They showed me a very pretty machine that counts and weighs three thousand sovereigns per day. It hesitates a moment, and after a short deliberation throws the good sovereign to the right and the bad to the left. There is another that takes a bank bill, stoops and gives it, as it were, two little kisses, impressing on it marks that forgers have not as yet been able to imitate. Finally, I was conducted to the vaults, where I might have imagined myself in a grotto of the "Arabian Nights"; all filled with sacks of gold and ingots sparkling in the gaslight.

PARIS, *August*, 1861.—I do not know whether in consequence of too much turtle soup, or exposure to the sun, but I have again suffered from my former agonizing pains, which must resemble those of hanging, and which create in me no desire to be suspended. After six weeks of dinner parties I find it very comfortable not to don a white cravat. I passed a week in Suffolk County in a fine *château*, almost in solitude. It is a flat country, but covered with magnificent timber, with much water; it is very near the fens whence Cromwell came. The quantity of game is astonishing, and at every step one runs the risk of crushing partridges or pheasants.

Should Madame de Montijo go to Biarritz I shall join her and pass some days with her. She is inconsolable, and I find her even more sad than last year when her daughter died.

I see by your letter that you are as much occupied as a general-in-chief on the eve of battle. I remember reading in " Tristram Shandy," that in the house with a newly born babe all the women believe themselves entitled to tyrannize over the men; and I feared to be treated with the disdain inseparable from your present height of grandeur. For myself, I am but slightly inclined to love children; nevertheless, I can imagine that one may be attached to a little girl as to a kitten, an animal to which your sex bear a strong resemblance. There is perfect solitude here, by

15

which I profit in preparing something promised to my master, and which I wish to take to Biarritz. I read little except Roman history ; nevertheless, I have read M. Thiers's
nineteenth volume with great pleasure. It strikes me as
being written with greater negligence than its predecessors,
but full of curious matter. In spite of his desire to speak
ill of his hero, he is continually carried away by his involuntary love. He gives exceedingly amusing stories of
Montrond, to whom I only regret not having related them
while he was living. M. Thiers paints him correctly as an
adventurer in love with his trade, and honest toward his
employers during the period of his service, much the same
as Dalgetty in the "Legend of Montrose."

BIARRITZ, *September*, 1861.— I am still here, dear friend,
like a bird on a branch. It is not the custom here to
make plans in advance, indeed they are resolved on only
at the last moment. It is excessively cold after dinner, it
being impossible to keep warm with the system of doors
and windows that has been contrived here. The sea air is
of service, and I breathe more easily, but sleep badly, as
I am immediately on the shore, for the slightest wind
rouses the waves to a terrific uproar. Time passes here as
in all imperial residences — in doing nothing and in waiting that something may be done. I work a little, sketch
from my window, and walk a great deal. There are but
few persons at the Villa Eugénie, and all agreeable. Yesterday we took a charming walk along the Pyrénées, sufficiently near the mountains to see them in all their beauty
and escaping the discomfort of constant ascents and de-
scents. We lost our way and found only people who were
ignorant of our fine French tongue : and this happens as
soon as one quits the suburbs of Bayonne.

Yesterday the Prince Imperial gave a dinner party to a
troupe of his young friends. The Emperor himself mixed
the champagne with seltzer-water, but the effect was the
same as if they had drunk the pure wine. They were all
tipsy a quarter of an hour afterward, and my ears still
ache with the noise they made. I boldly undertook to
translate a Spanish memoir respecting the site of Munda

for His Majesty, which I begin to perceive is terribly difficult reading. I am working like a negro for my master, whom I shall go to see in a few days.

COMPIEGNE, *November*, 1861.—Our anticipated *fêtes* have been postponed by the death of His Majesty of Portugal. As lions we have four Highlanders in kilts, the Duke of Athol, Lord James Murray, with the son and nephew of the Duke. It is droll enough to see these eight bare knees in a drawing-room where all the men are in knee breeches or pantaloons. Yesterday His Grace's piper was introduced, and they all four danced in a way to alarm the company when they whirled about. But there are some ladies here whose crinoline is still more alarming as they enter a carriage. As lady guests are not obliged to wear mourning, legs of every color are seen, the red stockings having a very good effect. In spite of walks through damp, icy woods, and red hot drawing-rooms, I have escaped a cold; but I am oppressed and do not sleep.

I was present at the great ministerial comedy, where we were in expectation of several additional victims. The faces were a study, the speeches still more so; inasmuch as M. Walewski, the tottering Excellency, paraded his griefs indiscriminately to friends and enemies. An inveterate prejudice is the strongest provocation to the utterance of nonsense, especially when one is in the habit of it. Oh human platitude ! His wife, on the contrary, was wonderfully cool and self-possessed. What is said of the Emperor's letter? He has a way peculiar to himself of saying things, and where he speaks as a sovereign contrives to convey the impression that he is of a finer porcelain. I believe it to be precisely what is needed by our high-toned nation which has no love for common clay.

Yesterday the Princess of ——, when taking tea, asked a footman, in her German accent, " *De lui aborder ti sel bour le bain.*" After a quarter of an hour the man returned with thirty pounds of bay salt, supposing that she wished to take a salt bath.

A picture by Müller, representing Queen Marie Antoinette in prison, was lately brought to the Empress. The

Prince Imperial asked who this lady was and why she was not in a palace. They explained to him that it was a Queen of France, and told him the meaning of a prison. He immediately ran off to ask the Emperor to be pleased to pardon this Queen whom he kept in prison. He is an odd child, and sometimes TERRIBLE. He says that he always bows to the people because they drove away Louis Philippe who was not on good terms with them. He is a charming child.

CANNES, *January*, 1862.— I have here as neighbor and companion M. Cousin, who has come to be cured of laryngitis, and who talks like a one-eyed magpie, eats like an ogre, and is surprised he does not get well under this beautiful sky, which he sees for the first time. He is, moreover, very amusing, for he has the tact to draw out every one around him. I believe that when he is alone with his servant he talks with him as with the most coquettish Orleanist or Legitimist Duchess. The Cannites, *pur sang*, cannot get over their astonishment, and you may fancy their look on being told that this man, who talks on every subject, and talks well, has translated Plato and is the lover of Madame de Longueville. The inconvenient part of it is that he does not know when to stop talking. For an eclectic philosopher it is a misfortune not to have adopted the conspicuous virtue of the sect of peripatetics.

How do you govern the little children who absorb you so much? It appears to be an interesting occupation. The worst thing about children is their tardy development which leaves us so long uncertain if they have mind or power of reasoning; it is vexatious that their struggling intelligence cannot be demonstrated by themselves. The main question is to know whether we shall talk sense or nonsense to them; each system has its pros and cons. I have made the acquaintance of a poor cat that lives in a cabin deep in the woods; I carry it bread and meat every day, and it runs a quarter of a league to meet me. I regret not being able to carry it off, for it has marvelous instincts.

LONDON, *British Museum*, *May*, 1862.— Frankly, the Exhibition is something of a failure. True, everything is not yet unpacked, but the building is horrible; although very large it does not impress one with its size, and one must walk and be lost in it to appreciate its extent. The English have made great progress in taste and the art of arrangement ; we make furniture and painted paper assuredly better than they, but we are in a deplorable path, and if this continue we shall be distanced. Our jury is presided over by a German who speaks English that is nearly incomprehensible, and nothing can be more absurd than our conferences ; no one even understands what subject is under discussion. Nevertheless, we vote. The worst of it is, that in our division there are some English manufacturers, and medals must necessarily be given to these gentlemen, who do not merit them. I am bombarded by speeches and routs. Two days ago I dined with Lord Granville. There were three small tables in a long gallery, which arrangement was expected to promote general conversation, but as the guests were but slightly known to each other nearly a general silence prevailed. In the evening I went to Lord Palmerston's, where the Japanese Embassy wore great swords which kept getting caught in all the women's dresses. I saw some women who were very beautiful and others who were very ugly ; both making a complete exhibition of their personal charms ; some attractive, others quite the reverse ; but each one displaying the same assurance.

LONDON, *June*, 1862.— I read my report yesterday to the International Jury, in the purest Anglo-Saxon, not a word drawn from the French. In vain do the Commissioners appeal and beat the drum, they cannot attract a crowd. Since the price has been reduced to a shilling fashionable people no longer go, and the lower class seem to find little pleasure in it. The restaurants are detestable, the American restaurant being the amusing feature, where may be found more or less diabolical beverages that one drinks through a straw : mint julep or " RAISE THE DEAD." All of these drinks are disguised gin. I am tired out with British hospitality and dinners which give the idea of all being prepared by the same inexpert cook. You cannot imagine how I long for a plate of soup from my own *pot-au-feu*.

I do not know which of two recent important events has produced the greatest effect,— one, the defeat of the two Derby favorites by an unknown horse ; the other, the defeat of the Tories in the House of Commons. The number of mournful faces in London was really ludicrous. A young married lady at the races fainted on learning that Marquis was beaten a head's length by a rustic without pedigree. Mr. Disraeli puts a better face on the matter and shows himself at every ball.

PARIS, *July*, 1862. — Madame de Montijo arrived last week, so changed that it is distressing to see her. Nothing consoles her for the death of her daughter, and I find her less resigned even than on the day of her death. I dined last week at Saint-Cloud with a small circle quite agreeably, and where the feeling struck me as being less papistic than is generally supposed. I was permitted to scandalize matters without being called to order. The little prince is charming. He has grown two inches and is the prettiest child I have seen.

BAGNÈRES-DE-BIGORRE, *The Upper Pyrénées*, 1862.— I have arrived here with M. Panizzi after a little tour beneath a terrible sun, and find weather worthy of London : fogs and an imperceptible rain that penetrates to one's bones. The physician of this watering-place is an old comrade of mine who has auscultated me and punched my chest and back, discovering two mortal ailments of which he undertakes to cure me, provided that I drink daily two glasses from the hot mineral spring, which is not ill-tasting ; and that I bathe in a warm spring that is very agreeable to the skin. Already I am better. There are not many persons here, the English and the grapes having failed this season. In point of beauty we have Mademoiselle A. D——, who formerly captivated Prince ——. I have only seen her back, and she wears the vastest crinoline to be found in all the country. Balls are given twice a week, which I shall not attend, and amateur concerts, which I shall religiously avoid. Yesterday I was compelled to undergo a musical mass, to which I was conducted by gensdarmes; but the *soirée* given by the Sub-Prefect I declined, not to accumulate too many catastrophes in a single day. I should like to show you the incomparable verdure of this region, to talk with you beneath the shade of the great beech-trees, and make you drink the bright water for which crystal would be no fitting comparison. The petty quarrels and occupations of which you complain are lamentably incidental to a provincial place, and one can only deplore the fate of persons condemned to live there. Nevertheless it is certain that in the course of a few months one sinks to the level of the natives, and becomes interested in provincial inanities. The confession is sad, but human intelligence accepts the aliment offered and with satisfaction.

Last week I made a mountain excursion to see a farm belonging to M. Fould. It is on the shore of a small lake, facing one of the finest panoramas imaginable, surrounded by great trees, a rare thing in France; and one breakfasts there most capitally. He has many magnificent horses and oxen, the whole managed with English order.

Have you read "Les Misérables," and heard what is said of it? This is another of the subjects in respect to which I find the human species below that of the gorilla. The world becomes more stupid every day.

BIARRITZ, *Villa Eugénie, September,* 1862.—Dear friend, I am here on the sea-shore, breathing more easily than for a long time. The waters of Bagnères made me ill, a proof, it was said, of their beneficial action; but on leaving them I began to revive, and now the sea-air and perhaps also the superb *cuisine* have perfected my cure. There are but few guests at the Villa, and only amiable persons whom I have long known. There is no crowd in the town, not many French, the Spaniards and Americans predominating. At the Thursday receptions at the Villa the Northern and Southern Americans have to be placed on different sides of the salon, lest they should eat each other.

On these occasions there is full dress, but usually there is not the least toilet; the ladies dine in high dresses, and we of the ugly sex in morning coats. There is not a *château* in France or England where one is so free and without etiquette, nor where the chatelaine is so good and so gracious to her guests. We take beautiful walks in the valleys skirting the Pyrénées, returning with prodigious appetites. The lady bathers are, as usual, very odd in the matter of costume. There is a Madame ——, the color of a turnip, who arrays herself in blue and powders her hair, — the powder, however, is said to be ashes, with which she sprinkles her head because of her country's misfortunes.

Have you seen Victor Hugo's speech at a dinner of Belgian booksellers and other swindlers at Brussels? What a pity that this good fellow, who has such fine imagery at his command, should not possess an iota of common sense, nor the discretion to refrain from uttering plaudits unworthy of so clever a man! I find more poetry in his comparison of the tunnel and railway than I have met with in any book these five years. But they are, after all, merely metaphors, containing nothing of depth, solidity, or judgment. He is a man who intoxicates himself with his own words and does not take the trouble to think. The twentieth volume by Thiers pleases me, as it does you. I have read it a second time with renewed pleasure, and shall do so again. It was immensely difficult, in my opinion, to extract anything from the confused rubbish of the St. Helena conversations as reported by Las Cases, and Thiers has come out of it wonderfully well. I am also pleased with his comparison of Napoleon with other great men, although he is somewhat severe upon Alexander and Cæsar; nevertheless, there is much truth in what he says as to the absence of virtue on the part of Cæsar. It attracts great interest, here, and I fear that there is not overmuch love for the hero; for instance, they will not concede the anecdote of Nicomedes, nor you either, I fancy. Adieu — keep well, and do not sacrifice yourself too much for others; they will come to accept it as a habit, and what is now a pleasure to you, will perhaps some day become an irksome duty.

PARIS, *October*, 1862. — I returned from Biarritz with my Sovereigns. We were all quite doleful, having been poisoned, as I believe, by verdigris. The cooks swear that they scoured their saucepans, but I do not credit their oaths. The fact is, fourteen persons at the Villa were seized with vomiting and cramps, and having been formerly poisoned with verdigris, I know the symptoms and hold to my opinion. What with the poisoning and the political stir, I have led an agitated life. I have been divided between the desire that M. Fould should remain in the Ministry, in the interest of our master, and the wish that he should resign for the sake of his own dignity and personal advantage. It has ended by concessions which have benefited no one, while, in my opinion, they have lowered the *dramatis personæ*. The joke of the matter is that Persigny, whom the non-papist Ministers cannot endure, has become their standard bearer, and that he shall continue in office they have made the condition on which they retain their portfolios. So, Thouvenel, an intelligent, very good fellow, has been dismissed, while Persigny, who is crazy and understands nothing of business, remains. Here we are then, in the clutches of the clergy, and you know where they lead their friends.

I am now reading a book that may entertain you : the history of the " Revolt of the Netherlands," by Motley. There are not less than five thick volumes; but although not over and above well written, it is smooth in style and interesting. He yields too much to anti-Catholic and anti-Monarchical prejudice, but he has made immense researches, and though an American, is a man of talent.

I am suffering with my lungs. You will learn some day that I have ceased to breathe for want of this organ, which should induce you to be very amiable to me before this misfortune shall occur.

CANNES, *January*, 1863. — I have received the last novel by M. Gustave Flaubert, the author of " Madame Bovary," which I believe you have read, though you will not confess it. The new romance is " Salammbô," a crazy production ; but the writer has talent which he fritters away under the pretext of realism. One obtains an amusing idea of the author, and a still more ludicrous one of his admirers, the *bourgeois*, who discuss such things with decent people. I recommend you to read a romance by M. de Tourguenieff, the proofs of which I am expecting for the *Revue des Deux Mondes*, and which I have read in Russian. It is called *Les Pères et les Enfants*. It offers a contrast between the passing and coming generation. The hero, the representative of the new generation, is a socialist, materialist, and realist, nevertheless a sensible and interesting man. This novel has produced a great sensation in Russia, and a great outcry against the writer, who is accused of immorality and impiety. When a work excites such public exasperation, it is, in my opinion, a signal proof of success.

Before leaving Paris I consulted an eminent physician, wishing to ascertain how long a time would be allowed to prepare for my funeral ceremonies. I was satisfied with the consultation, first, because the ceremony would not take place so soon as apprehended ; secondly, because he explained clearly and anatomically the seat of my malady — not the heart, but the lungs. True, I can never be cured, but there are alleviations for my suffering. I have been in bed a week from an attack of spasms and suffocation, having contracted a painful lumbago, the effect of this fine climate, where, so long as the sun remains above the horizon one may fancy it to be summer ; but as soon as it disappears we have a quarter of an hour of damp cold that penetrates to one's very marrow.

It appears that they are becoming more and more religious in Paris. I receive sermons from people from whom I should have expected something quite different. I am told that M. de Persigny has shown himself ultra papist on the Senate's committee of address. I do not believe that there was ever a period when the world was more senseless (*bête*) than now. Last as long as it may, the end is ominous.

PARIS, *April*, 1863. — Of all the Italian cities, Florence appears to me to have best preserved her characteristics of the Middle Ages. As to Rome let me give you two bits

of advice: first, never to be a moment in the air at night-
fall, for fear of the Roman fever; but a quarter of an hour
before the Angelus go to St. Peter's and wait until the
strange, damp precipitate in the air shall pass by. There
is nothing finer for meditation that this great church
at that hour, the indistinctness of its vast proportions
makes it truly sublime. Think of me when there. My
second recommendation is to employ a rainy day in seeing
the Catacombs. When there, turn into one of the narrow
corridors debouching from the subterranean streets, extin-
guish your taper and remain alone for a few moments.
You will tell me your sensations. I should have great
pleasure in the experience with you, but perhaps our sensations would not be the same. I never succeeded in Rome in
carrying out my programme of sight-seeing, for at each
street corner one is drawn off by something unforeseen, and
the great charm is to yield to impulse. As regards objects
of art, study the frescoes, and the views as to nature and
art combined. At the Capitol make them show you the
wolf of the Republic, which bears trace of the thunderbolt
that struck it in the time of Cicero. It is not a thing of
yesterday. Try to understand that you cannot see the
hundredth part of all that is interesting, and do not regret
it; there will remain one great, harmonious memory worth
more than a crowd of souvenirs in detail. Do not forget
to see Pompey's statue, at the foot of which Cæsar was assassinated. Rome is pervaded with a gentle, agreeable
melancholy which one recalls with pleasure; for a vivid
comparison with which it would be well to pass a week at
Naples. Of all transitions it is the most abrupt and amusing; it is comedy succeeding tragedy; and sends one to bed
the mind filled with ludicrous images.

I do not know whether the *cuisine* has made any progress in the States of the Holy Father, but in my time it
was the "abomination of desolation," while in Naples it
was possible to subsist.

Society here is astir with the actual or reputed eccentrici-
ties of Madame de ——. Certain it is that she is crazy
enough to be placed under restraint. She beats her servants,
cuffs, boxes the ears, and makes love to her favorites in

the same breath. She carries her Anglo-mania so far as to drink brandy and water, that is to say, much of the former with little of the latter. The other evening she presented one of her friends to M. Troplong, saying: "*Monsieur le President*, I bring you my DARLING." To which M. Troplong politely replies, that he is happy to make the acquaintance of M. Darling. If all that is told me of the manners of the *liounes* be true, it is to be feared that the end of the world is near. I dare not tell you all that takes place in Paris among the young representatives of the generation that is to bury us.

CHÂTEAU DE FONTAINEBLEAU, *July*, 1863. — No one has time here for anything, and the days pass one knows not how. The chief occupation is eating, drinking, sleeping: I succeed in the first two, in the last very badly, after passing several hours in knee-breeches, in rowing on the lake and getting a frightful cough. There are many well-assorted guests here, fewer officials than usual, which does not, however, detract from the prevailing *entente cordiale*. Sometimes we walk in the woods, after having picnicked on the grass like tradesmen from the Rue St. Denis.

Two days ago some very large chests arrived from his Majesty Tu-Duc, Emperor of Cochin China. They were opened in one of the court-yards. Within the large cases were smaller ones painted in red and gold, containing two very yellow elephant's teeth, two rhinoceros' horns, and a package of moldy cinnamon, the whole exhaling inconceivable odors. There was also a large quantity of narrow gauze-like stuffs, of every ugly color, more or less soiled, and all musty. Medals, that were among the expected gifts, were absent, and probably remained in Cochin China; from which it appears that the great Tu-Duc is a swindler. Yesterday we attended the manœuvres of two regiments of cavalry, and were all cooked by the heat; all the ladies had a sun-stroke. To-day we are to have a Spanish dinner in the Forest, and I am intrusted with the *gaspacho*, that is to say, imposing raw onions on the ladies, who would swoon at the mere mention of the vegetable. I have forbidden that they be warned, and after they have eaten it, I shall make my confession to them in the style of Atreus.

LONDON, *August*, 1863.— I expected to find London empty, and in fact such was my first impression ; but at the end of two days I discovered the great ant-hill to be still swarming, and, alas ! that they dined quite as often and as interminably as last year. Is not the slowness of the dinners inhuman in this country ! It really deprives me of appetite. We are never less than two hours and a half at table, and if the half hour during which the men leave the women to speak ill of them be added, it is always eleven o'clock when we return to the drawing-room. This would be but a demi-evil could one eat all the time ; but, with the exception of the roast mutton, I find nothing to my taste.

The great men seem to me to have grown somewhat old since my last visit. Lord Palmerston has given up his false teeth, which changes him very much ; but has preserved his whiskers, and has the air of a gay gorilla. Lord Russell looks less good-humored. The great beauties of the season have left town, but they are not very enthusiastically lauded. The toilets, as usual, struck me as very inferior and crumpled ; but nothing can resist this climate, of which my throat is also a proof. I am hoarse as a wolf, and suffer from suffocation. On my return to Paris, Panizzi will join me, and we are to be carried off to Biarritz by my gracious Sovereign Lady, who will lodge us for some time on the sea-shore.

Have you read Renan's "Life of Jesus"? It is the stroke of an ax to the edifice of Catholicism. The Bishop of Tulle has issued an order that all the nuns of his diocese shall recite *Aves* in M. Renan's honor, or rather to hinder the devil from flying off with everybody because of this same Renan's book. The author is so frightened at his own audacity in denying the Divinity, that he loses himself in hymns of admiration and adoration, to the disparagement of the philosophical intelligence by which alone the doctrine is to be judged.

CHÂTEAU DE COMPIÈGNE, *November*, 1863.— Since my arrival here I have led the perturbed life of a manager, having been author, actor, and director. We have played with success a rather immoral piece, of which I will tell you the story on my return. We have had very fine fireworks, though a woman who examined the fusees too closely was killed outright. You do not tell me what has become of the charming child in whom you are interested. Train her, I beg of you, so that she be not a fool like the majority of women of the present day. If those in the Provinces are worse than in Paris, I do not know in what desert we shall seek refuge. We have here a fine slip of a girl, five feet four inches tall, with the pretty ways of a grisette, and a mixture of ease and honest timidity sometimes very amusing. Some fear was entertained lest the second part of a charade should not correspond with the beginning — (a beginning of which I was the author) : "It will go off very well," said she : "We shall show our legs in the *ballet*, and that will make up for all." — N. B. Her legs are like flageolets and her feet are far from aristocratic.

CANNES, *January*, 1864.— I am charmed that Aristophanes is so fortunate as to please you. There are doubtless many things that shock your prudery, but which will interest you now that you have learned from Cicero something of ancient morals. You ask if the Athenian ladies attended the theatre. Learned men are divided in opinion on this point. It is probable that tolerance and intolerance prevailed at different periods in the same country, but it is certain that women never appeared on the stage, their rôles being enacted by men, which was the more easy from the custom of wearing masks during the performance. In Algeria you would have found, doubtless, women at the play. In the East, they have not now, and never had in ancient times, the prudery that prevails with women at the present day. An extraordinary point about Aristophanes is the unrestrained way in which he speaks of the gods, even on the occasion of their festival, for it was at the Dionysia that "The Frogs" was represented, in which Bacchus plays so singular a part. The same thing took place in the first ages of Christianity. Comedies were played in church. There was the mass "des sots," and the mass "de l'Ane," the text of which still remains in a very curious manuscript. Apart from the nonsense that Aristophanes threw into his comedies as a seasoning of coarse salt, there are choruses of the finest poetry. My venerated master, M. Boissonade, was of opinion that no Greek had surpassed them. I recommend you to read "The Clouds," the masterpiece of Aristophanes. There is in it a dialogue between the Just and the Unjust, of the most elevated style. I think there is truth in his reproaches against Socrates; even after listening to him in Plato, one is tempted to forgive the hemlock. A man is a pest who, like Socrates, proves every one to be only a fool.

PARIS, *April*, 1864.— I rarely go into society, but I wished to pay my respects to my masters, whom I found in excellent health ; which gave me also an opportunity of seeing the new fashions, which I admire but indifferently. It is a sign of old age. I cannot become accustomed to the mode of dressing the hair. Not a woman adopts the style suited to her own face ; but all model themselves after the barber's blocks. One of my friends presented me to his wife, a young and pretty person, who was whitened, daubed with rouge, and her eyelashes painted. I was horrified.

Have you read About's book, *Le Progrès?* I do not know if it is successful, but it is very witty. Perhaps the clericals have had the good sense to withhold the excommunication that never fails to insure wide circulation to a work. It was their fulmination that secured Renan great pecuniary profit ; his idyl having brought him one hundred and seven thousand francs. I keep subject to your order Taine's three thick volumes on the history of English Literature. The style is of a somewhat studied elegance, but very pleasant reading.

LONDON, *British Museum*, *July*, 1864. — From eight o'clock in the evening until midnight my life is passed at dinner parties, and the morning in looking at books and

statues : or I work at my great article on the son of Peter
the Great, which I am strongly inclined to entitle, "The
Danger of being a Fool"; for the moral drawn from the
work is that intellect is a necessity. You may find here
and there something to interest you; notably, how Peter
the Great — a detestable man and surrounded by detestable
canaille — was deceived by his wife. I have carefully, and
with some difficulty, translated his wife's love letters to
her lover, who was impaled for his pains. These letters
are really better than could be expected from the age and
the country in which they were written; but love works
wonders. The misfortune is that she knows nothing of
orthography, thereby rendering her meaning somewhat obscure to a grammarian like myself.

Nothing is talked of here but the marriage of Lady
Florence Paget, the beauty of London, the last two seasons. It would be impossible to find a prettier face on a
more delicate figure, too slight and small for my special
taste. She was noted for her flirtations. Mr. Ellice's
nephew, Mr. Chaplin, of whom you have often heard me
speak, a tall young fellow of twenty-five, and with twenty-
five thousand pounds per annum, fell in love with her. She
trifled with him a long time, finally became engaged to him,
and, it is said, accepted from him jewels and six thousand
pounds with which to pay her mantuamaker's bills. The
wedding day was arranged, and last Friday they went together to the park and the opera. On Saturday morning
she left home alone, and proceeding to St. George's
Church was married to Lord Hastings, a young man of her
own age, very ugly, and possessed of a slight fault — a
passion for cards and wine. After the ceremony they
started for the country, and at the first station she wrote
to her father, the Marquis of Anglesey : "Dear Papa — As
I knew you would never consent to my marriage with
Lord Hastings, I was wedded to him to-day. I remain
yours, etc." She also wrote to Mr. Chaplin : "Dear
Harry — When you receive this I shall be the wife of Lord
Hastings. Forget yours, very truly, Florence." Poor Mr.
Chaplin, who is six feet high and has yellow hair, is in
despair.

MADRID, *October*, 1864.— It is terribly cold and damp, and every one is ill, the bad weather having come upon us with excessive violence, according to the custom of this country, where gentle transitions, of whatsoever nature, are unknown. Imagine the misery of people who live on an elevated plateau exposed to every wind of heaven, their only stove being a *brasero*, a very primitive contrivance, giving one the choice of being frozen or asphyxiated. Civilization has made great progress here, but without a corresponding improvement. The women have adopted your absurd hats and wear them in the most uncouth fashion. The bulls are worthless, and the men who kill them are stupid and cowardly.

CANNES, *January*, 1865.— What do you think of the Pope's encyclical? I delight in reading the letters from the Bishops. There is a Bishop here, a man of wit and good sense, who veils his face. There are few attorneys more subtle than these gentlemen ; but the most ingenious is M. D——, who makes the Pope say precisely the contrary of his encyclical and he may possibly be excommunicated at Rome. It is vexatious to serve in an army the general of which exposes one to defeat. Do they hope at Rome that the Marches, the Legations, and the County of Avignon will be restored to them by a miracle? The misfortune is, that the world is so stupid that to escape the Jesuits it may be necessary to throw ourselves into the arms of mere blusterers.

The number of English here becomes more alarming every day. A hotel as large as that of the Louvre has been built on the sea-shore, which is always filled with these Islanders. One can no longer walk without meeting young Misses in Garibaldi *caracos* and hats with impossible feathers, making a pretense of sketching. There are croquet and archery parties of a hundred and twenty persons. I regret the good old times when one never met a soul.

Do you know that I received compliments from every quarter on my appointment as successor to M. Mocquard? I believed nothing of it, but by dint of seeing my name in the newspapers of various countries I began to be uneasy.

16

With my disposition you may believe how well the position and I should agree!

Imagine my reading Lamartine's "Entretiens," in which I fell on a life of Aristotle, wherein he states that the retreat of the ten thousand took place after the death of Alexander. Would it not really be better worth while to sell steel pens at the gate of the Tuileries than to utter such enormities?

CANNES, *April*, 1865.— Your friend Paradol is Academician through the will of the burgraves, who for this purpose obliged the poor Duc de Broglie to return to Paris in spite of his gout and eighty years. It will be a curious sitting. Ampère once wrote a very bad history of Cæsar, and you may imagine all the allusions that M. Paradol will take occasion to make to this work, now forgotten by every one save the burgraves. Jules Janin remains outside of the door, as also my friend Autran from Marseilles, who, assuming the clerical, was abandoned by his religious friends.

You have heard, perhaps, that Mr. William Brougham, brother of Lord Brougham, and his successor in the peerage, has been caught in the fact in a very ugly matter of cheating. It causes great scandal here among the English colony. Old Lord Brougham puts a good face on it, and is, of course, a perfect stranger to all such villainy.

To teach myself patience, and to woo sleep, I am reading a book by Mr. Charles Lambert, who demolishes holy King David and the Bible. I find it very ingenious and rather amusing. Serious and pedantic books at which ten years ago no one would have dreamed of glancing, have now, thanks to the clergy, become popular and widely read. Renan has gone to Palestine to make new studies of landscape; Peyrat and this Charles Lambert are writing books still more serious and learned which sell like bread, my bookseller tells me.

LONDON, *British Museum, August*, 1865.— I have been here about six weeks, catching a few days of "the season," and have undergone some terrible dinners and two or three of the last routs. Lord Palmerston strikes me as having grown singularly old, notwithstanding the success of his elections, and it seems to me more than doubtful if he be equal to the approaching campaign. His retirement will insure a fine crisis. I have just passed three days with his probable successor, Mr. Gladstone, who did not amuse, but interested me, for I still find great pleasure in observing varieties of human nature, and here they are so different from our own as to excite an inexplicable wonder that within ten hours' distance bipeds without feathers should so little resemble those of Paris. In some respects Mr. Gladstone appears to me a man of genius, in others a child. There is in him something of the child, the statesman, and the *fou*. Five or six deans were at his house, and every morning the guests regaled themselves with a little prayer in common. I did not attend that of Sunday which must be something very curious. What surpassed everything was a sort of half-cooked roll that is taken hot from the oven for breakfast, the digestion of which gives one infinite trouble the rest of the day. In addition to this we had hard *civrn*, that is to say, Welsh ale, which is very celebrated. You doubtless know that only red hair is worn. Nothing could be easier in this country, and I am quite sure it is not dyed. Not a single horse is to be seen in Rotten Row; but I rather like a great city in this state of semi-death. I profit by it to see the lions. Yesterday I passed an hour at the Crystal Palace watching a chimpanzee nearly as large as a child ten years old, and whom it so strongly resembled in its actions as to humiliate me by the incontestable relationship. I begin to tire of London, and thought for a moment of going to Scotland, but I should have fallen among sportsmen, a race I abhor.

LAMARTINE

TWENTY-FIVE YEARS OF MY LIFE

ALPHONSE DE LAMARTINE

THE public career of Alphonse Marie Louis de Prat de Lamartine was a varied one and is generally familiar.

He was born in 1790 and died in 1869. He began his political life as a legitimist, then he leaned to the royalist cause. Later on he was a constitutionalist and a republican. The times were stormy for stronger men than Lamartine ever was. His chief work, the "History of the Girondists," paved the way for the revolution of 1848. Its author was at once hoisted into public office. The task of sailing the ship of State was beyond his strength and not wholly to his taste. In less than a year his political star had risen and had set forever.

As poet and descriptive writer Lamartine will live, though his verse had become moribund before he died. He wrote his histories and memoirs as a poet, which gives their pages the graceful charm that perpetuates them. These passages from his youthful career were not published until after his death.

(247)

TWENTY-FIVE YEARS OF MY LIFE

As to the interest which these memoirs will have in a literary or political sense, I do not exaggerate it one way or the other; but the following are the reasons which make me think I shall at least be forgiven for their publication.

I was born in the very midst of the French Revolution — a time of passion, folly, and fury of parties on all sides. My first recollections are of a father in prison; of a mother a captive on parole in her own house, under a revolutionary guard; of the songs of the " Marseillaise " and the " Ça ira," sung in the streets, and echoing, as it were, the anguish in the bosom of the families around us; of the dull THUDS which followed the stroke of the guillotine in our public squares; of the march of half-scared troops all day long on the highway. I used to sing myself the songs I heard others sing — poor, little, unintelligent echo that I was of a world into which I had just entered amid smiles and tears! My poor mother used to look at me sadly enough. One day a change came: the soldiers overpowered the demagogues; the guillotine was swept away, and my own family could breathe freely again. We went to seek a humble shelter among our faithful peasants in the country. Little by little we obtained the kind of security granted to proscribed persons. Year after year my sisters came to brighten the home, which our devoted servants always maintained on the most comfortable footing; and here I grew and throve in the midst of our people.

My mother taught me the existence of that mysterious and Divine Being who is Justice, Power, and what we call Providence. This was to me a great joy: my little mind had been always working; now I had found a key to the problem of life — the only real and true foundation — in a word, I believed, and prayed. My heart opened to these

(249)

pious influences ; the spirit of a man began to develop itself in me ; in a word, the child was being matured.
Then came my school and college life, when rude hands
fashioned me, in sad contrast to the gentle, loving training
of my home. I passed through this ordeal, and came out
of it transformed, but not improved. I was an excitable
lad, like a will-'o-the-wisp, with no very fixed ideas, and willing
enough to float down the flowery stream of life. The Revolution broke out again, and I looked upon it as solving
for me the mystery of the future. I went into the army :
I loved the Bourbons, and thought I would die to serve
them. But when peace came I was soon sick of a military
life. Napoleon returned, and there was an end of my
dreams of glory. I accompanied the Bourbon princes to
the frontiers of France, but I did not go beyond — I felt
that I belonged to my country above all else. Then came
the bloody field of Waterloo : the 20th of March was
avenged, and the Bourbons were reinstated. I again took
my place in their guard, both from a feeling of honor and
of fidelity. But I did not remain there long : I could not
stand a life of inactivity and of discipline without glory ;
so I again became a vagabond and a wanderer on the face
of the earth. Traveling not only dispels our *ennui*, but interests and fills the heart. I led a life of pleasure and of
love for several years ; then followed sadness, dissatisfac-
tion, and remorse. I resolved at last to do something, and
went into diplomacy, for which I felt I was well qualified.
Not long after I married a good and accomplished woman
who brought me back to all virtuous and domestic habits,
and I became once more satisfied, calm, and happy.

The Revolution of 1830, which drove the elder branch of
the Bourbons into exile, induced me to share their fate, in
spite of the wishes of the Orleans princes, whom I was
very willing to respect, but whom I could not serve. I
started for the East, and for two years diverted my mind
by traveling in Turkey, the Archipelago, the Holy Land,
Syria, and the Lebanon. I came home. My reputation had
grown during my absence. I found myself elected a member of the Senate. I resolved to abstain from party votes
or passions, and to devote myself entirely to the good of

my conntry ; thus giving up any chance of promotion or
public employment, but preserving my own principles and
self-respect. I conquered at last a certain position for myself, but with difficulty. Certain literary successes at this
time added slightly to my reputation. After ten years,
party strife and passions got the upper hand. The very
men who had brought about the Revolution of 1830, and
the Government of the Orleanists, turned against their own
work. I opposed them vigorously ; but I refused everything save the pleasure of defeating and overthrowing them.
I could not bear that my indignation should be attributed
to any other feeling than one of right. I repudiated all
idea of intrigues and revolutionary banquets. I struggled
at one and the same time against the coalition and the royalists of 1830. I had the happiness of being understood by
the country and the King, who sent for me and begged me
to take office. I refused, though with respectful firmness.
I chose to have no rôle but that of a volunteer : all for my
country, nothing for myself. The crisis became imminent :
there were risings in various places ; the Ministers lost their
heads ; the coalition disbanded itself ; the King lost his
presence of mind ; the people were in a ferment. At last
the Revolution, with which I had nothing on earth to do,
was declared. I was only mixed up in it during the last
few hours, after the flight of the King. I appeared like
Fate, to repress, and, if possible, keep it within bounds.
It has been said and written that such and such a faction
or secret society brought it about. This is not true. I can
appeal to the ocular testimony of thousands — not in defense
of myself, but to bear witness to the fact that, finding the
Revolution inevitable, it was I who organized it ; and unless
we had been content with utter anarchy, what else was
there to be done ? I asked it of the whole of France. It
was a bold step ; but it was a necessary one. The alternative was only a continued and aggravated anarchy. *Felix
culpa !* The Republic once proclaimed, I found the means
of moderating its action. France behaved admirably. For
four months we governed in the midst of the storm, without what one may call a government at all. Afterward
everything was changed. I refused what was offered to me,

and returned into obscurity. I had not the vanity to pretend to that to which neither my birth nor my talents entitled me. I bore without complaint fifteen years of unjust reproaches and of continued misfortunes, under which I am now sinking. I worked on courageously, however : I am working still. These events may interest my readers — I write them in good faith. May God be my helper !

I was just beginning to see and understand something of outside things when my father and mother carried us off — a whole tribe of children, in a long file of bullock wagons — to establish us and all our worldly goods at Milly. Our dear mother was in the first carriage with two of my sisters on her knees, and another at her breast ; a quantity of loose packages filled up the lumbering vehicle. My father went on foot as a sportsman, carrying his gun, cheering my mother, and helping the carriage when it got into any bad ruts. Two dogs in a leash followed him, and then two more wagons full of maids and nurses and household goods of every description, going at a foot's pace. Then came a carriage containing Mlle. de Monceau and her maid. All this formed a regular procession of old-fashioned equipages rolling and tumbling about in the mud, for the public roads in those days were execrable. The cries of the drivers, the lowing of the bullocks, the clamor and fright of the women servants, and the hearty laughter of the children at each fresh misfortune, made up a picturesque scene, which was partly amusing and partly touching. We did not arrive at Milly for five or six hours, although it was hardly more than twelve miles.

Milly was then a poor little village built on the ridge of a hill planted with vines, at some distance from St. Sorlin, which was the rural capital of the country.

Ever since the spring, my father had come to Milly from time to time to prepare the house for his family. The revolutionists had, to a certain degree, spared the old place, and contented themselves with turning the drawing-room into a dancing saloon on Sundays for the benefit of the neighboring peasantry. The sabots of the dancers had broken the old encaustic tiles into a thousand bits ; not from pure mischief, but simply from a sort of pleasure at profaning a nobleman's house. We stumbled among the broken fragments of pavement until a workman had clumsily repaired it with large square common bricks. There was not much more damage done. The vines continued to bear and the fruit trees to blossom, so that the traces of the Revolution in Milly might be said to be restricted to the ball-room. Every one — father, mother, aunt, children, and servants — had soon found his or her place in the house. Our only furniture were a few beds, tables, and chairs. The kitchen, soon filled by the peasant women, once more sent up the cheerful smoke from its wide, inglenooked chimney. The nurse and children walked and played in the corridor. My father spent his days in hunting or shooting on the mountains. My mother was occupied in writing, in the care and superintendence of the house, or in visiting the sick and suffering, with whom she at once made friends, and was beloved as readily as she herself loved all around her.

Do you wish for a description of these my first happy days at Milly? The account of one day will serve for all the rest.

No sooner had the first rays of the sun lit up my mother's room, than my father, who was a very early riser, went out walking. A maid used to fetch me and put me into my father's place, by the side of my darling, gentle mother, who used to kiss and pet me, and then teach me to lisp my little prayers. I did not know very well the meaning of the words, or understand what that Invisible and Omnipotent Power was, called God; but I knew I was doing like mamma, and that was more than enough for me. Most good things are done from imitation. To try and be like what one loves, that is the first instinct of man. At any rate, it was mine. Reasoning one may dispute, but not that which has become a habit. My father was not a very religious, but he was an honest and an honorable man. The love and respect of his wife, whom he adored, made him pious almost in spite of himself.

After prayers we went to breakfast, I on my nurse's knee, off the vinedresser's soup, which I used to think the best in the world. Then I trotted off into the vineyards to play with my companions (the children of our peasants), or else, like them, to keep the goats and sheep in the mountain forests. We used to return when the bell of the old steeple rung the midday *Angelus*. Then a fuming hot soup with bacon and vegetables awaited us round the homely wooden table ; a repast which I infinitely preferred to the pure white tablecloth and more delicate dishes served to my parents. I remember even now with appetite the little two-pronged, two-penny forks which doubled into our pocket clasped-knives, and with which we used to pick out and eat the *boulli* of our soup, in little bright red or green varnished earthenware bowls ! Soup has ever since appeared a luxury to me. A cabbage or celery leaf, with a radish, just stirred in what is called "tea-kettle broth," with a bit of black bread, this is the true food of the country peasant. My simple life made me relish the homely fare of the cottager as much as a child who had known nothing else. When I grew older, and was no longer allowed to run wild, and the age of lessons and schools came, I was obliged to give up this simple food of goat's cheese, cabbage, onions, and the like, and made to eat meat, which disagreed with me so much that I had a regular illness in consequence ; and, ever since, I have never lost the early tastes contracted at that time. Even when we dined up-stairs, my mother never could persuade us to eat anything but vegetables.

After dinner, my father used to go back to his shooting on the mountains, sometimes alone, at other times in company with one of his head vinedressers, of whom he had made both a guide and friend. This man, who was in every way superior to his class, was called Claude Chanut, and became quite a favorite with us all.

Sometimes it happened that we passed the whole winter at Milly, as in a kind of domestic convent, completely snowed up, but visited from time to time by certain old friends of my father's, who were living in hiding, as it were, in the neighboring villages. First, there was the doctor of the canton, who lived with his wife at St. Sorlin, with a son, who became my great friend, and a daughter, whom I should have fallen in love with, if I had been of the right age. Then there was the Chevalier de La Cense, a retired officer in the Guards, living with his sister, Mademoiselle de Moleron, in the same village, a cheery, jovial, good-natured man, whose arrival brightened the whole house. Then there was M. de Vaudran, of the Bruys family (one of twenty children, all distinguished in their different careers), living at Bussières, in the parish of Milly. M. de Vaudran, who was an old friend of my father's, had been secretary to M. de Villedeuil before the Revolution, and initiated into all the political secrets of the highest society in Paris. He was a Royalist of the good old school—moderate, impartial, and just toward every one, even toward the men who had mingled in the Revolution, without having [imbrued their hands in crime and blood. He took pity on my somewhat neglected education, and gave me my first writing-lessons on a little table in the dining-room, for which I have remained eternally grateful to him. His three sisters — simple, gentle, loving, agreeable women, and great friends of my mother's — often accompanied him to Milly. Although obliged, from political circumstances, to live continually in the country, and only associate with people of a humbler class, the natural distinction of their manners, and the companionship of their brother, who always spent part of the year with them, gave them a high-bred tone which could not be mistaken; and their entire absence of affectation made their reception of friends in their own home most pleasant; while their natural grace and dignity gave a special charm to their conversation.

The Curé de Bussières their near neighbor, young, handsome, mundane, amiable, and of elegant and refined habits, was full of respect and deference for these ladies, and he was also a favorite shooting companion of my father's.

At a quarter of a league from our house, buried in the wooded gorges of the mountains of St. Point, was a site which has enshrined itself in my memory and imagination forever. I mean the village and *château* of Pierreclos — the habitation of the old Count de Pierreclos, whom I have before mentioned. Walter Scott has nothing more romantic or original in his descriptions of the nature, habits, and dwelling-places of the Scotch lairds. Now for a description of the *château* itself, its inmates, and the life they led there.

We used to go and dine there every Sunday after high mass; that is, at a quarter before twelve. After having clambered on foot to the summit of the Csaz mountain, which threw a long gray shadow over the Milly valley behind my father's garden, a steep and rapid descent to the right brought us into the Pierreclos valley. A rough path, full of rolling stones, but shaded by old walnut-trees, led us by several barren hamlets to the head of the valley. There the aspect of the scenery changes; the hills, covered with vineyards, slope down toward the rich meadows, irrigated by bright and rushing streams, and shaded by poplars cutting the sky-line, like the cypresses of the South. Very soon the valley widens, and the eye is lost in a distant vapory forest of pines and beech. The background is formed of dark mountains, covered here and there with snow, which lies in deep patches in the hollows. After having walked on a little way on the high-road, we used to perceive a mass of smoke and vapor coming out of the mouths of the village furnaces, which blackened even the walls of the old steeple of Pierreclos. But it was church time, and we hurried into the chapel, where the priest was saying mass. The old lord and his family occupied a bench to the right of the altar. The family consisted of the master of the *château*, a gouty old man, but with a proud and determined countenance, who looked down with a sort of insolence on his old vassals; his brother, M. de Berzé, who bore the name of the old Gothic *château* of which we spoke just now, between Milly and Cluny; his five daughters, all very pleasing-looking, both in face and figure; and a young son, of about the same age as myself, with whom hereafter I was to be bound in the ties of a warm friendship. As soon as we appeared they made room for us in the church, and we were soon kneeling in our proper seats. The mass being over, the peasants separated. The old lord mounted his horse (with the help of his servants), and rode up to the castle by a steep paved road. We followed on foot with the rest of the family, and winding through the vineyards, soon arrived at the iron gates of the *château*. Nothing could be more imposing than its appearance as you entered. A vast courtyard, which led you through a high subterranean passage, or covered way, to the keep, from which you suddenly emerged into an open sunny space brilliant with flowers, growing up to the very foot of the steeple of the old chapel, which was built on a high terrace to the extreme left of the castle. Then the ground suddenly fell, like a drop-scene in the opera, and revealed to you a mass of towers and pinnacles and quaint Gothic windows and ornaments, the whole lit up and illuminated, as it were, by the setting sun.

On first entering the large courtyard, I was struck at the sight of a new building not yet finished, on the windows of which the workmen, in fact, were still at work. It was evidently intended to replace the old Gothic castle, which, being mainly composed of keeps and square towers, circular staircases, irregular turrets, and pointed roofs, was more picturesque than comfortable, and rather gave one the idea of an aerial village. This old fortress, in reality, had been built on the edge of a promontory, and followed the sinuosities of the rock both above and below, from the summit to the valley. The upper part formed an oval terrace, upon which all the doors opened, whether of the kitchens or drawing-rooms.

The apartments with the exception of a great stove in an angle of the dining-room, and a magnificent fire-place of black marble in the drawing-room, large enough to burn whole trees at a time, had the appearance of rooms recently restored after a fire the day before. The mortar scarcely filled up the spaces between the stones ; and the walls, guiltless of whitewash, seemed never to have been smoothed by the mason's trowel. The flames had licked the paint off the ceilings, which bore the traces of an incendiary fire, seemingly scarcely put out.

" Look ! " exclaimed the old Count, showing me the marks of the above-mentioned destruction ; " look at the traces of the passage of those brigands ! Here was the torch of one, there the hatchet of another, a pickaxe was the tool of the third. Ah ! the rascals ! I know them well ; and never in

17

my lifetime will I suffer the remembrance of these horrors to be effaced."

In truth in 1790, in the famous and inexplicable day called *du Brigandage*, this grand old castle had been completely ravaged, and nearly burnt to the ground, by the peasants from the mountains, who had determined to avenge the supposed wrongs of the villagers, and took advantage of the unpopularity of the owner, who was hated by the people, to carry out their nefarious designs. The pillage and devastation were indeed complete.

His wife and daughters were saved by the fidelity of two or three of their tenant farmers, and concealed in the neighboring forest. The Count and his son escaped by a miracle, and swore to be avenged. His eldest son emigrated the next day. As to the old Count himself, he returned after a time to his ruined home, and went on living there till the day when they came to carry off the cannons of his terrace to Mâcon, at the same time that his whole family were thrown into prison by the agents of the Revolutionary government. My father, who in 1790 was on leave at Monceau, armed and mounted the young men of Mâcon, and pursued the incendiaries to the Château of Cormatin, killing several in an engagement in the neighborhood of Cluny, and hanging others on the trees by the roadside, — a service never forgotten in the grateful memory of the old Count. The insurrection was at an end, and order was everywhere restored, until the day when the Government, in its turn, had given the signal for persecution, and imprisoned, as we have said, the whole family as Royalists.

The head of the family had been formerly captain of cavalry during the Seven Years' War. He had been taken prisoner by the Prussians, and used to tell us how the Queen of Prussia, delighted with his good looks and cleverness, used to knock every morning at his door in the corridor, calling out, "Count Pierreclos! get up and follow the King's hunting party! Your horses are waiting." "At these words," he added, "I gladly rose, and started for Sans Souci, where we used to eat delicious sour-krout." The Queen of Prussia was always brought into the conversation.

On returning from Potsdam, he sent in his resignation, and married a young girl of good family from the neighborhood of Lyons. She bore him five or six children, and they lived constantly in the Château of Pierreclos, the old Count being the object of the timid fear of the peasantry, and the ridicule of the middle classes. He was not a bad man at all but absurdly vain and boastful, with a good heart at bottom, though often violent and rough in his manners. His wife had died during their imprisonment. The eldest of his sons had emigrated; the youngest who was called the Chevalier de Pierreclos, was a boy of my own age, brave, clever, and intelligent, left to nature and with scarcely any education; but giving promise of what he afterward became — a brilliant adventurer, like the Chevalier de Grammont, a hero of the civil wars, of romantic love affairs, of duels, horses, and all that is comprehended in the old term of a " free lance." We were intimate from children, and shared in all boyish sports.

His sisters, older than himself, were handsome, *piquante*, and original. As they had no mother, they had consequently little or no education, properly so called; they, in fact, brought up one another. There was certainly in the château an old aunt, the only sister of the Count, a clever woman, and as strange as himself; but who could only have taught cards to her pretty nieces, that being the one occupation of Madame de Moirode from morning till night. She used to come into the drawing-room at eight o'clock in the morning, and sit on a curtained seat, like Madame du Deffant! Then lowering the curtains round her on three sides, to keep out the draught, she would offer cards to all comers: brothers, sisters, nephews, nieces, friends — no matter who! playing without a moment's intermission from one meal to another; resting for a few minutes, perhaps, in the middle of the day, and beginning again with any new-comers till supper-time.

The Chevalier de Berzé, an old cavalry officer like his brother, the Count de Pierreclos, ran through his whole fortune very early in life, and now had accepted the posts of agent and gardener to the family. In the drawing-room his only functions seemed to be to provide fresh cards, and to bring in fresh logs for the fire. He was a thoroughly good-natured, "serviceable" fellow, ready to do a kind turn to everybody, and universally beloved. I saw him live, grow old, and die, like a living piece of furniture, having no idea in life but that of saying "Yes" to everything proposed by his brother; of bringing the finest melons from the garden to the dining-room, the most beautiful flowers to his nieces, and fresh faggots for the inexhaustible fire-places in both apartments.

But when the time of the vintage drew near, everything assumed an aspect of work and life and gayety, which metamorphosed the whole country. The peasants loaded their carts with water thoroughly to cleanse the deep wine-presses which were to hold the grapes. The bullocks, coupled together and harnessed at dawn, lifted their intelligent heads and velvety eyes under the heavy yoke; or else ruminated, by the side of the pole, the armfuls of hay which the children gave them. The women, lifting us up in their arms, would help us to scramble up by the axle of the wheels into the vat. This was a large, oval kind of bath, in which the vine-dresser goes to the vineyard, and which he there fills with great bunches of cut grapes to bring them back to the wine-press. Then we were lifted out by the workmen, and our places filled by the contents of their baskets. A quantity of sticky flies and wasps, drunk with the juice of the grape which had already begun to ferment, fell with the fruit into the vat, but either instinct or satiety prevented their stinging us.

Thus we went joyfully from one vine to the other, helping to cut the rich bunches and fill the baskets or bins of one set of reapers after the other. The cleverest and handiest girls from the neighboring villages formed themselves into bands, slept in the barn at Milly, and were hired as cutters by the owners of the vineyards. They used to walk singing, their pails on their heads, or their baskets on their arms, behind the one who served as guide in the narrow paths between the vines; and then placing themselves by twenties or thirties, each at the foot of a vine stock, would quickly clear the whole stem with careful, skillful hands, of its rich white or blue burden, squash them in their fingers, and throw them into the bins, which the boys would then carry off to the carts. The very vineyards seemed to sing as their rich produce fell under the scissors; the earth, as it were, rejoiced at her spoil. We, children, used to follow the carts dripping with their juicy burden; our little pinafores all stained with the blood of the grape, and meeting with joyous cries each fresh band of workers. The joy ran like the wine from hill to hill. Then we helped to empty the grapes from the vat to the wine-press; or gathered bunches of fresh grapes to refresh the tired bullocks, whose carts creaked under their heavy load. Then we would count the number of bins, and run to tell our father, who would calculate the numbers of tuns of wine which would be the final result, and which, in reality, formed our whole income for the year. A few days after, the same work was begun again, until the leaves of the vine, all yellow and seared, had no more fruit to conceal; until, in fact, the vintage being over and the barrels filled to the brim with wine, the vines were left desolate, the goats picked off the few remaining leaves, and the once busy paths were still as death.

Then began the spinning of the flax and hemp in the evenings at home; or else the cracking of the walnuts, which was the last gay work of the season for the villagers. The mistress of the house, by the light of a rustic lamp called a *creuse-yeux*, gathered round the large kitchen table, children, servants, visitors, and neighbors. The men went to the cellar and brought out huge sacks of nuts, of which the husk, already half rotten, was easily detached from the shell, and threw them on the floor. Every one, armed with a hammer, set to work on a heap of this rich fruit before him, to crack the nuts carefully, and take out the kernel (if possible entire) and put them in little heaps, either for sale or for the oil mill. Gay laughter and innocent conversation echoed from one end of the room to the other, and made the work seem like play. When all was done, dancing began, and generally continued till midnight.

It was the same with the weaving of the hemp and flax, which used to occupy the winter evenings in the great barn until the tow merchant came round and bargained for the long hanks of yarn and vegetable silk, the produce of which was the gain of the wives and daughters and women-servants of the house, and often served to keep them in clothes altogether. We used to take our share in all these works with our servants and peasants, as was the custom in those primitive days. The presence of our gentle mother was a check on any light or improper word or action ; for she had won the respect and love of the whole neighborhood.

Our conversations at these gatherings was generally on the subject of the good or bad crops ; the price of wine or wheat ; the marriage of this or that village lad or girl ; the wages of the women-servants, which generally consisted of ten crowns (thirty francs) a year, six yards of un-bleached linen for shifts, two pairs of *sabots*, a few yards of stuff for petticoats, and five francs as a present on New Year's Day. These were the current wages of servants in those days. They are now at least ten times as much ; but I doubt if the people themselves are one whit richer or happier. Money only represents, under one denomination or other, a certain amount of wants. All is equal, except in the mind of man.

Very often, on coming out of some sanguinary revolution-ary crisis, very terrible at the time, perhaps, but quickly forgotten, the talk among the elder men became political — that is to say, military. Itinerant hawkers used to come round to our doors, crying out, " Great battle between the French, under command of General Bonaparte, in Italy, and the English or Germans " (or else it was " Moreau on the Rhine," or " Massena in Switzerland," or " Macdonald in Suabia," or " Hoche in the Palatinate," or " Marceau in Germany "). Then the peasant would rush out of his cabin, while the hawker unrolled to his admiring eyes highly-colored portraits of heroes, and he listened with all his ears to the startling tale of battles won, and heroic escapes, or glorious death-scenes ; and bought for a penny the true(?) history of all these feats of arms. He would then nail them up on his wall, or get his wife to sew them on the serge curtains of his bed, where they remained for himself and his family as a true history of France and of her doughty deeds to all time.

The first political enthusiasm with which I was myself fired was in the village square adjoining our own courtyard. There was a young man named Janin, a little better educated than his neighbors, who taught the village children the elements of reading and writing. One day he stepped out of the cabin which served as a school, and sounding a drum and a clarionet of which he had somehow become possessed, he quickly attracted all the boys and girls in Milly; to whom he commenced showing off a quantity of pictures of military heroes, which he had obtained from one of these hawkers, who was standing by his side. "Look," he exclaimed, "at this picture of the battle of the Pyramids, gained by General Bonaparte! He is this little dark, thin man, whom you see here mounted on a horse as yellow as gold, which is rearing and plunging, with his long sabre in his hand, before that mass of cut stone which is called the Pyramids, and who is saying to his soldiers, 'From up there, forty centuries look down upon you.'"

But his eloquence was rather lost on his audience, who did not understand a word of it, and preferred Augereau galloping on a white charger and crossing the Rhine with one bound, as if he had been carried on the wings of Victory herself; or Berthier, tearing a swan's quill from his floating plume to write the staff orders with a pensive countenance. But Kléber with his drum-major's figure and size, carried the day, and excited the enthusiasm and plaudits of the whole hamlet.

The hawker passed the morning selling these pictures of national glory from house to house, with Janin to explain the subjects of each. His enthusiasm spread the excitement over the whole country, and no one shared in it more vividly than myself. It was thus that I first began to understand what was meant by military glory. A horse, a plume, a sabre were henceforth to me symbolical of great things. The people were fired with a military ardor, which lasted a long time. All through the winter evenings nothing was talked of but the hawker, and Janin was continually summoned to explain again the text of these wonderful, and of course TRUTHFUL pictures.

Time went on, and I was eleven years old. My father began to talk seriously of sending me to school; but it was difficult to decide, because, since the Revolution, no public school existed, if we except certain private houses, more or less famous at Paris or at Lyons, and a College of Jesuits (who were then called FATHERS OF THE FAITH), whom the uncle of Bonaparte, Cardinal Fesch, protected on the frontiers of Italy, in the little town of Belley, in Bugey. My mother very much wished that my father would decide on sending me to this college, which had a very high reputation for piety and learning. The greater portion of the noble familes of Piémont, Lombardy, Turin, Alessandria, and Milan, sent their children there. But my mother was opposed by all the rest of the family, who wished me to go to a private house in Lyons, called the house of *La Caille*, at la Croix Rousse, and which also was well spoken of. My uncle, M. de Lamartine, did not much like the Jesuites; my father was indifferent, but above all wished to please his brothers and sisters, on whom my future fortune depended. So that he ended by saying "Yes," and my mother rather sorrowfully took me to Lyons.

How sad was my departure from Milly! It was the first deep wound my heart had received, and I felt it bitterly. How broken-hearted I was at saying good-by to the old servants, who all loved me, and I them, and especially Janette, a charming and beautiful girl from the mountains, whom I cried terribly at parting with, and whom I left equally bathed in tears! Janette came to kiss me in my little bed, and I started for Lyons as if it were (as in reality it was to me) for the other world. From that hour Milly, its rocks and vineyards, its peasants and servants, and all belonging to it, seemed to be graven in my memory as a warm and living thing which formed a part of my very self. Alas! I have had to part with it all since, down to the very stones. And when I pass by the road, I turn away my head, that I may not see it, and do not look round till the ruined steeple and vine-covered hills have altogether disappeared from my sight.

Hardly had I returned to Milly than I felt what a difficulty a young man of my age and class must be to my father and mother. What was to be done with a youth too old to remain idle, too distinguished in his studies not to be ambitious, and too aristocratic to serve the new Government? The *embarras* was great, and helped to strengthen my besetting sins of indolence and indecision. I should not have minded going into the law courts, where many of my companions were learning to become future counselors or judges; but the pride of my family revolted against the law as a profession. To join the army, which I should have preferred, would have involved me in the service of the present dynasty, which my parents might recognize, but whom they would not allow me to serve. To be auditor of the Council of State (which was offered to me) would result in my being forced to be a flatterer and a tool of the Imperial *régime*. Not one of these positions was possible to one of my birth, society, or antecedents; so that there was no alternative but to wait.

Things remained in this state of indecision during the autumn and winter which followed my leaving college.

But, at the end of the following year, my father and mother took us to pass the winter at Mâcon, in a large house which they had just bought, and in which we installed ourselves. There I first learned to understand what was meant by a serious passion. It was my first real love. Now, it appears to me to have been only the shadow of it; but the impression it left on my mind was deep and lasting. The lady who awoke this feeling in my heart died not long ago; therefore I can speak of her without fear; and, indeed, there was nothing in the smallest degree to throw a shade on her memory in the reciprocal affection of two children, for such we both were.

There was, then, at that time in Mâcon, a young girl of fifteen or sixteen, of whom all the town spoke in raptures, not only on account of her great beauty, but of her singular talents and modest grace. Her name was Mlle. P. On her mother's side she was noble: on her father's of the middle class; so that both held her in equal honor, and she was received with the most flattering distinction in both sets of society. She had one brother, a vulgar, commonplace man, who seemed to have united in his own person all the defects of the father; while his sister had reproduced all the beauty and refinement of the mother, who, in fact, only cared for her. The father never appeared in the drawing-room; he lived alone in his own apartments. The son mixed with the lowest set in the town. Everything was as aristocratic about the wife as it was plebeian about the husband. There were, in fact, two houses under the same roof; and, in visiting the mother, you were not *censé* to know the father, although he was a man of the strictest probity and honor. These contradictions rarely occur but in small country towns.

Mlle. P. wore on her face the signs of this strange destiny. She had the most delicate and beautiful figure which any sculptor ever idealized in a sylph. She danced as the dragon-flies skim over the water, her feet scarcely touching the ground. At every ball at which she was present, when the orchestra struck up a waltz, a circle was sure to be formed round her; the women to envy, the men to rave about her; but she never seemed to be conscious of it. This wonderful grace was part of her very nature. Her little oval head resting on her small white neck was beautifully formed. Her eyebrows were finely marked, and her long eyelashes shading her soft downcast eyes, made her look like a statue of Purity. Her half-shut eyes, her little half-open mouth, her delicate features, and her clear and transparent complexion, gave her face an expression which it was impossible to forget.

It was thus that this beauty suddenly appeared to me, and love first said to my heart, "Here I am." I felt a longing desire to go out of the ball-room and breathe the cold fresh air on the borders of the Saône. I did so, and came back when the orchestra struck up a second waltz — then went out — then came back again, till my friends burst out laughing at my proceedings, and called out to me, as I was disappearing a third time, "Stop! Mlle. P. is going to dance." She heard them, and cast a grateful glance at me in passing, as much as to say, "I saw you, and I shall think of you even when waltzing with another."

Every time she passed me, she gave me the same kind, fixed look. That is how our acquaintance began.

When the ball was over, I staggered out like a drunken man. I followed a whole troop of young men who escorted her to her door. I saw that, after having wished them good-by, she still sought some one else. I did not dare advance, or go back. I stopped still. The door, which opened on some turning steps, as is often the case in Mâcon, was suddenly thrown open, and threw her back down the first step. Her mother uttered a cry of fear. I rushed forward and caught her, as she was falling, in my arms. Directly after I wanted to retire, but her mother called me back. " Ah, sir ! " she said, " you must give us leave to express our thanks ; come in ; and as our introduction has been so obliging a one on your part, I must insist on making your acquaintance, and my child will promise you the first dance at the next ball. " I followed her into the drawing-room where she gave us tea, and I asked permission to come the following day and inquire after the young lady. Her mother granted it with great kindness, her daughter thanked me with a look. I went out of the house mad with joy. For a long time I watched from the angle of the quay, the lights from her window, which gradually went out ; and I felt that that beautiful pure child was dreaming in her little bed. Did she think of me ? I wondered. I came home very late and alone ; but I could not sleep ; my heart was too overflowing with happiness.

The next day, when the salon of Madame P. opened to receive her friends, I was one of the first arrivals. I found Mlle. P. alone. She was evidently as much afraid of missing my visit as I was of not finding her. Thus our two hearts understood each other without a word ; the same electric spark of sympathy ran through us both. The mother came in soon after, and received me as if I had been an old friend of the family. She did not visit my mother, for they were not in the same set of society. She knew her, however, by sight, and had that affectionate respect for her character which every one felt in the country. But the pride of my uncles and aunts would not have per-

mitted the mixture of the old nobility with the new *régime*,
or allowed them to be invited to our house. We only met,
therefore, at the balls of the Prefecture, or at the *fêtes* occasionally given in the Town Hall, when there was, of
course, a mixture of classes.

Madame P. was proud of her daughter. She had given
her the education of an artist. She had learned every possible accomplishment, especially dancing; that silent art
which suited the dangerous times in which we lived, when
an imprudent or incautious word might have had serious
consequences. In those days a good dancer was as much
esteemed as a clever orator or writer is now. Mlle. P. was
really a modern Terpsichore. Her tall and elegant figure,
the perfect suppleness and grace of her movements, the
beauty of her arms, the delicacy of her feet, the soft languor of her expression, captivated every one even before
she moved; but when she began to dance, her lightness
was such that she seemed hardly to touch the ground.

Her mother never took her eyes off her child. You saw
that she was wrapt up in her, and that she was in fact
the pride of her life. She had heard people speak of me
as having had a brilliant career at college, of which not
only my family but all Mâcon was proud. She was consequently flattered that I should have become the admirer of
her daughter. She treated me as somebody and something
above the rest, and flattered my self-love almost to the extent of compromising her charming child. In the very
first conversation we had together she took care to make
me understand that there were but two beings among the
young people of Mâcon whom she considered worthy of attention — her daughter and myself: the one for her beauty and
talents; the other for my birth, and for the superiority I
had shown to all my academical rivals. She thus, as it
were, set us apart, in a little world, to ourselves — a position which we were nothing loth to accept. At our very
first meeting our eyes had said the same thing to each
other, and we did not want even her mother's help to fall
in love! Henceforth there was a sweet mystery between
us; that is, we adored each other, and despised every one
else. Her mother was a sort of accomplice, as she had

been, from the first, our confidante. I very soon became
the friend of both, and the *habitué* of the house. All the
town seemed to me to favor my suit. Every one was full
of the passionate affection which had broken out between
the queen of the balls, Mlle. P., and the young student
from Milly, who had so distinguished himself at college,
and had fallen in love at first sight. Men smiled and
women sympathized in our wooing. My family only either
did not or would not see what was going on; and I took
care not to enlighten them.

There was a lady in Mâcon, Madame L., who was noted
for her beauty, but of a rather doubtful reputation, and
who had married, late in life, an old Knight of St. Louis,
who was a near relation of my father's. She kept open
house, receiving every evening a large and somewhat mixed
society, among whom Madame P. and her daughter were
always found. When eight o'clock struck, Madame L. used
to retire to her own apartments; but the party went on,
and Madame P. and her daughter and a good number of
young people stayed chatting till midnight, or else got up
some music, with that easy, happy familiarity which is the
result of intimate acquaintance on all sides. One heard
bright jokes and merry laughter all round; but the happiest
were those who, like me, leaning over the piano, listened
breathlessly to the touching voice which spoke words understood only by ourselves. Such were our happy evenings;
and, when we parted, it was sadly, perhaps, but full of
hope for the morrow. We did not use to say much to each
other, but our silence was understood, and without words
we knew at what hour we should pass by a certain street
the next day, at what precise time we should meet in the
green paths of St. Clément, and exchange a look — without
stopping to speak, or awakening the suspicion of indifferent
people; sure of one another, and reckoning on making up
for our silence by a long talk in the evening. Until then
it was joy enough to have seen each other, if but for a
moment. When a ball drew near, the consultation as to the
dress to be worn, and the color of the bouquets to be chosen,
was quite sufficient to satisfy us. Each understood the
other, and our hearts needed no further symptoms of a love

which knew no bounds. Her mother did not attempt to interfere with us. I saw, on the contrary, that she enjoyed it. As to the father, he never appeared, either in his own house, or in any other society. He was constantly at magistrates' meetings, or in his own quarters; and only saw his child's dress as she crossed the road to go to the ball, of which she was the chief ornament.

Thus passed this happy and mysterious winter, which appeared to me to last but a day.

However, spring came, and the first green of the meadows gave a tender shade to the willow leaves by the river side. Walks outside the town, in which we always contrived to meet, had replaced the musical *soirées* at Madame de L.'s. A young lady of Mâcon generally accompanied Mlle. P., and by her amiable conversation enabled me to have many a *tête-à-tête* talk with her whom I loved. We profited by these moments, which friendship had so good-naturedly contrived for us; and it was very rarely that we met any one, or were interrupted. However, once or twice we met a man standing at the corner of the hedge close to the charming village of St. Clément, and he always bowed and looked at us with a certain amount of curiosity. This gentleman, whom I only knew by name, was, however, well-known in the town. He was an old friend of the family of P., and lived, since the Revolution, on a pretty little property in the village of St. Clément, where he was looked upon as a speculative philosopher, given chiefly to agriculture and contemplation. I appeared to be a special object of his attention, which rather annoyed me and made me anxious. I fancied that the rumor of my attentions to the young lady had reached him, and that he perhaps wished to judge by my appearance, if I were a man calculated to make her happy. I did not dare own my fears, however, to her who was the cause of them. But, before long, I did not fail to be enlightened on the subject.

Some days after, Madame P. told me that M. F. C. had the custom of giving a little *fête champêtre* every spring to her daughter and herself in his orchard at St. Clément; that his wife helped him to do the honors with her beautiful flowers and her fresh eggs and cream, which were noted

all over the country; that he had written to propose the
following Sunday in the afternoon for their visit; that, having seen us together several times, he had ventured to ask
me to join them, and had begged her to be the bearer of
the invitation. I was delighted to have my share in this
little family gathering, and concluded, in consequence, that
I was not displeasing to their old friend and counselor. I
saw that Mlle. P. was equally pleased, and prepared myself
joyfully for the Sunday's *fête*. Madame de L. and Madame
de X. were also invited; but I was the only MAN admitted,
which filled me with hope.

At last the Sunday came, and Madame P., her daughter,
her two friends, and I started separately for St. Clément,
not to attract the attention of the Mâcon gossips. We met
in the steep and narrow path which led to M. F. C.'s villa,
about half a league from the town, and in a few minutes
found ourselves at the door. Mons. and Madame F. C.
were waiting for us on the threshold, and received us as if
we were the only guests they expected in the course of the
year. Their first kind words were for me. "Young man,"
said the philosopher, "you are welcome to my hermitage;
and, as you are the friend of these ladies, you must look
upon us likewise as your friends, for we have none dearer
at Mâcon." Then, taking the arm of Mlle. P., while his
wife took the other ladies into the house, he led her and
me all over the gardens, kiosks, and orchards of his pretty
home, and made us eat the strawberries and cherries which
grew in his beds in such wonderful profusion. "What a
delicious place!" we exclaimed, "and how one would like
to live here forever!" "Yes," replied the old man, smiling; "but to be perfectly happy there must be TWO, must
there not, for nature only seems to grant happiness to man
on that condition?" Mlle. P. blushed and looked at me as
she hung down her head. I colored too. But our host
did not seem to perceive it, and went on gathering some
beautiful large gooseberries, and throwing them into her
lap, while our talk became more and more intimate, till at
last on suddenly turning a corner, we found ourselves opposite a thatched summer-house, where the luncheon was
already prepared. We went in with him, and exclaimed at

the beauty of the fruit, the richness and thickness of the cream, the great cheeses of St. Clément, the delicate cakes, so exquisitely light and varied, and all made by his wife; and at the good wines, both white and red, which were the produce of his own vineyard. "Let us sit down, dear children," said the old man, "while we are waiting for those ladies; let us have a little comfortable chat. Now tell me young man, what do you like best in my country retreat?" he added, with a kind smile. "I can feel nothing but the happiness of being here, sir," I replied. Mlle. P. looked at me again and colored. "But," he continued, "one sees the sun this year everywhere. So you do the running waters, and the shady nut avenues, and the flowers and the fruits. Can you not find all these equally at Mâcon?" I smiled, and replied, "Yes, certainly one can find these things elsewhere." "Well, then, it is not this which makes you so happy that you feel that you cannot be more so! What is it, then? Now to enable you to find out, I am going to leave you for a few moments, and go and seek those ladies. You shall tell me when I come back." And he went out with an air of secret satisfaction, and left us together.

As for me, I was certainly a thousand times happier than I had ever been in my life, but also a thousand times more timid and embarrassed. My looks, my sighs, and my attentions had often told her the state of my feelings; but I had never ventured on any actual avowal of my passion till this old man, as it were, forced it upon me. Covering my face with my hands, I remained silent.

"Let me go!" exclaimed the poor child, her shaking voice betraying her emotion; and she got up to escape. These words broke the spell, which seemed to enchain my speech. "Oh, no!" I at last cried, throwing myself at her feet. "You shall not go till my heart has spoken. Do not look at me; but let me only say that what makes me so intensely happy here is neither the sun, nor the trees, nor the flowers, nor the waters; but simply that I am here with you, and that I can at last tell you how I love you." A soft sigh was my answer. "Let us go," she repeated; "though I have said nothing, you will understand me." We went out after this double avowal, both of us scarlet with emotion, and soon met the old man, talking in a low voice with Madame P., who was leaning on his arm. We turned away, but he had seen our troubled faces, and understood all.

When we returned to the house, we found the rest of the company. Madame F. C. made us see the inside of her house, the library, the drawing-room, the court-yard, the pigeon and chicken-houses, until our emotion was a little calmed, and then they came to announce that the luncheon was waiting in the summer-house. A silent joy filled both our hearts, which were overflowing with tenderness and trust. At last we felt sure of our mutual love. The old man seemed as happy as we were. He talked to us all the time about the happiness of his country life, alone with the only human being he cared for, and who was his wife. Mlle. P. looked at me from time to time with a soft smile. I felt I had nothing more to wish for here below. I came back in the evening, walking before Madame P. and her friends, and telling her daughter all the thoughts of my heart — thoughts which I did not know I possessed till then, and which she alone could have inspired. Everything now was understood and clear between us, and we had only to wait till circumstances should enable us to consummate the happiness the first germs of which had been revealed to us in the summer-house.

A few moments later our hopes were rudely dashed to the ground. I had gone home with them, and we were sitting side by side on a sofa, while her mother was dressing in an adjoining room, of which the door opened into the drawing-room. We spoke low ; for who likes such confidences to be overheard, however innocent? The mother, who thought our silence strange, suddenly and softly opened her door, and while I (who had my back turned to the door) was whispering my fond hopes into the ear of her daughter, I felt a heavy hand laid upon my head ; while with the other arm, she violently pushed her child away from me. "Is this the *réticence* which you had promised me, and in which I was such a fool as to confide? Leave my house this instant, sir ; and you, mademoiselle, take care never to appear without me in a room where this

18

young man is present. You are both unworthy of my trust!" I sprung up, humbled and indignant, at this unexpected outburst. Taking my hat, I prepared to leave; but protesting against this unfair imputation on the purity of her child. The poor girl herself burst into tears, and indignantly repelled her mother's unworthy suspicions. Madame P. saw she had spoken precipitately, and coloring, made some excuse. After a time we made it up. We promised to hold our tongues, and be only to each other as a very dear brother and sister. Our love remained the same as ever — the dream of two young pure hearts, who had nothing to reproach themselves with but love.

It was, however, impossible to stop the gossip of the town, and the affair soon came to the ears of my family. My mother spoke to me about it. I answered by asserting that I never could love a more accomplished or charming girl. She was wise, and agreed with me as to the superiority of Mlle. P.; but she represented to me, tenderly yet firmly, that we were both too young to think of settling in life, and that we must wait many years before it would be prudent to think of marriage. This answer calmed and quieted us, without extinguishing our mutual passion. Not to argue or positively refuse, but to counsel hope and patience, is the wisest remedy for the insane desire of extreme youth. I felt that I must have some change of scene and thought. My family were of the same opinion, and arranged it as if by chance.

The daughter of Madame de Roquemont (that cousin of my mother's of whom I have before spoken) had just married at Lyons. The honeymoon was to be spent in Italy. Certain business reasons served as a pretext for the young couple to visit Milan and Leghorn, where their parents had correspondents in certain commercial houses. It was settled that I was to accompany them. Three months before they had come to Mâcon to see my mother, and now they returned to arrange about the time of our departure.

This journey to Italy was an immense joy to me. I left my love, it was true, but only for a few months, with the certainty that she would remain true to me, and with her equally firm persuasion that I should return with a heart as devoted to her as ever. The trial was short; the happiness certain. So I gave my whole mind to learning Italian, and devoted myself especially to Tasso, Ariosto, Alfieri, and others. Toward the end of that spring we parted. I had a perfect thirst for traveling. It seemed to me like the passion of the Infinite, which had no limits. Each new country appeared as a new world added to creation. My delighted curiosity seemed to grow at every turn of the wheel.

At last we got to Leghorn, on the borders of that exquisite Mediterranean — a visible infinity to infinite thought!

My traveling companions having the intention of spending some months here, took a house; while I went to a hotel in the next street, from whence I came every day to dine with the family. I passed several months in this way, hard at work all day at the Lingua Toscana; and all the evenings at the theatre or the opera; but I found time to write to my mother, and that with all the pride of my newly acquired knowledge. I may say that this time was my honeymoon of thought: my enthusiasm had found a new element on which to feed. I wrote also occasionally to Mlle. P.; but, at the risk of shocking my readers, I must own that my passion for her had a good deal cooled, and at last froze, like a globe which is removed from the sun. I had a pleasing remembrance of her, but that was all; my new passion for traveling had extinguished my rural flame of St. Clément. The remarkable faces of the Italian women had not perhaps more beauty than Mlle. P., but of a far more sensational kind. And then they were Tuscans, and their beautiful tongue seemed to me to have the accent of heaven itself.

The month of October drew near when we were to start for Rome and Naples. But letters from Lyons changed the plans of my companions. It was decided that they should return home at once, without proceeding any farther on that delightful tour which we had planned together! The blow was terrible; but I soon determined that their plans should not affect mine. I wrote to my father begging his permission to continue my journey, saying that I was only a few steps from Rome, that dream of my youth, and very few more from Naples, the centre of all human delights; that it would be too cruel to dash the cup from my lips, which I had only just begun to taste; that I had enough money to spend the winter at Rome; that, in the spring, I should obtain from M. Dareste de la Chavanne (a relation of my mother's living in Italy) the sum necessary to go on to Naples; and that, therefore, I was going to take his permission for granted and start for Rome where his answer would find me. It was a bold step on my part; but, after all, not an unreasonable one.

Having written, I waited a few days for a reply; determined, however, that, should it be in the negative, it would arrive too late; and then started joyfully back to Florence, to make the necessary arrangements for my solitary journey to Rome.

There were only two regular ways of traveling at that time in Italy — by post or *vetturino;* but the former was beyond my means, and the latter was too hopelessly slow. Sometimes one had to wait for five or six days before the driver had made up his party; and then, going on always with the same horses, which had to stop and bait continually on the road, you were an age reaching your destination.

From time to time, however, you could get a place in the mail-cart; and that I determined to try for. A man named Taglia Vino offered me a place in one of these conveyances; we were to sleep for two or three hours in an *osteria* in the mountains; but to reach Rome in four or five days. I agreed to be ready the following evening at night-fall in one of the *faubourgs* of Florence; and accordingly, at the given hour, Taglia Vino and his carriage made their appearance.

I found four persons already settled inside, but my curiosity as to my fellow-travelers had to wait till daylight, for they all went to sleep soon after we started.

The first was a young man toward whom every one showed great respect. Taglia Vino knew him and called him "M. Le Duc," and was constantly on the watch to do him some little service. This care seemed to me to be needful; for though the weather was excessively cold, and we had to cross the snowy mountains of Camaldoli, he wore the thinnest possible coat, with short breeches, silk stockings, and thin shoes, as if he had just come out of a ball-room. The very sight of him froze me; but he did not seem to feel it, and continued his journey with great gayety and good humor. The second was a young man with a charming countenance, who appeared to be the son of the actor Davide, an old and well-known singer, who was very famous at that time in Italy. You will very soon see why I said APPEARED TO BE THE SON. This young man had the long hair of a woman hanging over his shoulders; his features were soft and delicate, but his black eyes brilliant and bold. I could not help lowering mine when he looked at me. The third traveler was Davide himself, a cheery, fat, jolly old man, a good and rather comical talker, and reminding one of Lablache. Everything he said began with a joke and ended by a hearty laugh. No one could help liking him.

We were very soon all four fast friends. The pretended son of Davide seemed to be particularly attracted by me. He always followed me when we got out of the carriage to walk up the hills, and explained the country to me which he knew thoroughly. At Terni he pointed out the remains of the magnificent Roman bridge the arches of which unite the hills of Clitumna to the Roman Campagna. When we first caught sight of the Eternal City on her Seven Hills, the Duke, Davide, and his companion urged me to go and lodge with them in the Via Condotti, at the inn where they generally stayed, and which was the *rendezvous* of the greater portion of the French, German, and Swiss travelers. I accepted their proposal with joy; it made me feel at once at home, and as if my companions and myself had become one family; Taglia Vino even was less of a driver than a friend.

At last, toward evening, we perceived, above the fogs of the Tiber, something immense, which seemed to float in the heavens and which reflected the last rays of the setting sun. It was the dome of St. Peter's. The night was closing in when we reached the Piazza del Popolo. The

Via Condotti was to be our destination; they gave me a very pretty room, and the Duke went to the opera to see his illustrious parents; Davide and his son were lodged in an adjoining apartment. I could not sleep for thinking of Rome: it was, however, very sad and very desolate just then. There was neither Pope nor Cardinals; Bonaparte had made a clean sweep of them all. The Pope was at Savona.

The next morning on going down to breakfast I found the good Davide and his companion, the latter transformed into a beautiful woman. Her name was Camilla; she was a singer in Davide's theatre, whom he took about with him from kindness, so that she might be under his care and protection.

"One's clothes do not change one's heart," said Camilla to me, smiling at my astonishment. "Only you will no longer sleep on my shoulder, and, instead of receiving flowers from me, you must get me some." Davide and his pupil spent several weeks at Rome. Camilla knew the town by heart, and used to take me at the best hours for seeing this beautiful city — the morning under the dome of the stone pines in the Pincio; the evening under the shade of the grand colonnade of St. Peter's; by moonlight in the solemn inclosure of the Coliseum; and in the glorious autumn days to Albano, Frascati, or the Temple of the Sybil, echoing with the foaming cascades of Tivoli. Camilla was bright and gay, like a figure of eternal youth amidst these vestiges of bygone times; she danced on the tomb of Cecilia Metella; and while I was sitting dreaming on a funeral mole her beautiful but somewhat theatrical voice echoed through the Palace of Diocletian,

In the evening we returned to the city, our carriage full of flowers and fragments of marble, and rejoined her old companion Davide, whose affairs kept him at Rome, and who took us to finish our day in his opera box. The fair singer, who was a good deal older than I was, had no other feeling for me than a kind of brotherly liking. I was much too shy to show any other; but, besides, I did not feel any more affection than herself in spite of her beauty and my youth. Her man's dress, her easy familiarity, the male sound of her contralto voice, and the freedom of her manners, gave the impression of her being simply a handsome young man, whom I could treat as a companion and a friend. When Davide left the hotel in the Via Condotti, I went to seek a lodging for the winter elsewhere.

I had taken an Italian professor, who had been introduced to me by a German of great distinction, the brother of M. de Humboldt and an eminent diplomatist, who dined at the same *table d'hôte* as myself in the Via Condotti. This old professor was called Giunto Tardi. He was a very handsome man, and had married a Russian widow lady. He had been named consul at Rome during the short-lived reign of the Republic, which the French soldiers had quickly crushed. Giunto Tardi had gone quietly back to his position as a Roman citizen; but his moderation and justice, during his short tenure of office, had given him a high place in the esteem and consideration of his countrymen. He lived as a poor man, but much respected in the town which he had governed, and maintained himself by teaching rich strangers his native language. I took him not only to teach me Italian, but as a master of literature, and we became great friends. I shall have occasion later to mention his brother, who bore the same name, but who was a distinguished painter. I was his guest for a few days, and he set me the example of every Christian virtue.

M. de Humboldt, the Prussian diplomat, was a man whom I thought far superior to his brother, the author of "A Journey to South America," and "Cosmos," whom I also knew but esteemed less, in spite of his great name and reputation. A clever man he was; but without much real merit; it would be difficult to cite anything remarkable in his works, except his adulation of French philosophers and heroes of various shades of opinion, as he had discovered that theirs was the only real European glory. People speak of him as "the friend of Arago," "of Châteaubriand," "of Napoleon," "of Louis XVIII.," etc., etc.; he always, in fact, worshiped the rising sun, and managed to get a reflection from its rays. This reflection (accumulated during thirty years) made him appear to many as a bright light, while he was in reality only a flashing fire-work.

When one considers his extraordinary reputation and the
mediocrity of his talents, one is bound to acknowledge that
he was a master of *savoir faire*.   His brother, on the contrary, was a frank, modest, and clever statesman.   He flattered none, but won the good-will and esteem of every
one.   This is the feeling with which he inspired me at
eighteen, and I have seen no reason to change my opinion
since.   The other obtained his reputation by a cheat, which
is worse than not having deserved it.

When Davide, Camilla, and M. de Humboldt were gone,
I stayed alone in Rome with no other companions than the
monuments and ruins, which Camilla had made familiar to
me, and my Italian master.   I asked the latter if he would
allow me to make acquaintance with his brother, to which
he consented.   I went daily to see him.   His studio was an
isolated convent in an obscure corner of Rome.   He sold
me a charming picture of the Cascades of Tivoli for a few
Roman *scudi*.   It is a model of beauty and patient skill.   I
still have it at St. Point, and look at it whenever I wish to
remember those happy, peaceful days.

Another artist, a lady named Bianca Boni, did a beautiful copy of Guido for me which I have never parted with.
It is a Virgin, but with an exquisite expression.   The features are angelic, and the forehead, mouth, and neck are
positively radiant with light.   Her eyes are looking up-
ward, as if they could not think of sublunary matters.   A
large blue veil falls over her head, hides her hair, and
falls on her shoulders.   Everything in this composition is
ideal, chaste, and pure; it is better than a woman, and
more than an angel; it is the Virgin before the Annuncia-
tion.

I had my picture taken by Bianca for my mother; and
as she was young, gentle, and very attractive, I was fool
enough to fall in love with her, and let her see it.   She
was furious, destroyed the likeness she had taken of me,
and sent me back the money she had received for the portrait.   I wrote a humble note of excuse and apology, and
left the sum again at her door, telling her that I had been
justly punished in being deprived of the work of her
hands; but that it was not just that she should lose the

price of her time which was so precious to her; and so implored her to receive back the money. But she was inexorable, and made me feel that these great Italian artists are likwise women of high and unimpeachable virtue. I distributed the money she would not accept among the poor. Such was the result of my first adventure in Rome. Bianca Boni inspired me ever after with a respect which was worth a good deal more than my stupid affection.

The old painter, brother of Giunto Tardi, was another object of my esteem; I might almost say, of my veneration. He rarely left his studio but to go to mass with his wife and daughter, a young girl of sixteen, as virtuous and good as himself. Their house was a species of monastery where work was only interrupted by a frugal repast and by prayer.

One day, at the *table d'hôte* of the Via Condotti, I became acquainted with a young Lyons merchant, who, after a time, proposed that we should go together to Naples. This young man was gentle, good, and well educated. I accepted his proposal, and had no occasion to repent it. He was a very agreeable companion, and we started in his own carriage.

We slept at Terracina, the brigands having made night traveling too perilous. We went on the next day, and suddenly heard a succession of shots fired in an olive wood on our left. Soon we came upon a carriage half burned lying in the middle of the road, which was that of the courier from Rome to Naples. The bodies of two travelers were lying dead on the roadside, and a wounded horse lay in the middle. Some soldiers were guarding them, while others were pursuing the assassins, and firing on them as they fled from rock to rock of the mountains above us. We were very much shocked, and continued our journey not a little saddened by the scene we had just witnessed.

We arrived at Naples as the night fell; the noise and bustle of the streets and public thoroughfares positively deafened us; while the sea was lit up by the reflection of the countless lights which burned in the shop windows, or in the niches of the Madonna. We drove through the street of the "Florentines," which crosses that of "Toledo," and stopped at an hotel well known to my Lyons friend. After the silence and stillness of Rome we seemed to have passed into a new world. The next morning I was woke by some monks who sang verses in our honor, and brought us magnificent fruits from Castelamare, and other presents from the convent, for which, however, we had to pay handsomely. Then I got into a little carriage and went all over this enchanting town. I was quite delighted. No city had ever produced such a magical effect upon me; Rome was a monastery, Naples the Garden of Eden.

Nature and man seemed to have combined to produce this most perfect spot. From the moment of my arrival I was scarcely myself; I was boiling all over with emotion, and could not stay still in one place. I rushed off to the post-office; they spread out a quantity of letters on a board before me. I found one addressed to myself, which was given to me readily enough when I had paid the postage. It was from my old friend M. de Virieu, to whom I had written from Rome. He replied that he was just starting from Grand Lemps with his mother's consent, and with a letter of credit on Rome and Naples, and that he should join me almost as soon as I had received his letter.

In fact he arrived a very few days after. He met me at the hotel Fiorentino, where I had prepared a room for him, and where we became intimate with a young Calabrian gentleman, who initiated us into the mysteries of gambling. This was the first time that that wonderful temptation had assailed us. At that period in Naples the great game was the *trenta e quaranta*, played in a public room at the end of the Via di Toledo. This young Calabrian was married, but as inexperienced as ourselves. We used to spend hours in losing or spending a few *carlini*.

I had all this time a kind of compunction about certain letters of introduction which my mother had given me to M. de la Chavanne, director of the tobacco manufactory at Naples, and which I had hitherto neglected to deliver. Liberty without control seemed to me infinitely pleasanter. At last, however, I felt that I could no longer delay my visit. I inquired for his house and was directed to a magnificent establishment dedicated to St. Pietro Martyro, in

the most noisy quarter of the town. it was just midday;
I climed up a magnificent staircase of one hundred and
twenty steps till I got to the fifth or sixth story. Below
was a large garden surrounded with arcades. These arcades
and the lower story of the house were filled with vats,
workshops, and other things belonging to the state manufactory. I took in every detail of this picture, which remained indelibly impressed upon my mind, as it led to one
of the great events of my life, and in fact was to bring
about a decisive change in my existence.

Arriving out of breath at the top story, I rung at a
great door which gave entrance to a large and long cloister,
out of which opened different doors to the right and left.
At the end of this gallery were three large windows called
finestrati, which threw a brilliant light on the cloister itself. A number of young girls crossed and recrossed this
place every moment, carrying I knew not what in their
aprons. I found afterward that these children were employed in choosing the finest tobacco leaves for the manufacture of cigarettes. I was far from imagining that one
of these very girls would soon become GRAZIELLA, change
her occupation, and influence forever my future life. I did
not dare own the truth when in 1847 I wrote the novel of
" Graziella," which had such a success because every one
recognized that it was true to nature. I had from vanity
altered the first few pages, but all the rest was exact.
Now I am going to make a full confession of the whole
facts, and give you the true history of " Graziella."

At the end of the cloister to the right, I perceived an
open door and a good many servants, going backward and
forward, carrying plates and dishes, while inside the room
I heard the clatter of knives and forks. I saw I had in-
opportunely chosen the time of M. le Directeur's breakfast;
but it was too late to go back; I had already sent in my
card and was announced.

No sooner had he heard my name, than M. de la Chavanne rose and received me with open arms, exclaiming,
" He is the very image of his mother ! " He embraced me
with the greatest warmth and tenderness, and made me sit
down on a sofa under the window which lighted the

breakfast-room. I found out that this house had been a monastery, and that we were in the room of the old superior of St. Pietro Martyro. Two other persons were breakfasting with M. de la Chavanne: one from twenty to twenty-five years old, named Antoniella—a pleasing person but with nothing very striking about her; she was evidently on intimate and confidential terms with the director, and had, as I afterward found, the superintendence of the young girls employed in the cigar manufactory; the other was a most charming girl, but of her I shall speak later. Our conversation, in which neither young lady took a part, turned entirely on my mother and her family. M. de la Chavanne declared that he would never allow me to remain in a hotel at Naples, and that he would give me a charming little room in his house looking on the sea. He got up to show it to me, and I found a most comfortable room with a camp bed and a winding staircase leading up to the flat roof of this immense convent, from whence there was a glorious view of the sea, with Capri, Sorrento, and Vesuvius. A trellised wall sheltered a portion of this beautiful terrace from the wind; so that you were at the same time warmed with the genial Italian sun and your head shaded from its rays. I came down quite delighted with my little apartment, promising myself the pleasure of occupying it as soon as possible.

M. de la Chavanne, of whom my mother had often spoken to me, was a man of between forty and fifty years of age, and of remarkable goodness; his frank, cheery face and cordial manner made one love him at first sight. He was tall and large; his honest blue eyes looked you straight in the face, and his mouth alone would have told you his character; it was the very type of benevolence and sweetness. It was really impossible not to love him. He had served valiantly with his countrymen against the army of the Convention at the siege of Lyons. This siege had ruined him, and he had sought refuge in Italy. Here Murat, king of Naples, had given him the directorship of the state tobacco manufactory, a lucrative and honorable post. He established himself at Naples, and became rich and happy. He had left his wife and several sons in France, whom she had brought up admirably. From time to time she came to see him; he loved her devotedly, and was equally loved by her; the necessity of being so often separated from her was the only thing which ever embittered his life. He lived at Naples as an exile; but as one who endeavored to forget it by active work for those dear to him. He was adored by all the French in Naples and by the Neapolitans themselves, who knew him by the continual kind services which his position enabled him to render them. He was always kind and generous, fond of young people, and ever ready to contribute to their amusements. Such was the man into whose home I had thus been admitted, and I could have found no one so worthy of my esteem and affection. In taking leave of him, I felt the attraction which he universally inspired, and promised to return in a few days and take advantage of his generous hospitality. I had not then scarcely realized the secret and invincible charm which strengthened my resolution; i. e., the thought of seeing once more the fascinating face I had had a glimpse of at his table

On returning to Viricu, to whom I had to break my approaching separation from him in obedience to my mother's wishes, I went to the post and there found a letter directed to me in an unknown writing from Mâcon, which I opened with a trembling hand. It was from the old man of St. Clément, the friend of Madame P., and ran as follows:—

"Sir,— Your age and position made me believe that your affection for Mlle. Henriette P. (of which, as an old friend of her family, I had heartily approved), would result in a union which would secure your joint happiness; your departure and prolonged absence have given rise to certain doubts and scruples in my mind. Mlle. Henriette is very young, and so are you; you are not yet your own master, and you cannot answer for the wishes of your parents. I am, therefore, charged to tell you, in her mother's name, that proposals of marriage have been made to her by another person, whose character and fortune promise her that which, I fear, it would not be in your power to give her for many years. Be so good then, as to examine your own heart and conscience, and to let me know whether you still have the same feelings for this young lady as when you left Mâcon; and if her family may expect from you as favorable settlements as those which are now offered her elsewhere. We wait for your answer, and remain," etc.

This letter, which was evidently written with the concurrence of Madame P., if not of her daughter, troubled me very much. I took some days to think about it; I certainly was anything but free to choose; I had nothing, or next to nothing, of my own. I could only love her; but I could not, without great imprudence, answer for the consent of my family to a union, which I was not quite sure now of even wishing for myself. So I wrote a frank and prudent letter, explaining my position, and virtually leaving the decision in the hands of Mlle. P. herself.

I learned soon after that she was about to marry her other suitor. I regretted her; but I felt that her parents were right not to sacrifice the future of their child to an illusion of seventeen. Thus ended my first love dream, which was only a short but delicious bit of imaginary happiness.

I did not see her again for thirty years, when we met, with some regret perhaps, but with no bitterness. There are passages of this sort in most men's lives, which seem to be but dreams of our first youth. Mlle. P. was one of those fancies. She was very happy in her married life, and was united to one who was far more worthy of her than myself. I was still a child, and scarcely knew my own mind. But I wished to be sincere and loyal.

After having passed a day or two longer with Virieu in our hotel, I went to live with M. de la Chavanne. It was only a few doors off. I used to part with Virieu at night, sure to meet him early the next day; so that he became reconciled to our short separation. M. de la Chavanne was not at home when I arrived at his house. I was received by his old Neapolitan cook, and by that charming child, Graziella. She opened the door of the little room assigned to me, undid my portmanteau, and placed my things in the drawers, even kneeling down to take the creases out of my clothes. Every movement of hers was full of grace; only she seemed to me more shy and pale than the day I had seen her at breakfast. I scarcely dared raise my eyes to look at her, and felt distressed at her waiting upon me in this manner; but we scarcely exchanged two words. I felt as if she were one of my sisters, who had come as usual to do little things for me on my return from a long journey. The simplicity of her manner and dress added to my illusion.

After settling me in my room, we went back to the drawing-room, where she took up her work, and we began to talk a little. Antoniella came in from the large workroom where she had been superintending "her children," as she called them in the cigarette factory. Then came in the master, and the breakfast. We sat down to it as before. "Now I must introduce you properly to one another," exclaimed M. de la Chavanne, gayly. "This one is Antoniella. She is a good child, and very useful to me in the factory. She chooses, admits, or sends away the novices of my convent, who number some hundreds, and who are employed not exactly in saying their prayers, but in making cigars and cigarettes. She knows all the poor people and lazzaroni of the place, and finds out which of them have too many children to support, and wish to get work in my establishment. She manages all this quite admirably and lives with me, as you see, like my daughter, to receive and transmit my orders. Everybody is pleased and satisfied with her — employers and employed. My little workwomen are like her own sisters or children. She watches over them like a mother, and reports to their families if there be any cause of complaint in the workrooms; and so she helps me to keep perfect order and peace in the establishment. They call her in Naples ' *la madre delle cigarette.*' " At these words, Antoniella burst out laughing, and M. de la Chavanne, glancing at her with his kind, paternal face, smiled also. " Now," he continued, "as for this little girl " (pointing to Graziella, who colored up to the eyes), " who is still a child, Antoniella is teaching her French, that she may be some day my interpreter between the administration and the directors, who are our country-men. She is called Graziella, and is the daughter of a poor fisherman in the island of Procida, who has a whole tribe of children. She only receives the pay of a cigar workwoman, but she transmits it regularly, at the end of the month, to her mother, *La Procitana*. She does not, however, work with the rest but lives with us, so as to be under the immediate care of Antoniella, who is her friend and protectress. She superintends the house under her directions, and transmits my orders to the servants, who are Neapolitans, and whose *patois* she alone understands. She is still a child, as you see; but a good child, and beloved by everybody. I treat her more as a father than as a master. She orders everything here, and is our aide-de-camp, or rather our mouthpiece. Ask for whatever you wish. She is at your orders; only do not look at her dress, which is that of the children of Procitana, of the peasantry of an island from whence Naples obtains her most beautiful and her most useful servants. Their costume is, in fact, a mark of servitude in Naples, but of nobility in their own island. Go and dress yourself as a Procitana," he added, turning to Graziella; "Antoniella will help you."

The shy and beautiful child went out with Antoniella, and returned in a few moments entirely transformed. It was like a scene in a play. On her feet she had little yellow slippers without heels, of which the leather was finely embroidered in red and silver; her blue stockings seemed not to be knitted, but wove in some kind of bright stuff. A woolen petticoat, with a multitude of fine plaited folds, and of a dark yet bright brown shade, fell to her feet; a bodice of green velvet cut square, and made into a point before and behind, revealed her neck and bosom, both of which were modestly covered by a chemisette of fine lace and embroidery, closely buttoned down the front. The sleeves and waistband were trimmed with rich braiding and embroidery, and are alike for rich and poor. The head-dress, except on a journey, consisted of nothing but a profusion of raven black hair, rolled in a thick cable round the head, like a living turban. Her throat and ears were ornamented with a beautiful necklace and ear-rings of ancient Greek workmanship, and of very fine gold, the pendants of which clicked like the little bells of a horse in a circus. The blushing face of the child revealed a mixture of shame and bashfulness, partly with the consciousness of her own beauty, and partly with the sense of our appreciation of it. We looked at her with mute admiration ; and had she been less of a child, I should not have dared to lift my eyes. In a few seconds she disappeared, and ran off to put on her every-day dress. But the effect had been produced and the blow struck. I could not forget it, and henceforth never saw her in her ordinary costume without recalling the Procitana, and looking upon her merely as a shadow of her real self. The dress she generally wore was only a common, coarse, brown stuff, fastened close round her throat, without any ornament whatever, and a simple blue handkerchief tied round her neck. Her beautiful little feet were disguised in untidy, heavy, black shoes, generally down at the heel. Such was the chrysalis — but what about the butterfly?

Virieu came to see me in the course of the day. His father, as I before said, had commanded the cavalry at the siege of Lyons. M. de la Chavanne had followed him in his last charge, and had been all but a witness of his death. They talked a long time of this fatal day. Virieu dined with us, and was as much struck as myself with the marvelous Grecian beauty of *la Procilana*. That evening Virieu and I went out together, and I accompanied him to his hotel. In passing the Via di Toledo we went in, from curiosity, to the Palazzo Fiorentino, opposite the theatre. This was the public gambling house, permitted but superintended by the police. Immense tables, surrounded with silent players, filled the rooms : great heaps of gold and silver were piled on the green table by the side of each player. We were soon drawn in to join the game, risked some *scudi* and lost. That evening, and the next, and the day after, we did the same. We could not understand why the luck was always against us. While we were grumbling about it in the recess of one of the windows, an old Neapolitan came up to us, and told us, that as long as we played in that way, without sense or plan, we MUST lose ; that this game was not one of chance, but of skill and science ; that we were not to expect large gains but moderate profits ; that he himself had once been a victim like ourselves ; but that he now lived on what had formerly been his ruin. We listened to him with astonishment. He saw it, and lowering his voice, proposed to give us lessons at hazard, having been himself a croupier of a gambling table, and having masses of cards with which he could prove his theory to our satisfaction. With the ignorant and self-confident folly of youth, we accepted his invitation, and made an appointment with him the following evening in Virieu's rooms. The old man was punctual, and having thrown on the table a MASS of cards, that is, ten or twelve packs, the game began.

" Play as you will, gentlemen," he said quietly, " and I will bet you anything you like that, by the end of the evening, I shall have gained and you will have lost." He threw down the cards, we played and lost, his gains were very small, but he always won.

We tried twenty times and always with the same result. We were confounded. " Why then are you not yourself rich ? " I asked him at last. " Because riches are not the result of even successful gambling, but of honest labor," he replied. " I never promised that I should show you how to get millions, but small sums. Will you try again ? " " Yes," we answered. " Well, I am now going to show you my system, and explain on what it is based. Now listen to me. What is *trenta e quaranta ?* A game in which the player, playing against the bank, gains every time that the color BLACK or RED, on which he has betted, approaches nearest to the number forty, without going beyond it, for, if it goes beyond, the player is dead. He must, therefore, calculate, as nearly as he can, which is the color, whether black or red, which offers the best chance of arriving at the winning number, and conform his play to that. Understand, once for all, there is in reality no LUCK in it, only skill and memory."

The old croupier, without giving us more of his practice and experience, played for another hour, and following out the calculations he had suggested to us, went on winning, while we, trusting to luck, always lost.

He promised to return at the same hour on the following day. I was anxious to find out if it would always come to the same in the long run; and if he could ALWAYS reckon on small but certain sums. The next day, and for twenty days running, we were confirmed in this belief; he steadily won so many *scudi* a night, and we lost as many Napoleons. It was becoming serious, and I asked myself: "But what is the cause? for, after all, chance is but an effect of which we do not see the reason; let us go on and try to find it out."

All the winter the croupier came, and we devoted our evenings to him, either at Virieu's hotel or at M. de la Chavanne's. One saw nothing but cards. One heard nothing but *trenta e quaranta*. M. de la Chavanne's French friends came and chatted round the braziers, in which the olive wood chips burned without smoke or flame. Antoniella and Graziella worked on the sofa in the corner of the room. From time to time Graziella would look up at me and try to smile; but then her face would suddenly become grave, as if she said, "What a pity that so sensible a young man should have a taste for gambling!"

But the croupier cut his cards perseveringly, and we could discover nothing except the fact that he regularly pocketed our *carlini*.

In this way our Naples winter passed until the beautiful early spring lit up the waves and mountains of Castelamare. Vesuvius began to grumble and launch out angry puffs of smoke and flame, from time to time. Virieu was ill, and did not leave his room. I had met on the staircase of his hotel one day, M. Humboldt, the diplomatist, whom we had left at Rome. He received me like a son, and proposed to carry me off with him on a tour he was about to make in Calabria, after he had studied the volcano of which the threatened eruption had become more serious. I accepted his offer with joy; and yet I was sad at leaving Graziella when I thought of her. But as yet we had come to no explanation.

M. de Humboldt came to fetch me at M. de Chavanne's. At the moment of getting into his carriage he asked me: "Who was that beautiful child?" and I, looking up at

Graziella, saw that her eyes were full of tears. Why did she cry ; and why did she follow the carriage with her eyes till we were out of sight?

The horses rapidly took us on the road to Pompeii and Torre dell' Annunziata, a pretty village which you come to before arriving at Castelamare, and which is built at the foot of the mountain. We put up at a little inn still nearer to Vesuvius, and sent for guides and mules to conduct us to the hermit whose cell was built on the highest habitable cone. After two or three hours of fatiguing march, either upon cooling and slippery lava, or on hot ashes, of which the smoke nearly blinded one, we stopped on one of the lower spurs of the mountain. On turning round we felt as if we were floating in the sky : the sea, the islands, the capes, and Naples, all seemed to spring out of the earth at our feet. We could not resist an exclamation of pleasure. At last we reached the hermitage ; the hermit had ceased to sleep there at night, fearing to be surprised in sleep by a sudden outburst of the volcano. We sat down on the bench at his door, gazing at the wonderful scene beneath us, which the ether seemed to have evoked from the void below. At last the hermit himself arrived on his donkey, which carried besides a quantity of flasks of Lacryma Christi ; the hermit having catered for his guest as well as himself, and making us pay largely for the luxury. He was, however, a thoroughly good fellow, not belonging to any regular religious order, but one of those ambulatory friars who attach themselves to certain localities from whence they draw their means of subsistence. I should say that this monk was of the " Order of Vesuvius," and nothing else. He changed his cell according as the eruption changed its course. The rest of the time he entertained travelers ; his cell was a picturesque and sacred house of refreshment.

M. de Humboldt and I sat down on each side of his little table, and talked to him about the mountain and the general prelude to the eruptions. I resolved next day to study it nearer by descending the crater. It was of no sort of use my doing so, for I was neither a SAVANT, nor a naturalist. I did not even know the names of the scientific specimens which I proposed to bring back with me ; but I was just at the age when one wishes to be thought rather foolhardy, let it cost what it might; somewhat of the race of Empedocles, who left his sandals on the borders of Etna. I induced two of our guides to return to Torre dell' Annunziata to fetch the cords necessary for the perilous descent of the crater. M. de Humboldt laughed at my preparations, and endeavored to dissuade me from so rash an act without any possible object. But I was only the more strengthened in my pride and folly, and woke the next morning as determined as ever to carry out my plan.

Vesuvius had been silent through the night. The sunrise was magnificent; one saw nothing but a puff of yellow smoke belching forth at intervals from the pointed cone above our heads.

We started early, following our guides, who had brought the cords, which I had ordered during the night. It was no longer walking but scrambling. Several times we heard the stones and ashes falling round us, causing a sulphurous smoke which blinded us for a few moments until dispersed by the soft morning air. It would seem as if the spirits of this infernal region disputed every step with the human beings who ventured into their precincts. We often had to throw ourselves flat on the earth to avoid the rebound of the stones and pieces of rock as they fell; and only when the eruption ceased for a few moments, could we continue our route.

At last, we arrived at the mouth of the crater and sat down on the edge, measuring with our eyes, as far as we could, the frightful gulf, half in shade and half in lurid light, which yawned beneath our feet. It was the shape of an enormous funnel of which the base and the sides were colored, to windward, by the various streams of lava which recent eruptions had deposited on their course. On one side appeared a kind of crystallized salt, white as newly fallen snow; on another, fragments of sulphur as yellow as gold in the crucible. Farther on, the sides of the crater had taken the form of pointed, jagged, and still smoking rocks, with here and there bright stalactites which seemed to have frozen as they fell. One portion of this vast basin seemed filled with a brownish substance of which I did not know the name. But, toward the middle of the crater, masses of smoke belched forth, from the midst of which poured out at intervals rivers of flame lighting up the depths of this abyss of wonder and of terror, which might well have served for a picture of the infernal regions. My guides sat down with their cords and said, "What is the use of tempting Providence? How much more will you see if you do attempt the descent?" "I should actually have TOUCHED it," I replied. And rising from the hot sand on which I was sitting, I passed my arms through the knots of the cords, and prepared slowly to descend into the crater. Not one of the guides would consent to follow me; but they all hung on to the mouth of the basin, striving to direct my perilous course, and to induce me to return. I reached the flat brown surface I have before described in a few minutes; but the heat increasing in intensity as I neared the burning furnace in the centre, my shoes were at once almost burned off, and scarcely any sole remained to preserve my feet. I strove to stand on such portions of the sulphur as had cooled a little, and springing across one of the rushing torrents of liquid fire, tried to rest for a moment on a less burning crust. I felt I was lost if the wind, changing for an instant, had driven back upon me the sulphurous flame and smoke, which fortunately it drove, at present, on the opposite side of the crater. My guides called louder to me than ever to retrace my steps while there was yet time. I hastily knotted together in my handkerchief some specimens of the burning metals around me, and at last gave the signal to be drawn up again from this very hell upon earth. My ascent was accomplished in perfect safety, only my clothes and shoes were burned to rags. They hailed my return to terra firma with cries of joy, while M. Humboldt hastened to explain to me the names and characters of the specimens which I had brought up from the abyss. We went back to the hermit's cell, who could not recover his astonishment at my foolhardiness; and a good breakfast, with the help of the Lacryma Christi, made every one forget my folly.

That evening I would have given all the world to have had no part in this ridiculous adventure. If I had undertaken it as a man of science, to wrest some hitherto unknown secret from nature, it might have been sublime ; but undertaken by an ignoramus like myself, the attempt was simply ridiculous. My vanity met with its due punishment ; I had been egregiously vain — that was all ; but I reaped what I deserved — that most bitter feeling of a thorough contempt of one's self.

After our breakfast at the Hermit's we returned to Torre dell' Annunziata. The noise in the mountain seemed to increase in proportion as we went farther from it : the earth shook under our mules' feet. All the village had turned out. Every one, in mute despair, lifted their eyes and arms to heaven, and rushed from their houses to see which side of the cone of the crater would open out first and overwhelm with its burning stream of lava, the crops and the vineyards on which their whole existence depended. Every saint in the calendar was invoked in vain by these poor people. All of a sudden, at nightfall, a mighty cry burst forth — the problem had been solved. A great breach had been made in the cone to the south, and streams of liquid fire were pouring down the sides of the mountain with resistless speed. What direction would the eruption take during the night ? That was the anxious question. We got back to our little inn and supped, passing the greater part of the night at our windows watching the progress of this terrible devastation.

As soon as it was light, we ran, like every one else, out of the house to the base of the mountain. The heavy torrent of lava had made fearful progress during the night, and had already reached not only the vineyards, but the gardens and houses in the upper part of the village of L'Annunziata. Some of these cottages, perched on a little rising ground to the left, were already entirely encircled by the fire. The poor inhabitants were flying from their homes, with cries and tears, carrying with them whatever they could most easily save from the flames. It was a heartbreaking sight. Men were dragging great sacks of wheat, or bundles of Indian corn ; women, their cradles full of children, on their shoulders. The animals followed, driven by the boys, and trembling with fear ; the very cocks and hens, with half-burned wings, were fluttering and striving to hide themselves amidst the vines. It was exactly such a scene as Pliny describes at the overthrow of Pompeii. As the lava slowly but surely encircled its prey, you saw the green vine leaves shrivel up, crackle and groan, almost like living human beings ; and then the branches, despoiled of their now yellow leaves, in their turn becoming crisp, taking fire, and spreading the destructive element along the ground, which had become as a furnace. These agonies of nature were slowly repeated, till each vine had fallen a victim to the destroying element. For me the sight had a sort of fascination, and I forgot that I ran a like danger myself. We had certainly legs wherewith to fly ; but if for a moment we were to forget, or that the wind had changed its quarter, the same burning breath would have devoured us like the shrubs, and our calcined bones would have crackled as rapidly as the vine branches. I did forget it several times, and drawing nearer to this bed of fire, the very stick I held in my hand was shriveled up in a moment. We suddenly saw, from the lay of the ground, that the flames had changed their course, and that we were in imminent danger of being encircled by them, unless we rapidly returned to the shelter of the town. At last, the lava torrent chose for its bed a narrow valley which led to the sea, crossing the high-road to Naples, along which both horses and foot passengers were flying at full speed. But anxious to study this phenomenon to the end, which had been the object of M. de Humboldt's visit, we remained on that part of the road which led to Castelamare and Salerno, till the eruption had ceased. The only sights and sounds which met our eyes the following day, however, were the tears and lamentations of the poor ruined inhabitants. After witnessing this terrible calamity, M. de Humboldt returned to Naples, and I started alone for Castelamare.

After having driven through the picturesque forest of laurels which surround the beautiful villas in the neighborhood of Naples, I went to Sorrento, which gleamed on the horizon before me like a dream of Tasso's.

After some days spent in making expeditions from this lovely place, I hired, sometimes a *corricolo*, and sometimes a boat, to visit the Temple of Pæstum and La Cava, the most beautiful spot along the whole coast. After spending about a fortnight in these solitary excursions, I found that the high-road between Torre dell' Annunziata and Naples was again opened, a certain quantity of earth having been thrown upon the lava bed; so that I took a little carriage, and returned to Naples. My heart was still full of Graziella. I felt that all the emotions of which I could neither speak nor write would be shared in and sympathized with by that delicious child.

On going up-stairs at St. Pietro Martyro, I was startled at not hearing her bright voice as usual at the end of the gallery. Everything in the old convent seemed to be as still as death. M. de la Chavanne was in his counting-house. Antoniella was superintending the cigar-makers. My room was shut up. The only person I could find was the cook, who exclaimed, "Ah! you will no longer find Mlle. Graziella. She is gone back to the islands to her parents. No one has had any tidings of her since. We suppose she was taken to her grandmother's house at Ischia, from whence she will not come back till after the summer. Oh! by the bye, she left a little note for you, which she told me to give you on your return. Here it is."

I took the note, which was written, or rather scribbled, in Neapolitan *patois*, as follows: *Già che sei partito, non posser più restar. Non ti rivedrò mai. La damizella* ("From the moment you left, I felt I could no longer stay. I shall never see you again!") Two or three great tears had left their blots on the coarse yellow paper.

This note explained to me that which her eyes at parting had only partially revealed. I went into my room, threw myself on the bed, and burst out crying. Virieu came up a few minutes later, to know if I was returned. He found me in tears, and asked in utter amazement, what was the matter. Without speaking, I showed him the poor little note. "Oh," he exclaimed, "why, here's the beginning of a beautiful romance! You must go on with it. What a good thing; for I was bored to death!" "Don't joke about such matters," I replied. "Tears at her age are serious."

I waited till Antoniella came in, and asked her directly where her little friend was gone. "I do not know," she replied. "I went to ask her father on the quay of Pausilippo. There was no one there. The neighbors told me that he had left off coming to Naples, and that they believed Graziella was gone back to her grandmother's house at Procida. Since you went off with that clever German, she never spoke or told me any of her little secrets; only I remarked that she was often crying."

When M. de Chavanne came in from his counting-house, I asked him the same question. "Well," he answered, laughing; "it appears that you are at the bottom of the despair and the flight of poor little Graziella. We have tried in vain to find her out, and can only conjecture that to escape a sorrow which she could not conquer, she is gone back to her old grandmother at Procida. Her good common sense will soon make her see the folly of all this, and if you wish to meet her again, you may be sure to do so in the autumn."

I was destined to see her long before that. I knew where to find her, and I felt that she had left her comfortable position at M. de Chavanne's for no other earthly reason than disgust at my going off with M. de Humboldt. I knew that she loved me, and that her flight was nothing but a wild declaration of love. I was torn with grief. I felt I could not remain away from her any longer. I have described in my novel, how I rejoined her at Procida. The little details which I have now given to my readers, form the only difference between the fiction and the reality. It cost my pride too much to own that my first deep love had only a cigarette maker for its object, instead of a coral worker, as she became later. Where will not vanity find a peg on which to hang itself?

After this confession, I have nothing to add, but that the rest of the story is literally true. Graziella was as young, as naïve, as pure, as religious as I represented her in my novel. All the scenes therein described are drawn from life. The scene and the actors are simple daguerreotypes. The trade of the child was less vulgar in the novel, but that is all. Our voyage to Procida, and the purchase of the new boat as a present to the family, the joy of the grandmother at its reception, the exclamations of delight from the children, all this is not invented but simply related. So it is with our life in the island, and our mingled feelings of intense joy and sorrow, with our nights on the terrace where we had erected a tent, and our days under the shade of the vineyards where we lived the happy and simple life of the lazzaroni.

Toward the end of the month of May, my family wrote to Virieu for an explanation of the suspicious life I was leading at La Margellina. M. de la Chavanne had evidently written to warn my mother. Virieu, in his warm friendship for me, returned posthaste to Naples, and dragged me away almost by main force. I left Graziella drowned in tears, and as I got into the carriage she fainted away. I vowed to return to live and die at Procida. At Milan I halted for a few days after Virieu had gone, being resolved to try the *rouge et noir* system which he and I had so conscientiously studied at Naples with the old croupier. I faithfully promised Virieu not to retrace my steps to Naples till I had seen my family, but to rejoin them in a fortnight at Milly.

Milan had a gambling table which opened daily at the theatre of La Scala. It was there that I determined to try my luck. I was extraordinarily successful. I resolved to reduce the old croupier's theories to practice. I thought, without always arriving at making the number forty, there was more chance with a good many low cards than with five or six higher ones. Experience had shown me that high and low numbers were dealt out, as it were, in sets and not alternately. I therefore concluded that, by watching carefully the dealing of the cards, I could make pretty sure of those which were left. I followed this method steadily, and won as steadily every night.

I remained a fortnight at Milan, and then started for Lyons with a Swiss merchant from Lausanne and his servant, who took immense care of me on the road, and insisted on my staying a few days at their house, when we reached their home.

After resting two or three days at Lausanne, I took a little carriage and came back to Mâcon. My father was waiting for me, and received me with the greatest affection, without saying a word of my follies. I felt that I had come back pardoned, and that few sons had a father like mine. Still I was sad as death, though I did not say why. My poor mother cried for joy at my return, after so long an absence. If the rest of the family were displeased with me, they took care to conceal it. Everything seemed forgotten, except in my own heart and in the sick heart of my poor Graziella. Alas! I had not long to wait for news. A traveler passing through Mâcon brought me the tidings of her death, together with her letter of farewell. Her last thought had been for me.

I have now described my first loves, my happiness and my misery, and my first journey into Italy. Since that time, Italy became my own country, or, at least, the country of my affections. But my life was about to change entirely. We were in the year 1812–13. Bonaparte, like a man chased by the Furies, had returned from Moscow, where he never should have gone, while the other half of his forces were engaged in Spain, to which country he had no right to pretend. Of seven hundred and fifty thousand men whom he had had under arms, only a few thousand remained this side of the Vistula. But in the midst of his reverses he was grand. He never despaired. He gathered together the fragments of his glorious army, and with three hundred thousand men was fighting a brilliant campaign, though he could not recover the lost ground.

Austria offered him peace and neutrality. She proposed certain concessions not unacceptable to his ambition, or to his former glory. But he preferred fighting on for shadows, and threw the fate of the Empire and of France on one die. At Leipsic he lost all. He came back to Paris without an army. He brought but his genius, his pride, and his authority; in some eyes he became a hero once more, but a hero of adverse fortune. He was compelled to lay down his arms and the Empire at Fontainebleau, and went to the Isle of Elba to reflect upon his crime toward his country. It was the beginning of the end. St. Helena avenged Paris and France.

I had a great friend, who was an old *émigré* of Condé's army, living in the mountains of the Jura. I resolved to throw myself on his hospitality for a few weeks, and spend a little time with him in the heart of the Swiss mountains, from whence I could easily go farther if the state of things became worse.

This gentleman who was a good deal older than I, was one of those charming people who suit all ages. He was a Royalist, but not a very keen politician, and enjoyed life as he found it. He had that witty and keen sense of humor which rather laughed at enthusiasm or over-zeal, even in the cause of the King. He was a widower; his beautiful young wife was from Mâcon, and had died in her first confinement. His name was M. de Maizod. His little château was only a house dignified with that feudal title, but which the peasants considered as belonging to the village. His nearest neighbors lived at the little town of Moirans. There was an old middle-class family in Moirans, which was not far from St. Claude, who were immensely looked up to and respected in the country. They were called, like the Scotch clans, the Chavériats. Léonard Chavériat, who belonged to every one of note in Moirans, was looked upon with affectionate admiration by the whole population. He was, in fact, all powerful; being lawyer, sportsman, fisherman, and one who could turn his hand to anything, while his greatest delight was to be of use to everybody. He was a Royalist; but his opinions were subordinate to his instincts.

I spent a month in this quite solitude without being troubled by the convulsions which agitated the other provinces.

Chavériat told me one day that war had been declared, and that the Emperor had ordered that all the young men who had served in the King's household should be compelled to join the Imperial army. I decided instantly on my course. " I would rather fly or die than fight against the King!" Chavériat, offered to guide me to the Swiss frontier. I accepted his services. We parted at the frontier line. I cried aloud for joy at my deliverance and walked on to St. Cergues, and found the house of M. Reboul. He was a noble Swiss who had received Madame de Staël, Montmorency, Benjamin Constant, and many other distinguished persons during their exile.

I was welcomed by a young lady of great beauty, in the absence of M. Reboul. This young girl, or rather this angel, had nothing either in her face or dress like any woman I had ever seen. Her voice and features fascinated me. But her face, with her blue eyes, and her rose-leaf complexion, had a mingled expression of joy and sorrow, which struck me the moment I saw her. I did not then know that she had only lately lost her mother, and that time had not yet effaced the traces of her grief. She was plaiting a large straw hat with a wide border to defend her neck from the sun, and little bits of straw were scattered on the parquet floor at her feet.

She offered me a glass of wine while I was waiting for her father; and we began to enter into a quiet kind of conversation. She, with that calm soft voice, which thrilled me through and through, and I, with a totally new feeling which made my words tremble on my lips. I had a letter of recommendation from Léonard for her father, so that I had no alternative but to await his return. He came home very late, but by that time I had become accustomed to my hostess, and it was Reboul who appeared to me the only stranger.

I gave him Léonard's letter. He read it carefully, and then said we would speak of its contents on the morrow. He told his charming daughter to go and prepare my room for me. She left us at once, but my thoughts followed her. I do not know how it was that recollections of Graziella mingled with this new vision. I could not tell why this angelic apparition gave me at once such a feeling of security and such an inclination to cry.

I supped afterward with Reboul; his daughter waited on us. Her soft and holy face seemed to me a good omen on the threshold of an unknown future.

During supper, M. Reboul spoke to me openly of his adventures as guide to the many hundred proscribed or voluntary exiles who for the last fifteen years he had concealed and conveyed from one country to another. He began by Madame de Staël, whose château of Coppet was not far from St. Cergues. The wish he felt to save his friends had insensibly led him to make a habit of that which had at first been only the impulse of his kind heart. His reputation was spread throughout France and Switzerland, and he had always been fortunate in his ventures. He attributed his success to the protection of God, which the prayers of his saintly wife and child had obtained for him. At the mention of his wife his eyes filled with tears. His daughter turned her face away, and covered it with her apron to hide her tears. "Do not let us talk of this any more to-night," said her father. " It is time to go to bed. You will stay here till to-morrow," he added, turning to me, "and I will give you the best advice I can after I have heard your story, and have found out what I can do for you." His charming daughter helped the servant to make my bed, and I went to rest to dream of the future. But the face of the Graziella of the Alps prevented my sleeping for a long time.

The next day, at day-break, I was up and ready to accompany her father. She wished me good-by, recommending me tenderly to God's care. "You are very young," she said, "to be thus thrown by yourself into an unknown future. Your mother must have many anxieties on your account!" "Ah," I replied, "I have a mother and sisters also, who pray to God for me. They are younger, but not better or purer than you." She wrung my hand, and we parted.

After having walked for some time on the brow of the mountain which the dawn had hardly yet lighted, I suddenly burst into a cry of admiration. The whole horizon of Switzerland seemed to me to be emerging from the morning mist; it was like a second creation. At our feet the Lake Leman sparkled, half in light and half in shadow. The mountains of Meilleraie and the rocky Tooth de Jaman, so wonderfully described by J. J. Rousseau, formed the barrier on the Italian side. The Valais, a country of innocence and of shepherds, seemed nestled in a little hollow to the left. Then Vevay and the Château de Chillon shone like fallen stars in the lake. Never, not even at Naples, had I seen so wonderful and glorious a spectacle. At each rung of the marvelous ladder of terraces which we began to descend, new bays, new ports, new towns, new villas, new gardens opened out on our delighted gaze. It seemed as if we were really assisting at the creation of a new world. After we had walked for about two hours, always bearing toward the left, Reboul suddenly stopped and showed me a large and imposing modern castle, which rose like a fan with its succession of terraces above the village at the head of the lake.

" Look ! " he said to me. " We will wish one another good-by here. That is the Château of Vincy, to which I have led you. I will not go any farther, for you cannot lose your way. This castle, which is one of the most beautiful on the borders of the lake, belongs to the illustrious House of Vincy, Lords of Berne — once very rich, now ruined by the vile revolution of 1799. It is now inhabited by the youngest and last brother of those who commanded the Swiss troops in the service of France, and of whom one or two passed into Holland. Some of the other members of the family are married, and have become once more French proprietors. Others have seen long service in the household of the King, while this one spends his winters at Geneva, and his summers in this old family mansion. He is the best man I know to give you the information you seek, and to put you in the way of obtaining what you wish. He has, as it were, the kernel of a little French army, composed of men who wish to fight for the cause of the King of France without joining themselves to strangers. He is, in fact, the principal Royalist agent for the French in Switzerland. Go and introduce yourself to him in my name, and ask him to look at your papers. They will tell him all. "

I thanked Reboul, sent many heartfelt good wishes to his daughter, and strolled on alone for the *château* of M. de Vincy. I was not without some uneasiness as to the manner in which I should be received, for I had only this note from Reboul, and my personal appearance was certainly not in my favor. I went down the hill, therefore, rather reluctantly, and arrived, almost with a feeling of regret, at the iron gates which led to the castle.

I pushed open the gate for myself. One felt, by the solitude and the absence of any porter or servant, the ruin which had fallen on this noble and Royalist house. I walked on till I came to a magnificent flight of steps, and was admitted by a servant, who took in my card to M. de

Vincy. He was a wizened, ill-dressed little man, and everything about him indicated a certain degree of poverty. He
made me sit down in his own room, and asked me to what
circumstance he was indebted for the honor of my visit.
I presented M. Reboul's note in answer.

"I know nothing," he replied, "at this moment, of the
state of affairs in France. The armies gathered against the
Emperor are composed of English, Prussian, Russian, Austrian, and Italian troops. There are no Frenchmen, I fear,
except a handful gathered together by the Prince de Polig-
nac in a village near Neufchâtel called La Chaux-de-Fond.
The Abbé Lafond, Malet's only accomplice, is at the head
of this little troop. I will have your passport *viséed* for
Neufchâtel."

I thanked him, and stood aside while a multitude of
people and farmers came to transact different affairs with
him, or to receive his orders. The same servant introduced
them one after the other. I saw many of these men leave
miserable little sums in copper on his desk, which was
evidently their rent, and which he counted with the anxiety
of an apparently rich man who did not know where to
turn for the necessary expenditure of the house. Everything showed the pinching of penury in the midst of external opulence. I was filled with pity for him in spite of
my admiration for his magnificent home.

When the farmers had finished their payments M. de
Vincy came back to me and gave me my passport *viséed*.
I wished him good-by, feeling more and more for his unhappy position, and took my departure. Scarcely had I
taken half a dozen steps toward the iron *grille* than a carriage drove up and stopped at the steps. Two ladies and
a little child got out of it. They were a mother and
daughter, and a pretty boy of ten or twelve years old. I
glanced at them and raised my hat as they stopped for an
instant on the lower step of the staircase, where M. de
Vincy had joined them, and was speaking to them in a
low voice. During this conversation I had turned away
and had just reached the iron gates when a soft voice recalled me. It was Madame de Vincy. "Sir," she exclaimed,
"be so kind as to come back."

20

I did so, shyly enough. When I drew near them she added, " Sir, forgive me for having called you back without having the honor of knowing you. But when M. de Vincy told me the object of your visit, I feared you might not have dined, and as we are just going to sit down to dinner, I venture to ask you to share our humble repast. There is no inn in this village, and it is three hours' march from here to Rolle. Do not refuse us the pleasure of being your hosts to-day."

I refused on the plea of my dress; but they insisted more amiably than ever, and I was compelled to yield. The dinner was served immediately; my hostess was most indulgent and kind. Madame de Vincy, the mother, was one of the most beautiful and imposing women I ever saw. She was born a princess of some sovereign house in the Palatinate, of which I have forgotten the name. The Vincys had noble birth on both sides, but Madame de Vincy did not belie her origin. Her height, which was five feet and seven inches, gave her the majesty of a goddess without taking away her grace as a mortal, and the blue eyes of a German princess impressed a certain amount of dignity even on her smile. Her face alone revealed the goodness of her heart; the sound of her voice spoke to the heart even before it charmed the ear. Her civility was indeed true Christian courtesy. Never had I seen so remarkable a face. One felt that she was a mother, and there was something filial in the emotion with which her beauty inspired me.

Her daughter, who was infinitely less beautiful but as good and sensible as her mother, was gentle and sympathizing in manner; I saw that her soul was a reflection of Madame de Vincy's, and that she was a shoot of the same stem. She was about sixteen. The boy of twelve had a fine German countenance. Madame de Vincy had two other sons, one in the Dutch service and one in the household of Louis XVIII., who had followed the King to Ghent. They were fine well-grown lads; in fact, their mother was made to bring forth noble-looking sons.

Our conversation became more and more familiar. We had plenty of subjects in common in the political aspect of the times, and in the strangeness of my own position. They insisted on hearing my history, which I related simply and naturally. I saw that it made a great impression on my hostess, and that the father and son were of the same opinion. The dinner over, I took up my little bundle, and prepared to continue my journey. " But, sir," exclaimed Madame de Vincy, " an idea strikes me. My husband tells me that you are going, at all risks, to join the little gathering of French at La Chaux-de-Fond, in the neighborhood of Neufchâtel. I highly approve of your determination not to serve your country with strange troops, who any day may become our enemies. But if you find this French corps dispersed, what do you mean to do?"

" I really don't know," I replied.

" Well, then," she rejoined, " if you can put up with such accommodation as we can offer you here, why should you not stop a few days till we can obtain some information as to the state of things at Neufchâtel, and let us, for a time, replace to you your mother and sisters?"

I colored; but my face showed the pleasure I did not dare express. The ladies understood me at once, and Mademoiselle de Vincy, at a sign from her mother, taking my little bundle from my hands, laid it on the table.

" Well," added Madame de Vincy, smiling, " try and fancy that we are your mother and sister for the moment. You will not refuse to let us shelter you for some weeks till we can see our way a little more clearly; and will you not be as comfortable here as on the high-roads, or in some bad Swiss inn? Make up your mind to stop with us, for I already feel toward you as to a son."

" Ah! madame," I exclaimed with a broken voice, " how can I resist such kindness, and go against my own heart's leanings?"

" Well, well, then it's all settled," exclaimed husband and wife at once. " We will go and order your room, and I hope you will be as comfortable or more so than at the inn of Rolle."

They gave me a room with a most glorious view over the lake of Geneva, and I found myself treated in all respects as one of the family.

From that hour my life became most enjoyable. The mother and daughter took possession of me, while M. de Vincy, busy with his domestic troubles, was painfully collecting his rents from the tenants of Vincy. I had almost forgotten the object of my journey. But I soon found that the so-called French army, which had been organized in Switzerland by the Royalist agents of the Pays de Vaud, was reduced to nothing, or contented themselves with some insignificant movements without any result. In the meantime I reveled in the enjoyment of the confidence which my circumstances and age had inspired in the bosom of a hospitable and virtuous family.

One day during my stay with them I went to dine in the little town of Nyons, to try and glean some news to bring back to my hosts at the Château of Vincy. There was at Nyons an inn dear to all old emigrants, kept by a maiden lady, who was well known in the country. Madame de Vincy gave me a line of introduction for her, and I went there for a night. She received me as an old friend. There were about thirty guests at the *table d'hôte*, at which she presided. Hardly was I seated, without any intention of being remarked by anybody, than an angry squabble arose at the other end of the table between some people who had been quietly occupied in eating their dinner in silence, and a Swiss officer belonging to the canton of Berne. I could not help listening to the quarrel, which seemed to get warmer every moment.

"No!" at last exclaimed the officer, "I am not one of those mean Frenchmen who renounce the great man who has been the origin of all their glory in Europe, and who are at this moment forming wishes for his second fall from the armies of the allies. And if you don't like my principles, you may, if you please, call me to account for them. I am ready to answer any one who chooses to contradict me."

Everybody was silent. Some of the company went away. I was the youngest, the most unknown, and the farthest from the speaker, who was at the extreme end of the long table. I therefore held my tongue, when a young man and two very pretty women who were with him, started up close to a side door which led into the dining-room. Their speaking faces, the deep frown on their foreheads, and the eager eye with which they looked up and down the room seeking for one who would answer and avenge their cause, made me instantly resolve to break the silence.

"Very well, sir," I exclaimed, rising and turning to the officer from Berne, "as no one seems disposed to answer your insolent speech, I shall take it upon myself to reply in my quality as a Frenchman. Yes, sir, I am one of those Frenchmen whom you call mean, because they believed in the reality of abdications, and in the sacred nature of treaties; and did not think that the caprice of a voluntary exile in the island of Elba could dispose at his will of France and of Europe. They still hold to these opinions; and if you wish to be answered otherwise than by words, I am ready, and will meet you where you please."

At these words a low murmur of applause ran through the whole length of the table, which went on increasing till the officer, looking thoroughly ashamed of himself, retired, and I remained confused at the praise I had unexpectedly received. I sat down quickly, rather ashamed of my easy triumph, when the too pretty women, whose presence had inspired me to speak, rushed toward me, and drawing me toward the door I have before mentioned, carried me off through the corridor of the inn to their own room, and congratulated me in the terms which I have since heard in the House of Deputies.

"We are proud, sir, to be French women," they said, "and to have by chance heard one of the youngest of our countrymen avenge our country by such words after the insults of that miserable wretch, whose only admiration is for tyranny. As to ourselves, believe that we have never made a pact with those who look upon glory as the one good, and that we hailed the restoration of the Bourbons as the return to right and liberty. Tell us who you are, and pray make use of our little apartment here while you are staying in this hotel."

They brought some punch, and I drank to the health of my enthusiastic friends; after which, thanking them warmly for their kindness, I went back to Vincy. A note from the landlady of the hotel had preceded me: my little adventure, colored by her good-nature, seemed heroic. They received me in consequence as a Royalist hero. Fortune had served me. I had defended at the same time the cause of the Bernese aristocracy, and that of the King of France.

These two ladies were Mesdames de Bellegarde, doubly famous from the part they had played during the French Revolution of 1792 and 1793, and by their enthusiasm for the restoration on the return of Louis XVIII. in 1814. Although very different in expression, they were still very beautiful, a beauty which had exposed them in former times to all the snares of human love and admiration. The eldest, the Countess de Bellegarde, had a face like that of Judith by Allori. She was tall, large, dark, with passionate black eyes, a living picture in fact of enthusiasm. The youngest, also tall and with a beautiful figure, was a great contrast to her sister; she was fair, delicate, and sensitive, with blue dreamy eyes, which often wore an expression of great sadness. They were natives of Sardinia, the daughters of a Count de Bellegarde, and had been left orphans very young. Their father had been in the service of the House of Austria, and their name had long been distinguished among the generals whom the Emperor was fond of selecting from the Italian states, such as the Montecuculli and others. Left in the country home of their ancestors during the beginning of the French Revolution, they lived in a magnificent *château* called Des Marches, in the midst of the beautiful valley of Grésivaudan. After having conquered Savoy and Geneva, the revolutionary general, De Montesquieu (then in the full height of his power, though soon after proscribed), had taken refuge in the mountains of Switzerland, to wait for better times, and the province of Savoy had been given up to the proconsul Hérault de Séchelles. Before the days of the Convention, Hérault had been a magistrate and a philosopher, and a model of honorable and high-principled conduct. His beautiful face and figure resembled that of Antinous; he was the "Barbarossa" of the aristocracy. Elected unanimously by the legislative assembly, he had obtained a high position there, not only by his eloquence and the dignity of his bearing, but by his Jacobin enthusiasm. With his great zeal, his voice, and his expressive face, he became the idol of the neophytes of those days; but, insensibly dragged on by the revolutionary torrent beyond his own convictions, he had, like Le Pelletier de St. Fargeau, yielded to the popular tumult, and sacrificed the King to the exigencies and barbaric violence of the republic. Popular favor, however, had rewarded him for this weak compliance as if it had been a virtue. Sent soon after to republican Savoy, he was at the same time a conqueror and conquered: he came to the Château of Marches, and saw these two beautiful orphans without a guardian or protector; the one in all the splendor of her grown-up beauty, the other with all the tender grace of budding girlhood. A passionate love for the Countess de Bellegarde took possession of his heart; while his burning eloquence inspired these young girls with an enthusiasm for his own opinions. The two sisters had been introduced by him as models to the fanatical people of those provinces. A little later he became unpopular with his party from his moderation, and Hérault de Séch elles followed Danton to the scaffold, and died an honest republican, a victim to the crimes of the people.

The Countess of Bellegarde and her innocent sister wished to share his fate; but even these brutal judges, dazzled by their youth and beauty, would not condemn them. They had lived ever since that time in the Château of Marches, sharing in the society around them, and in the reaction against the Terrorists, of whom they had so nearly been the victims. The events of the 20th of March had revolted them; they had quitted their *château* and come to Nyons to live with the Royalists. It was thus that I first became acquainted with them, and in their enthusiastic declarations I recognized the pupils of him in whose political school they had been brought up.

Two days after, I resolved to profit by my near neighborhood to see, at least once before her death, Madame de Staël, who had long been the object of my antipathy on account of her father, and of my enthusiasm as regarded herself. Coppet, which was the abode of M. Necker, had been previously bought by my grandfather, who had kept it a long time without living in it; but all of a sudden the canton of Berne passed a law refusing the rights of proprietorship to any Catholic; so that he ceded it to I know not whom, and bought in its stead the beautiful castle of Ursy, in Burgundy. I felt that it would hardly be right for me, as a guest of the Vincys, to go and introduce myself at the Château of Coppet as a pilgrim at the tomb of M. Necker, whom it was impossible for me to admire or to love. "I should be wanting to two persons," I said: "to Madame de Vincy and to myself. I will not go!" Only, as the high-road is the property of everybody, I thought a cat might look at a king, and that a glimpse of her would satisfy without compromising me. I knew that Madame de Staël went twice a week to Geneva with certain friends of hers, among whom were two beautiful women, one Madame Récamier, her great friend, exiled, like her, from all countries under the dominion of the Emperor; the other, Mlle. de Constant, a German, of still wider reputation; but, at this period of my life, the admiration of genius extinguished all other in my heart.

I got up, therefore, very early one Saturday, which was the day they told me Madame de Staël made her weekly expedition to Geneva, and putting a piece of bread in my pocket, I hid myself at a turn of the road from Coppet to Geneva, being partly concealed by a great ditch on the high-road, by the side of which her carriage must necessarily pass. I remained there from nine o'clock in the morning till two o'clock in the afternoon, hidden by the shrubs at the side of the road; during which time I amused myself by reading "Corinne" (that beautiful work of that modern Sappho), and listening with a quick ear to the least sound of a carriage coming from Coppet. In spite of the poetic interest of this beautiful book on Italy, the day appeared to me rather long, and I at last determined to quit my hiding-place, when to my great joy I heard the rolling of two carriages, which left me no doubt as to their occupants. They passed like the wind; the first contained only two gentlemen with Mlle. Constant; a beautiful person in the flower of her age. I could only, however, snatch one look at her, which was followed by an involuntary cry of admiration. The next carriage, which was an open one, contained two women, whom it was impossible not to recognize. One was Madame Récamier, whose angelic face could bear no other name, and of whom it was said that one look sufficed to bind your heart to her forever; but her beauty, although it dazzled, did not distract me. Her companion, who was speaking to her in a loud voice, was, however, the person of whom I was in search. I had time to take in her features thoroughly, for the horses slacked their speed at a little rise there was in the ground. Madame de Staël was, as usual, dressed in an Indian turban, of which the varied and well-assorted colors seemed to be magically reflected upon her forehead. The forehead was large, prominent, and high, as if to give space to a whole world of thought and new ideas; it shaded to prominent eyes of magnificent shape and brilliancy; all her expression, in fact, lay in these eyes; they spoke more than her mouth. Her nose was short and finely shaped; her lips thick and open, made for eloquence or for love; her complexion was pale, but brightened by a look of inspiration. Her arms, which were always in movement, and exposed by short, open sleeves, were white and magnificent; her whole person, though large, was not wanting in a grace which called forth admiration; in fact, it commanded it. The little hill had been climbed. The horses started again at a trot, and nothing remained to me but the dust they left behind them. Genius had passed me with its escort of beauty; but what remained on one's memory was the genius. I could not finish the volume of "Corinne" after having seen its author! I came back very late and found my friends waiting for me for supper. I was obliged to own to Madame de Vincy what had been the cause of my long absence. "Why did you not tell me of your very natural admiration?" replied this noble woman; "in spite of some differences of opinion, we have for Madame de Staël as much enthusiasm as yourself. We would have taken and introduced you to her. It is impossible to see without admiring her, or to be her neighbor without loving her. Her faults are those of her training and her wit; her good qualities belong to her own heart; the foundation of all her glory is really her goodness." " No," I replied to my kind hostess. " I would rather have seen her quietly without knowing her; I have had a glimpse of genius, and it was as rapid and fugitive as itself;" and then we began to talk of other things.

I had spent three weeks in this delightful house in a delicious intimacy with the Vincy family; but I knew the extreme poverty of the house, and I was afraid of being indiscreet, and perhaps burdensome. I settled, therefore, to delay no longer my start for Neufchâtel and La Chaux-de-Fond, to seek the French royalist military gathering. They smiled at my enthusiasm, but they let me go. A gentleman from Lyons, who was a great agriculturist, came in the same way that I had done to present himself to Monsieur de Vincy, and gave me a pretext for departure. I took leave of my kind and generous hosts with a pang; it appeared to me as if I were again parting from my own family. Madame and Mlle. de Vincy had tears in their eyes at wishing me good-by. I started with my Lyons companion, but promised to return if the gathering at La Chaux-de-Fond disappointed my expectations. At Rollo we chartered a kind of Swiss car to conduct us to Neufchâtel. Our *vetturino* brought us there in three days, the road winding round the base of the Jura mountains, amidst the most beautiful scenery possible, with the Lakes Leman, Yverdun, and of Neufchâtel to the right, and grand rocks and pine forests to the left. We were perfectly charmed with our expedition, and as our opinions were identical, there was nothing in our conversation to mar our enjoyment of this magnificent scenery. The first question we asked on arriving at the hotel at Neufchâtel was about the French military gathering at La Chaux-de-Fond. No one had an idea of what we meant! I began to fear our royalist visions would vanish in smoke. My companion was so discouraged that he decided to return to his Lyons property. I, however, was determined to persevere in the search, and next day started on foot for La Chaux-de-Fond. The path led through a beautiful forest of sombre pines and magnificent waterfalls, and I did not arrive there till the morning

of the following day.   La Chaux-de-Fond was then a poor little
Swiss village, situated on the extreme frontiers of France,
and inhabited by peasants who were all clock-makers.   Its
picturesque wooden houses were scattered here and there
over the plain which led to the pine wood.   My appearance and dress were rather those of a journeyman watch-
maker, who was coming to seek employment from one of
the clock-makers in the district.   I went into the first
public-house I came to, and asked for the address of the
head of the staff of the French army.   The people looked
at one another with surprise, and after having said something in a *patois* unintelligible to me, concluded with a
smile that I was wishing to find a French priest named
L'Abbé Lafond, who had been living in the only decent
hotel in the village for one or two months, and to whose
lodging they proposed to conduct me.   I began to doubt
the existence of a staff corps, which thus disappeared like a
mirage, and which seemed to be represented by an abbé in
a wild village on the side of the Alps; however, having
come so far, I was determined to see, and I saw.   What
was called the great hotel of La Chaux-de-Fond was a little
house at the end of a long solitary street, on the opposite
side to that by which I had come into the village.   A
young girl, who had volunteered to be my guide, said smiling to the innkeeper, " Here is a gentleman who is looking for the French army; they told him at our house
that its head-quarters were with you, and that its general was L'Abbé Lafond! "   " It's quite true, " replied
the innkeeper; " we have got here a gentleman who calls
himself the Abbé Lafond, but who says he is a major-general
in the French army.   If you, sir, " he added, turning to
me, " wish to speak to him, I will go and ask him to come
down-stairs; in the meantime, here is a little table with
some fresh bread and cheese, and beer, to refresh you after
your hot walk. "   They brought me, accordingly, this primitive breakfast, and I sat down to eat it in the best parlor of
the little inn.

I was hardly seated at the table, however, before I saw
a little man with a beaming face, between thirty and forty
years of age, come rapidly down a little wooden staircase.

"Oh! there is Monsieur l'Abbé Lafond," exclaimed the servant, and she brought him to where I was sitting. He was
dressed in a brown great-coat, which was half military, half
ecclesiastical. His black stockings carefully drawn up over
his well-made calves, reminded one of a priest; while the
black cravat and military collar made me fancy that he was
an officer. He thus represented a double character, the ecclesiastic below and the soldier above; he was, in fact,
made to suit every taste. I got up and bowed, while he
came forward smiling, and asked me, "What had brought
me to see him in this out-of-the-way part of the world?"
I begged him to sit down. He said he would breakfast
with me, and ordered some eggs, and we entered into conversation while filling our glasses with beer. "You have
come from Monsieur de Vincy," he said to me at last.
"Here is a letter from him," I replied. He read it, and
then said quietly; "This is just what I had supposed." I
continued: "I am come to join the little army which is
being organized, I am told, under your orders, at La Chaux-
de-Fond. I will not serve with strangers against France,
but I am dying to fight for the King against the Emperor;
where is the army?" "The army!" he exclaimed; "why,
it is I! there is no other. Was not I alone, two years
ago, the army of a general, who, with the help of a single
man, put a whole ministry in prison, and an empire in his
pocket? Men after all are nothing; it is the idea which is
all in all; the idea is mine, and if I can persuade every
one from here to Besançon (as I have done) that a formidable army has been formed on this frontier, ready to act
when the time comes, is it not as useful, and as much
dreaded by the enemy as if indeed numberless battalions
were prepared to enter France by this route, to bear succor
to the Royalists? Without money, without pay, without
soldiers, without arms, I keep a whole province in check,
and paralyze both Besançon and Belfort. You see that you
come yourself to join us, and you find only a head instead
of arms; believe me, it is enough; stay with me, we shall
be two instead of one; and when the Emperor has been
defeated in the open fields by the armies of Europe, we
shall have been believed to have led a general insurrection,

and the East of France will think that their deliverance is owing to us." I fairly burst out laughing. "From this statement, Monsieur l'Abbé, am I to imagine that shadows are as powerful as bodies, and that imagination surpasses reality?" He replied: "Have I not already clearly proved in 1813, that if General Hulin had consented to allow himself to be convinced by a ball in his jaw that the Emperor was dead, the empire would have died in reality?" "You are right, Monsieur l'Abbé," I answered; "but a surprise is not a revolution. Some man comes, more curious, or perhaps, you will say, more obstinate than others. Instead of a well-appointed army he finds nothing but an ecclesiastic; and if he does not want to pass for an adventurer, he blows upon the shadow, and its nothingness is made apparent. Let us have our breakfast together in peace, and I will take leave of you afterward. I shall not believe again so lightly in representations from a distance, and shall content myself with waiting; while you must be satisfied with my good wishes." He saw that his army would never arrive at more than one man; but he comforted himself by giving me all the details of Malet's conspiracy, in which he had played the principal part. Fifteen or twenty innocent Bonapartists had been shot to convince the Emperor of the reality of the conspiracy; the Abbé Lafond, who was the only guilty one, escaped. He evidently hoped to play the same game a second time; but I refused to act as his second. I must do him the justice to say, that he was a man of wonderful genius and resources. When he was the chaplain of a madhouse close to one where General Malet was expiating a previous sentence, he felt that he wanted a soldier to pull the strings of a military conspiracy, and persuaded him to undertake it. He had but one man, it is true, but he very nearly succeeded. He was confident of succeeding again, but miracles do not happen twice in a man's life. It was impossible to hear any one relate a story which one might think little to the credit of an ecclesiastic, with more confidence in the purity of his motives. He was really a master in political intrigue; but he had not the art of varying his subject; he always played the same tune. After having studied him for one whole evening, although immensely

struck by his genius, I left him the next day without
regret, and went back to Neufchâtel, my illusory search
after military glory being dispelled. I came back by Berne
to the Château de Vincy, where I gave them a full account
of the puerilities of the Abbé Lafond. I always wonder
what has become of him since, but I never could find out.
He lives, and probably conspires still. I have always been
astonished not to hear of him as having been shot in some
great conspiracy strangled at the birth; but I believe that
there is a special Providence which watches over men of
this sort, and that L'Abbé Lafond will probably go to his
grave in peace.

At Paris, the Emperor could not live long on the conspiracy of Elba, and the Royalists and Liberals gave him
little time to decide on any line of conduct. He was continually promising reforms; but his only real hope was in
the army. Before he was really ready, he made up his
mind to take the field. Waterloo was to cut the knot;
that day, so fatal to military France, was drawing near!
In the meanwhile I resolved to pass into Savoy on the
other side of the lake.

There was a boatman in the Savoyard village of Narnier
who spent his time in ferrying over the inhabitants of the
two countries, from the Swiss to the Savoyard side of the
lake. He was known to Mademoiselle ——, the mistress
of the hotel where the Mesdames Bellegarde lived. I took
leave a second time, therefore, of my kind hostesses at the
Château de Vincy, and went to Nyons. I begged the mistress of the inn to recommend me to the boatman of Narnier as a good Royalist flying from Imperial France, and
only wishing to live in peace until the political horizon
brightened. The boatman, himself a devoted Royalist, consented on these terms to ferry me over. I embarked in
his little open felucca, which was loaded with cattle, toward the end of June; but it was one of those stormy
days which made the Lake Leman as tempestuous as the
Archipelago. We had, in consequence, a very dangerous
crossing, and the waves increasing in violence as we approached the shores of Savoy, prolonged our voyage till far
into the night. Luckily, one billow, larger than the rest,

threw us safely on the sand. At Narnier I went to lodge in the house of the boatman himself, who consented to shelter me for some hours. During supper I asked him if there were any lodgings in this place which would receive me at a very low price, for my journey to Neufchâtel and Berne had made a great hole in my fifty pounds; and if my exile were to be prolonged some time longer, I began to think I must pass over to England or to Russia, and earn my bread by teaching French. The boatman spoke to his daughter (a young woman of about twenty years of age) about a little empty house on the borders of the lake, which had been used as a guard-house by the custom-house officers of the King of Sardinia until the breaking out of the war; but which he would be very willing to let to me if I could content myself with such humble accommodation, and if the hay of his poor neighbors, which he yearly deposited there, was no inconvenience to me. "The house," he said, turning to me, "is about a quarter of an hour's walk from Narnier: if this arrangement should be agreeable to you, I would let you the apartment for two-pence-halfpenny a day, and would feed you for sevenpence halfpenny a meal; without meat certainly, but with excellent bread, lake trout, and cheese." That would come to ten-pence a day, and his proposal suited not only my purse, but fully satisfied my love of solitude; so that the bargain was struck, and the very next day his daughter took me to my new quarters.

On leaving the village of Narnier, an unfrequented little path leads across some beautiful meadows by the side of the lake. After walking for some minutes in silence with my guide, I heard the regular noise of the waves of the lake grating on the rocky promontories, and dying away softly on the yellow sand of the shore, while the fresh breeze from the lake refreshed my whole frame. At a little distance I perceived a square and solitary building very much like the hull of a shipwrecked vessel; the walls on the shore-side had only a low door, which was partly hidden by a group of osiers; on the water-side was a little window, low and narrow, like a loophole, from whence you could watch the lake without being yourself observed.

Window and door, all was shut; there was no sign of life
about the place, nor a sound in the house or out of it; it
reminded one of the dwelling of a leper in the Middle
Ages, such as Xavier de Maistre described in his "Solitude"
some months before; only there was no leper. "Here is
the house, sir," said the young boat-woman to me, not,
however, without a look of some anxiety, as if she were
afraid that the mournful appearance of everything would
disgust me with the place.

While speaking she put a great wooden key into the lock,
and the heavy door rolled on its hinges. A bat, the only
inhabitant of the place, flew in my face, blindly knocking
its wings against the wall; but I was not thereby dismayed,
and we went up-stairs to the only room in the house, which
had served as the head-quarters of the custom-house officer.
The room was not more than eight or ten feet in diameter,
with the exception of a window, which remained open to
give some air to the forage. Everything was full of hay.
"This is the room," said hesitatingly and modestly the girl;
then, as if ashamed to offer so extraordinary a lodging to
a stranger, she hastily added, "But of course, it will be
emptied and cleaned; and we shall put a nice bed and
table in the place of the hay." As she spoke she gave un-
intentionally a little kick with her sabot to the dried grass
before us, and out rushed a whole army of mice, which began racing about the room. "Oh! what pleasant bed-fel-
lows," I said, laughingly, to the girl: "Bats and rats!
Well," I added, after a few minutes, putting my head out
of the window and contemplating the beautiful waves which
dashed gently against the walls of the cottage, the glorious
scenery of the mountains of the Pays de Vaud in front of
me, and the two promontories which formed the bay of
Narnier, "well, I find the house charming, and I will take
it." Her face expanded with pride and satisfaction, while I
sat quietly down on the hay. "I don't want any other
bed," I continued; "a pair of sheets and a counterpane are
all I need; I shall do very well here. I am used to cam-
paigning, and the smell of the hay is rather pleasant to
me than otherwise. Are you married mademoiselle?" "No,
sir," she replied; "my father is a widower and old. He

would remain quite alone here if I were to leave him ; there would be nobody in the house to make his soup; no one in the boat to mend his sails ; no one at the helm to guide the rudder. I could not make up my mind to leave my father." "You are a good and noble girl," I answered, "and God will bless you for it." I looked at her with an expression which seemed to say, "Any man would have been happy to have won so fair a face." She rowed me quietly back, without speaking, to her father's house. "I will bring you some fresh bread and milk and cheese every morning for your breakfast," she said, as we landed ; "and I will fry your fish and make you some coffee at home for your dinner ; that is all I can do, I am afraid as I am not a great 'artiste' ; you will forgive, monsieur, such plain country fare ; it is not like the inn at Nyons, you see ! "

The boatman was very much pleased to find that his strange little house on the lake would answer my purpose. Everything was arranged that evening to my satisfaction. I dined at Narnier with my host, and in the evening I went and installed myself in my new abode. All my baggage went in a pocket-handkerchief, and consisted of some books brought from Nyons and a pair of pocket-pistols, which I placed in front of my window. I slept on the hay as one sleeps at eighteen. The troubled mice ran about all night, trying to find their accustomed holes, and the bats cried out at dawn of day ; but that only showed me that I was not alone. The swallows knocked their wings against my window early in the morning, and were very much astonished to find the panes of glass which had been put in the night before by the young boat-woman. I got up and opened the window, and they flew fearlessly about my room ; then I took my pencil, and looking beyond the lake to the little white speck which marked the Château of Vincy, I wrote the following verses : —

> *Pourquoi me fuir, passagère hirondelle ?*
> *Viens reposer ton aile auprès de moi.*
>
> *Pourquoi me fuir quand un ami t'appelle ?*
> *Ne suis-je pas voyageur comme toi ? etc.*

The daughter of the boatman came to knock at my door at the very moment I was finishing these verses, which I mentally addressed to Vincy. I gave them to nobody, and I was very much astonished some years after to hear them sung at Paris and attributed to Monsieur de Châteaubriand. They were not worth his while to disown, nor mine to claim. We all remember his touching romance,

> Ma sœur, te souviens-tu encore
> Du château que baignait la Dore,
> Et de cette tant vielle Tour
> Du More,
> Ou l'airain sonnait le retour
> Dù jour?

Châteaubriand was a great poet in prose, and I was nothing but the nightingale stammering by chance a plaintive air in my solitude. . . .

I continued to live alone in my empty dwelling with my dumb companions. Oh! how happy I should have been if Providence had granted me a dog! One, at last, came to me from a castle near Narnier, who attached himself to me because I petted him, and he found me alone. Whenever a person is unhappy, God sends him a dog; I have proved it twenty times, although man does not always perceive it. The moment the dog adopted me, my solitude ceased; for he never left me. We loved one another, and so we walked, eat, and slept together; and he understood me as thoroughly as I did him. I had now two friends, the dog and the boatman's daughter, and my days were calm, peaceful, and delicious.

The news of the battle of Waterloo came to me one morning in a little boat rowed by a messenger from Madame de Vincy. I watched it at sunrise out of my window like a seagull whose wings are colored by the rays of the morning, never dreaming that this little skiff bore for me a new fate — the fate of the whole world. The boat grounded on the sand; I put my head out of the window and the messenger asked me if I knew a young Frenchman who had taken refuge at Narnier? I replied that I was the person of whom he was in search. He gave me directly a long letter from Madame de Vincy, and a quantity of newspapers from Geneva. The letter ran thus: " I do not know whether you will be able to rejoice at the misfortunes of your countrymen ; but as far as we are concerned we cannot help being delighted at the victory of Europe over tyranny. Bonaparte has been bitterly punished for his rash enterprise ; he has been entirely defeated and put to flight at Quatre Bras. He is already at Paris, and has no longer any army. Oceans of blood have flowed on all sides, — the French are completly beaten ; our own son is badly wounded ; but the world is saved. I send you all the details in the inclosed packet of newspapers ; send them back to us." The boat was moored to the shore ; the morning breeze carried off the letter. I fell eagerly on the papers which were at my feet but I could scarcely sit still and read of our disasters. It was impossible to rejoice at the destruction of the whole French army ; but, if Bonaparte had won, the cause of the King would have been lost. I was silent and undecided from conflicting emotions. Finally I burst into tears. Was it from sorrow as a Frenchman, or from joy as a partisan ? I could not explain this even to myself. Every one will understand this conflict of feeling ; but no one can express it : my tears said what words could not. This is the misfortune of the bad actions into which the ambition of one man drags his country. . . .

ROMANCE

SALAMMBO

GUSTAVE FLAUBERT

GUSTAVE FLAUBERT

THE appearance of "Madame Bovary" in 1857 started the realistic movement which ran to the verge of a craze. Its photographic fidelity to life, including trivial details which, in less able hands, would have overwhelmed the dramatic interest, drew public attention to its method and tendency. A prosecution was instituted but failed, and the author was justified in the public eye.

In 1862 he issued the powerful romance of ancient Carthage which bears the name of "Salammbo," its heroine. Flaubert had qualified himself for the writing of this remarkable work by residence in Africa and long studies in archæology and history. It, too, is realistic in the strongest sense Once read it remains a fixed picture in the memory. Flaubert was a favorite pupil of Balzac. Nothing is hurried or merely sketched. There is at least the genius of infinite painstaking in all his work, and its impressive massiveness will insure its permanence among the masterpieces of the century. Flaubert was born in 1821 and died in 1880.

SALAMMBO

THE moon was rising just above the waves, and on the town which was still wrapped in darkness there glittered white and luminous specks — the pole of a chariot, a dangling rag of linen, the corner of a wall, or a golden necklace on the bosom of a god. The glass balls on the roofs of the temple beamed like great diamonds here and there. But ill-defined ruins, piles of black earth, and gardens formed deeper masses in the gloom, and below Malqua fishermen's nets stretched from one house to another like gigantic bats spreading their wings. The grinding of the hydraulic wheels which conveyed water to the highest stories of the palaces, was no longer heard; and the camels lying ostrich fashion on their stomachs, rested peacefully in the middle of the terraces. The porters were asleep in the streets on the thresholds of the houses; the shadows of the colossuses stretched across the deserted squares; occasionally in the distance the smoke of a still burning sacrifice would escape through the bronze tiling, and the heavy breeze would waft the odors of aromatics blended with the scent of the sea and the exhalation from the sun-heated walls. The motionless waves shone around Carthage, for the moon was spreading her light at once upon the mountain-circled gulf and upon the lake of Tunis, where flamingoes formed long rose-colored lines amid the banks of sand, while further on beneath the catacombs the great salt lagoon shimmered like a piece of silver. The blue vault of heaven sank on the horizon in one direction into the dustiness of the plains, and in the other into the mists of the sea, and on the summit of the Acropolis, the pyramidal cypress trees, fringing the temple of Eschmoun, swayed murmuring like the regular waves that beat slowly along the mole beneath the ramparts.

Salammbo ascended to the terrace of her palace, supported by a female slave who carried an iron dish filled with live coals.

In the middle of the terrace there was a small ivory bed covered with lynx skins, and cushions made with the feathers of the parrot, a fatidical animal consecrated to the gods, and at the four corners rose four long perfuming-pans filled with nard, incense, cinnamomum, and myrrh. The slave lit the perfumes. Salammbo looked at the polar star; she slowly saluted the four points of heaven, and knelt down on the ground in the azure dust which was strewn with golden stars in imitation of the firmament. Then with both elbows against her sides, her fore-arms straight and her hands open, she threw back her head beneath the rays of the moon, and said : —

" O, Rabetna — Baalet — Tanith ! " and her voice was lengthened in a plaintive fashion as though to call some one. " Anaïtis ! Astarte ! Derceto ! Astoreth ! Mylitta ! Athara ! Elissa ! Tiratha ! By the hidden symbols — by the resounding sistra — by the furrows of the earth — by the eternal silence and by the eternal fruitfulness — mistress of the gloomy sea and of the azure shores. O ! Queen of the watery world, all hail ! "

She swayed her whole body twice or thrice, and then cast herself face downward in the dust with both arms outstretched.

But the slave nimbly raised her, for according to the rites some one must catch the suppliant at the moment of his prostration; this told him that the gods accepted him, and Salammbo's nurse never failed in this pious duty.

Some merchants from Darytian Gætulia had brought her to Carthage when quite young, and after her enfranchisement she would not forsake her old masters as was shown by her right ear, which was pierced with a large hole. A petticoat of many-colored stripes fitted closely on her hips, and fell to her ankles, where two tin rings clashed together. Her somewhat flat face was yellow like her tunic. Silver bodkins of great length formed a sun behind her head. She wore a coral button on the nostril, and she stood beside the bed more erect than a Hermes, and with her eyelids cast down.

Salammbo walked to the edge of the terrace; her eyes swept the horizon for an instant, and then were lowered upon the sleeping town, while the sigh that she heaved swelled her bosom, and gave an undulating movement to the whole length of the long white simar which hung without clasp or girdle about her. Her curved and painted sandals were hidden beneath a heap of emeralds, and a net of purple thread was filled with her disordered hair.

But she raised her head to gaze upon the moon, and murmured, mingling her speech with fragments of hymns:

"How lightly turnest thou supported by the impalpable ether! It brightens about thee, and 'tis the stir of thine agitation that distributes the winds and fruitful dews. According as thou dost wax and wane the eyes of cats and spots of panthers lengthen or grow short. Wives shriek thy name in the pangs of childbirth! Thou makest the shells to swell, the wine to bubble, and the corpse to putrefy! Thou formest the pearls at the bottom of the sea!

"And every germ, O Goddess! ferments in the dark depths of thy moisture.

"When thou appearest, quietness is spread abroad upon the earth; the flowers close, the waves are soothed, wearied man stretches his breast toward thee, and the world with its oceans and mountains looks at itself in thy face as in a mirror. Thou art white, gentle, luminous, immaculate, helping, purifying, serene!"

The crescent of the moon was then over the mountain of the Hot Springs, in the hollow formed by its two summits, on the other side of the gulf. Below it there was a little star, and all around it a pale circle. Salammbo went on: —

"But thou art a terrible mistress! Monsters, terrifying phantoms, and lying dreams come from thee; thine eyes devour the stones of buildings, and the apes are ever ill each time thou growest young again.

"Whither goest thou? Why dost thou change thy forms continually? Now, slender and curved thou glidest through space like a mastless galley; and then, amid the stars, thou art like a shepherd keeping his flock. Shining and round, thou dost graze the mountain-tops like the wheel of a chariot.

"O, Tanith! thou dost love me? I have looked so much on thee! But no! thou sailest through thine azure, and I—I remain on the motionless earth.

"Taanach, take your nebal and play softly on the silver string, for my heart is sad!"

The slave lifted a sort of harp of ebony wood, taller than herself, and triangular in shape like a delta; she fixed the point in a crystal globe, and with both arms began to play.

The sounds followed one another hurried and deep, like the buzzing of bees, and with increasing sonorousness floated away into the night with the complaining of the waves, and the rustling of the great trees on the summit of the Acropolis.

"Hush!" cried Salammbo.

"What ails you, mistress? The blowing of the breeze, the passing of a cloud, everything disquiets you just now!"

"I do not know," she said.

"You are wearied with too long prayers!"

"Oh! Taanach, I would fain be dissolved in them like a flower in wine!"

"Perhaps it is the smoke of your perfumes?"

"No!" said Salammbo; "the spirit of the gods dwells in fragrant odors."

Then the slave spoke to her of her father. It was thought that he had gone toward the amber country, behind the pillars of Melkarth. "But if he does not return," she said, "you must nevertheless, since it was his will, choose a husband among the sons of the Ancients, and then your grief will pass away in a man's arms."

"Why?" asked the young girl. All those that she had seen had horrified her with their fallow-deer laughter and their coarse limbs.

"Sometimes, Taanach, from the depths of my being there exhale as it were hot fumes heavier than the vapors from a volcano. Voices call me, a globe of fire rolls and mounts within my bosom, it stifles me, I am at the point of death; and then, something sweet, flowing from my brow to my feet, passes through my flesh — it is a caress enfolding me, and I feel myself crushed as though a god were stretched upon me. Oh! would that I could lose myself in the mists of the night, the waters of the fountains, the sap of the trees, that I could issue from my body, and be but a breath, or a ray, and glide, mount up to thee, O, Mother!"

She raised her arms to their full length, arching her form, which in its long garment was as pale and light as the moon. Then she fell back, panting on the ivory couch; but Taanach passed an amber necklace with dolphin's teeth about her neck to banish terrors, and Salammbo said in an almost stifled voice: "Go and bring me Scha-habarim."

Her father had not wished her to enter the college of priestesses, nor even to be made at all acquainted with the popular Tanith. He was reserving her for some alliance that might serve his political ends; so that Salammbo lived alone in the midst of the palace. Her mother was long since dead.

She had grown up with abstinences, fastings, and purifi-cations, always surrounded by grave and exquisite things, her body saturated with perfumes, and her soul filled with prayers. She had never tasted wine, nor eaten meat, nor touched an unclean animal, nor set her heels in the house of death.

She knew nothing of obscene images, for as each god was manifested in different forms, the same principle often received the witness of contradictory cults, and Salammbo worshiped the Goddess in her sidereal presentation. An influence had descended upon the maiden from the moon; when the planet passed diminishing away, Salammbo grew weak. She languished the whole day long, and revived at evening. During an eclipse she had nearly died.

But Rabetna, in jealousy, revenged herself for the virgin-ity withdrawn from her sacrifices, and she tormented Sa-lammbo with possessions, all the stronger for being vague, which were spread through this belief and excited by it.

Unceasingly was Hamilcar's daughter disquieted about Tanith. She had learned her adventures, her travels, and all her names, which she would repeat without their having any distinct signification for her. In order to penetrate into the depths of her dogma, she wished to become acquainted, in the most secret part of the temple, with the old idol in the magnificent mantle, whereon depended the destinies of Carthage, for the idea of a god did not stand out clearly from his representation, and to hold, or even see the image of one, was to take away part of his virtue, and in a measure to rule him.

But Salammbo turned round. She had recognized the sound of the golden bells which Schahabarim wore at the hem of his garment.

He ascended the staircase; then at the threshold of the terrace he stopped and folded his arms.

His sunken eyes shone like the lamps of a sepulchre; his long thin body floated in its linen robe which was weighted by the bells, the latter alternating with balls of emeralds at his heels. He had feeble limbs, an oblique skull, and a pointed chin; his skin seemed cold to the touch, and his yellow face, which was deeply furrowed with wrinkles, was as though contracted in a longing, in an everlasting grief.

He was the high priest of Tanith, and it was he who had educated Salammbo.

"Speak!" he said. "What will you?"

"I hoped—you had almost promised me—" She stammered and was confused; then suddenly: "Why do you despise me? what have I forgotten in the rites? You are my master, and you told me that no one was so accomplished in the things pertaining to the Goddess as I; but there are some of which you will not speak. Is it so, O father?"

Schahabarim remembered Hamilcar's orders, and replied: "No, I have nothing more to teach you!"

"A Genius," she resumed, "impels me to this love. I have climbed the steps of Eschmoun, god of the planets and intelligences; I have slept beneath the golden olive of Melkarth, patron of the Tyrian colonies; I have pushed open the doors of Baal-Khamon, the enlightener and fertilizer; I have sacrificed to the subterranean Kabiri, to the gods of woods, winds, rivers, and mountains; but, can you understand? they are all too far away, too high, too insensible, while she — I feel her mingled in my life; she fills my soul, and I quiver with inward startings, as though she were leaping in order to escape. Methinks I am about to hear her voice, and see her face, lightnings dazzle me and then I sink again into the darkness."

Schahabarim was silent. She entreated him with suppliant looks. At last he made a sign for the dismissal of the slave, who was not of Chanaanitish race. Taanach disappeared and, Schahabarim, raising one arm in the air, began: —

"Before the gods darkness alone was, and a breathing stirred dull and indistinct as the conscience of a man in a dream. It contracted, creating Desire and Cloud, and from Desire and Cloud there issued primitive Matter. This was a water, muddy, black, icy, and deep. It contained senseless monsters, incoherent portions of the forms to be born, which are painted on the walls of the sanctuaries.

"Then Matter condensed. It became an egg. It burst. One half formed the earth and the other the firmament. Sun, moon, winds, and clouds appeared, and at the crash of the thunder intelligent creatures awoke. Then Eschmoun spread himself in the starry sphere; Khamon beamed in the sun; Melkarth thrust him with his arms behind Gades; the Kabiri descended beneath the volcanoes, and Rabetna like a nurse bent over the world pouring out her light like milk, and her night like a mantle."

"And then" she said.

He had related the secret of the origins to her, to divert her from sublimer prospects; but the maiden's desire kindled again at his last words, and Schahabarim, half yielding resumed: —

"She inspires and governs the loves of men."

"The loves of men!" repeated Salammbo dreamily.

"She is the soul of Carthage," continued the priest; "and although she is everywhere diffused, it is here that she dwells, beneath the sacred veil."

"O father!" cried Salammbo, "I shall see her, shall I not? you will bring me to her! I had long been hesitating;

I am devoured with curiosity to see her form. Pity! help me! let us go?"

He repulsed her with a vehement gesture that was full of pride.

"Never! Do you not know that it means death? The hermaphrodite Baals are unveiled to us alone who are men in understanding and women in weakness. Your desire is sacrilege; be satisfied with the knowledge that you possess!"

She fell upon her knees placing two fingers against her ears in token of repentance; and crushed by the priest's words, and filled at once with anger against him, with terror and with humiliation, she burst into sobs. Schahabarim remained erect, and more insensible than the stones of the terrace. He looked down upon her quivering at his feet, and felt a kind of joy on seeing her suffer for his divinity whom he himself could not wholly embrace. The birds were already singing, a cold wind was blowing, and little clouds were drifting in the paling sky.

Suddenly he perceived on the horizon, behind Tunis, what looked like slight mists trailing along the ground; then these became a great curtain of dust extending perpendicularly, and, amid the whirlwinds of the thronging mass, dromedaries' heads, lances, and shields appeared. It was the army of the Barbarians advancing upon Carthage.

BATTLE OF THE MACARAS

THEN Hamilcar grew extraordinarily pale, and those who were leaning over the pit outside saw him resting one hand against the wall to keep himself from falling.

But the jackal uttered its cry three times in succession. Hamilcar raised his head; he did not speak a word nor make a gesture. Then when the sun had completely set he disappeared behind the nopal hedge, and in the evening he said as he entered the assembly of the Rich in the temple of Eschmoun:—

" Luminaries of the Baalim, I accept the command of the Punic forces against the army of the Barbarians ! "

On the following day he drew two hundred and twenty-three thousand kikars of gold from the Syssitia, and decreed a tax of fourteen shekels upon the Rich. Even the women contributed ; payment was made on behalf of the children, and he compelled the colleges of priests to furnish money — a monstrous thing according to Carthaginian customs.

He demanded all the horses, mules, and arms. A few tried to conceal their wealth, and their property was sold ; and, to intimidate the avarice of the rest, he himself gave sixty suits of armor, and fifteen hundred gomers of meal, which was as much as was given by the Ivory Company.

He sent into Liguria to buy soldiers, three thousand mountaineers accustomed to fight with bears ; they were paid for six moons in advance at the rate of four minæ a day.

Nevertheless an army was wanted. But he did not, like Hanno, accept all the citizens. First he rejected those engaged in sedentary occupations, and then those who were big-bellied or had a pusillanimous look ; and he admitted those of ill-repute, the scum of Malqua, sons of Barbarians, freedmen. For reward he promised some of the New Carthaginians complete rights of citizenship.

His first care was to reform the Legion. These handsome young fellows, who regarded themselves as the military majesty of the Republic, governed themselves. He reduced their officers to the ranks ; he treated them harshly, made them run, leap, ascend the declivity of the Byrsa at a single burst, hurl javelins, wrestle together, and sleep in the squares at night. Their families used to come to see them and pity them.

He ordered shorter swords and stronger buskins. He fixed the number of serving-men, and reduced the amount of baggage and as there were three hundred Roman pila kept in the temple of Moloch, he took them in spite of the pontiff's protests.

He organized a phalanx of seventy-two elephants with those who had returned from Utica, and others which were private

22

property and rendered them formidable. He armed their drivers with mallet and chisel to enable them to split their skulls in the fight if they ran away.

He would not allow his generals to be nominated by the Grand Council. The Ancients tried to urge the laws in objection, but he set them aside; no one ventured to murmur again, and everything yielded to the violence of his genius.

He assumed sole charge of the war, the government, and the finances; and as a precaution against accusations, he demanded the Suffet Hanno as examiner of his accounts.

He set to work upon the ramparts, and had the old and now useless inner walls demolished in order to furnish stones. But difference of fortune, replacing the hierarchy of race, still kept the sons of the vanquished and those of the conquerors apart; thus the patricians viewed the destruction of these ruins with an angry eye, while the plebeians, scarcely knowing why, rejoiced.

The troops defiled under arms through the streets from morning till night; every moment the sound of trumpets was heard; chariots passed bearing shields, tents, and pikes; the courts were full of women engaged in tearing up linen; the enthusiasm spread from one to another, and Hamilcar's soul filled the Republic.

He had divided his soldiers into even numbers, being careful to place a strong man and a weak one alternately throughout the length of his files, so that he who was less vigorous or more cowardly might be at once led and pushed forward by two others. But with his three thousand Ligurians, and the best in Carthage, he could form only a simple phalanx of four thousand and ninety-six hoplites, protected by bronze helmets, and handling ashen sarissæ fourteen cubits long.

There were two thousand young men, each equipped with a sling, a dagger, and sandals. He reinforced them with eight hundred others armed with round shields and Roman swords.

The heavy cavalry was composed of the nineteen hundred remaining guardsmen of the Legion, covered with plates of vermilion bronze, like the Assyrian Clinabarians. He had

further four hundred mounted archers, of those that were
called Tarentines, with caps of weasel's skin, two-edged
axes, and leathern tunics. Finally there were twelve hundred Negroes from the quarter of the caravans, who were
mingled with the Clinabarians, and were to run beside the
stallions with one hand resting on the manes. All was
ready, and yet Hamilcar did not start.

Often at night he would go out of Carthage alone and
make his way beyond the lagoon toward the mouths of the
Macaras. Did he intend to join the Mercenaries? The
Ligurians encamped in the Mappalian district surrounding
his house.

The apprehensions of the Rich appeared justified when,
one day, three hundred Barbarians were seen approaching
the walls. The Suffet opened the gates to them; they
were deserters; drawn by fear or by fidelity they were
hastening to their master.

Hamilcar's return had not surprised the Mercenaries; according to their ideas the man could not die. He was
returning to fulfill his promise; a hope by no means absurd,
so deep was the abyss between Country and Army. Moreover they did not believe themselves culpable; the feast
was forgotten.

The spies whom they surprised undeceived them. It
was a triumph for the bitter; even the lukewarm grew
furious. Then the two sieges overwhelmed them with
weariness; no progress was being made; a battle would be
better! Thus many men had left the ranks and were
scouring the country. But at news of the arming they returned; Matho leaped for joy. "At last! at last!" he
cried.

Then the resentment which he cherished against Salammbo was turned against Hamilcar. His hate could now
perceive a definite prey; and as his vengeance grew easier
of conception he almost believed that he had realized it
and he reveled in it already. At the same time he was
seized with a loftier tenderness, and consumed by more
acrid desire. He saw himself alternately in the midst of
the soldiers brandishing the Suffet's head on a pike, and
then in the room with the purple bed, clasping the maiden

in his arms, covering her face with kisses, passing his hands over her long, black hair; and the imagination of this, which he knew could never be realized, tortured him. He swore to himself that, since his companions had appointed him schalishim, he would conduct the war; the certainty that he would not return from it urged him to render it a pitiless one : —

He came to Spendius and said to him : —

" You will go and get your men ! I will bring mine ! Warn Autaritus ! We are lost if Hamilcar attacks us. Do you understand me? Rise ! "

Spendius was stupefied before such an air of authority. Matho usually allowed himself to be led, and his previous transports had quickly passed away. But just now he appeared at once calmer and more terrible ; a superb will gleamed in his eyes like the flame of a sacrifice.

The Greek did not listen to his reasons. He was living in one of the Carthaginian pearl-bordered tents, drinking cool beverages from silver cups, playing at the cottabos, letting his hair grow, and conducting the siege with slackness. Moreover, he had entered into communications with some in the town and would not leave, being sure that it would open its gates before many days were over.

Narr' Havas, who wandered about among the three armies, was at that time with him. He supported his opinion, and even blamed the Libyan for wishing in his excess of courage to abandon their enterprise.

" Go, if you are afraid ! " exclaimed Matho ; " you promised us pitch, sulphur, elephants, foot-soldiers, horses ! where are they? "

Narr' Havas reminded him that he had exterminated Hanno's last cohorts — as to the elephants, they were being hunted in the woods, he was arming the foot-soldiers, the horses were on their way ; and the Numidian rolled his eyes like a woman and smiled in an irritating manner, as he stroked the ostrich feather which fell upon his shoulder. In his presence Matho was at a loss for a reply.

But a man who was a stranger entered, wet with perspiration, scared, and with bleeding feet and loosened girdle ; his breathing shook his lean sides enough to have burst them, and speaking in an unintelligible dialect he opened his eyes wide as though he were telling of some battle. The king sprang outside and called his horsemen.

They ranged themselves in the plain before him in the form of a circle. Narr' Havas, who was mounted, bent his head and bit his lips. At last he separated his men into two equal divisions, and told the first to wait; then with an imperious gesture he carried off the others at a gallop and disappeared on the horizon in the direction of the mountains.

" Master! " murmured Spendius, " I do not like these extraordinary chances — the Suffet returning. Narr' Havas going away —— "

" Why ! what does it matter? " said Matho disdainfully.

It was a reason the more for anticipating Hamilcar by uniting with Autaritus. But if the siege of the towns were raised, the inhabitants would come out and attack them in the rear, while they would have the Carthaginians in front. After much talking the following measures were resolved upon and immediately executed.

Spendius proceeded with fifteen thousand men as far as the bridge built across the Macaras, three miles from Utica; the corners of it were fortified with four huge towers provided with catapults; all the paths and gorges in the mountains were stopped up with trunks of trees, pieces of rock, interlacings of thorn, and stone walls; on the summits heaps of grass were made which might be lighted as signals, and shepherds who were able to see at a distance were posted at intervals.

No doubt Hamilcar would not, like Hanno, advance by the mountain of the Hot Springs. He would think that Autaritus, being master of the interior, would close the route against him. Moreover, a check at the opening of the campaign would ruin him, while if he gained a victory he would soon have to make a fresh beginning, the Mercenaries being further off. Again, he could disembark at Cape Grapes and march thence upon one of the towns. But he would then find himself between the two armies, an indiscretion which he could not commit with his scanty forces. Accordingly he must proceed along the base of

Mount Ariana, then turn to the left to avoid the mouths of the Macaras, and come straight to the bridge. It was there that Matho expected him.

At night he used to inspect the pioneers by torchlight. He would hasten to Hippo-Zarytus or to the works on the mountains, would come back again, would never rest. Spendius envied his energy; but in the management of spies, the choice of sentries, the working of the engines and all means of defense, Matho listened docilely to his companion. They spoke no more of Salammbo — one not thinking about her, and the other being prevented by a feeling of shame.

Often he would go toward Carthage, striving to catch sight of Hamilcar's troops. His eyes would dart along the horizon; he would lie flat on the ground, and believe that he could hear an army in the throbbing of his arteries.

He told Spendius that if Hamilcar did not arrive within three days he would go with all his men to meet him and offer him battle. Two further days elapsed. Spendius restrained him; but on the morning of the sixth day he departed.

The Carthaginians were no less impatient for war than the Barbarians. In tents and in houses there was the same longing and the same distress; all were asking one another what was delaying Hamilcar.

From time to time he would mount to the cupola of the temple of Eschmoun beside the Announcer of the Moons and take note of the wind.

One day — it was the third of the month of Tibby — they saw him descending from the Acropolis with hurried steps. A great clamor arose in the Mappalian district. Soon the streets were astir, and the soldiers were everywhere beginning to arm surrounded by weeping women who threw themselves upon their breasts; then they ran quickly to the square of Khamon to take their places in the ranks. No one was allowed to follow them or even to speak to them, or to approach the ramparts; for some minutes the whole town was as silent as a great tomb. The soldiers as they leaned on their lances were thinking, and the others in the houses were sighing.

At sunset the army went out by the western gate; but instead of taking the road to Tunis or making for the mountains in the direction of Utica, they continued their march along the edge of the sea; and they soon reached the Lagoon, where round spaces quite whitened with salt glittered like gigantic silver dishes forgotten on the shore.

Then the pools of water multiplied. The ground gradually became softer, and the feet sank in it. Hamilcar did not turn back. He went on still at their head; and his horse, which was yellow-spotted like a dragon, advanced into the mire flinging froth around him, and with great straining of the loins. Night — a moonless night — fell. A few cried out that they were going to perish; he snatched their arms from them, and gave them to the serving-men. Nevertheless the mud became deeper and deeper. Some had to mount the beasts of burden; others clung to the horses' tails; the sturdy pulled the weak, and the Ligurian corps drove on the infantry with the points of their pikes. The darkness increased. They had lost their way. All stopped.

Then some of the Suffet's slaves went on ahead to look for the buoys which had been placed at intervals by his order. They shouted through the darkness, and the army followed them at a distance.

At last they felt the resistance of the ground. Then a whitish curve became dimly visible, and they found themselves on the banks of the Macaras. In spite of the cold no fires were lighted.

In the middle of the night squalls of wind arose. Hamilcar had the soldiers aroused, but not a trumpet was sounded: their captains tapped them softly on the shoulder.

A man of lofty stature went down into the water. It did not come up to his girdle; it was possible to cross.

The Suffet ordered thirty-two of the elephants to be posted in the river a hundred paces further on, while the others, lower down, would check the lines of men that were carried away by the current; and holding their weapons above their heads they all crossed the Macaras as though between two walls. He had noticed that the western wind had driven the sand so as to obstruct the river and form a natural causeway across it.

He was now on the left bank in front of Utica, and in a vast plain, the latter being advantageous for his elephants, which formed the strength of his army.

This feat of genius filled the soldiers with enthusiasm. They recovered extraordinary confidence. They wished to hasten immediately against the Barbarians; but the Suffet made them rest for two hours. As soon as the sun appeared they moved into the plain in three lines — first came the elephants, and then the light infantry, with the cavalry behind it, the phalanx marching next.

The Barbarians encamped at Utica, and the fifteen thousand about the bridge were surprised to see the ground undulating in the distance. The wind, which was blowing very hard, was driving tornadoes of sand before it; they rose as though snatched from the soil, ascended in great light-colored strips, then parted asunder and began again, hiding the Punic army the while from the Mercenaries. Owing to the horns which stood up on the edge of the helmets, some thought that they could perceive a herd of oxen; others, deceived by the motion of the cloaks, pretended that they could distinguish wings, and those who had traveled a good deal shrugged their shoulders and explained everything by the illusions of the mirage. Nevertheless something of enormous size continued to advance. Little vapors, as subtle as the breath, ran across the surface of the desert; the sun, which was higher now, shone more strongly; a harsh light, which seemed to vibrate, threw back the depths of the sky, and, permeating objects, rendered distance incalculable. The immense plain expanded in every direction beyond the limits of vision; and the almost insensible undulations of the soil extended to the extreme horizon, which was closed by a great blue line which they knew to be the sea. The two armies, having left their tents, stood gazing; the people of Utica were massing on the ramparts to have a better view. At last they distinguished several tranverse bars bristling with level points. They became thicker, larger; black hillocks swayed to and fro; square thickets suddenly appeared; they were elephants and lances. A single shout went up: " The Carthaginians! " and without signal or command the soldiers at Utica and those at the bridge ran pell-mell to fall in a body upon Hamilcar.

Spendius shuddered at the name. "Hamilcar! Hamilcar!" he repeated, panting, and Matho was not there! What was to be done? No means of flight! The suddenness of the event, his terror of the Suffet, and above all, the urgent need of forming an immediate resolution, distracted him; he could see himself pierced by a thousand swords, decapitated, dead. Meanwhile he was being called for; thirty thousand men would follow him; he was seized with fury against himself; he fell back upon the hope of victory; it was full of bliss, and he believed himself more intrepid than Epaminondas. He smeared his cheeks with vermilion in order to conceal his paleness, then he buckled on his knemids and his cuirass, swallowed a patera of pure wine, and ran after his troops, who were hastening toward those from Utica.

They united so rapidly that the Suffet had not time to draw up his men in battle array. By degrees he slackened his speed. The elephants stopped; they rocked their heavy heads with their chargings of ostrich feathers, striking their shoulders the while with their trunks.

Behind the intervals between them might be seen the cohorts of the velites, and further on the great helmets of the Clinabarians, with steel heads glancing in the sun, cuirasses, plumes, and waving standards. But the Carthaginian army, which amounted to eleven thousand three hundred and ninety-six men, seemed scarcely to contain them, for it formed an oblong, narrow at the sides and pressed back upon itself.

Seeing them so weak, the Barbarians, who were thrice as numerous, were seized with extravagant joy. Hamilcar was not to be seen. Perhaps he had remained down yonder? Moreover what did it matter? The disdain which they felt for these traders strengthened their courage; and before Spendius could command a manœuver they had all understood it, and already executed it.

They deployed in a long, straight line, overlapping the wings of the Punic army in order to completely encompass it. But when there was an interval of only three hundred paces between the armies, the elephants turned round instead of advancing ; then the Clinabarians were seen to face about and follow them ; and the surprise of the Mercenaries increased when they saw the archers running to join them, So the Carthaginians were afraid, they were fleeing ! A tremendous hooting broke out from among the Barbarian troops, and Spendius exclaimed from the top of his dromedary : "Ah ! I knew it ! Forward ! forward !"

Then the javelins, darts, and sling-bullets burst forth simultaneously. The elephants feeling their croups stung by the arrows began to gallop more quickly ; a great dust enveloped them, and they vanished like shadows in a cloud.

But from the distance there came a loud noise of footsteps dominated by the shrill sound of the trumpets, which were being blown furiously. The space which the Barbarians had in front of them, and which was full of eddies and tumult, attracted like a whirlpool ; some dashed into it. Cohorts of infantry appeared ; they closed up ; and at the same time all the rest saw the foot-soldiers hastening up with the horsemen at a gallop.

Hamilcar had, in fact, ordered the phalanx to break its sections, and the elephants, light troops, and cavalry to pass through the intervals so as to bring themselves speedily upon the wings, and so well had he calculated the distance from the Barbarians, that at the moment when they reached him, the entire Carthaginian army formed one long straight line.

In the centre bristled the phalanx, formed of syntagmata or full squares having sixteen men on each side. All the leaders of all the files appeared amid long, sharp lance-heads, which jutted out unevenly around them, for the six first ranks crossed their sarissæ, holding them in the middle, and the ten lower ranks rested them upon the shoulders of their companions in succession before them. Their faces were all half hidden beneath the visors of their helmets ; their right legs were all covered with bronze knemids ; broad cylindrical shields reached down to their knees ; and the horrible quadrangular mass moved in a single body, and seemed to live like an animal and work like a machine.

Two cohorts of elephants flanked it in regular array; quivering, they shook off the splinters of the arrows that clung to their black skins. The Indians, squatting on their withers among the tufts of white feathers, restrained them with their spoon-headed harpoons, while the men in the towers, who were hidden up to their shoulders, moved about iron distaffs furnished with lighted tow on the edges of their large bended bows. Right and left of the elephants hovered the slingers, each with a sling around his loins, a second on his head, and a third in his right hand. Then came the Clinabarians, each flanked by a negro, and pointing their lances between the ears of their horses, which, like themselves, were completely covered with gold. Afterward, at intervals, came the light-armed soldiers with shields of lynx skin, beyond which projected the points of the javelins which they held in their left hands; while the Tarentines, each having two coupled horses, relieved this wall of soldiers at its two extremities.

The army of the Barbarians, on the contrary had not been able to preserve its line. Undulations and blanks were to be found through its extravagant length; all were panting and out of breath with their running. The phalanx moved heavily along with thrusts from all its sarissæ; and the too slender line of the Mercenaries soon yielded in the centre beneath the enormous weight.

Then the Carthaginian wings expanded in order to fall upon them, the elephants following. The phalanx, with obliquely pointed lances, cut through the Barbarians; there were two enormous, struggling bodies; and the wings with slings and arrows beat them back upon the phalangites. There was no cavalry to get rid of them, except two hundred Numidians operating against the right squadron of the Clinabarians. All the rest were hemmed in, and unable to extricate themselves from the lines. The peril was imminent, and the need of coming to some resolution urgent.

Spendius ordered attacks to be made simultaneously on both flanks of the phalanx so as to pass clean through it. But the narrower ranks glided below the longer ones and recovered their position, and the phalanx turned upon the Barbarians as terrible in flank as it had just been in front.

They struck at the staves of the sarissæ, but the cavalry in the rear embarrassed their attack ; and the phalanx, supported by the elephants, lengthened and contracted, presenting itself in the form of a square, a cone, a rhombus, a trapezium, a pyramid. A twofold internal movement went on continually from its head to its rear ; for those who were at the lowest part of the files hastened up to the first ranks, while the latter, from fatigue, or on account of the wounded, fell further back. The Barbarians found themselves thronged upon the phalanx. It was impossible for it to advance ; there was, as it were, an ocean wherein leaped red crests and scales of brass, while the bright shields rolled like silver foam. Sometimes broad currents would descend from one extremity to the other, and then go up again, while a heavy mass remained motionless in the centre. The lances dipped and rose alternately. Elsewhere there was so quick a play of naked swords that only the points were visible, while turmæ of cavalry formed wide circles which closed again like whirlwinds behind them.

Above the voices of the captains, the ringing of clarions and the grating of lyres, bullets of lead and almonds of clay whistled through the air, dashing the sword from the hand or the brain out of the skull. The wounded, sheltering themselves with one arm beneath their shields, pointed their swords by resting the pommels upon the ground, while others, lying in pools of blood, would turn and bite the heels of those above them. The multitude was so compact, the dust so thick, and the tumult so great that it was impossible to distinguish anything ; the cowards who offered to surrender were not even heard. Those whose hands were empty clasped one another close ; breasts cracked against cuirasses, and corpses hung with head thrown back between a pair of contracted arms. There was a company of sixty Umbrians who, firm on their hams, their pikes before their eyes, immovable and grinding their teeth, forced two syntagmata to recoil simultaneously. Some Epirote shepherds ran upon the left squadron of the Clinabarians and, whirling their staves, seized the horses by the mane ; the animals threw their riders and fled across the plain. The Punic slingers scattered here and there stood gaping. The phalanx began to waver, the captains run to and fro in distraction, the rearmost in the files were pressing upon the soldiers, and the Barbarians had re-formed; they were recovering; the victory was theirs.

But a cry, a terrible cry broke forth, a roar of pain and wrath: it came from the seventy-two elephants which were rushing on in double line. Hamilcar having waited until the Mercenaries were massed together in one spot to let them loose against them; the Indians had goaded them so vigorously that blood was trickling down their broad ears. Their trunks, which were smeared with minium, were stretched straight out in the air like red serpents; their breasts were furnished with spears and their backs with cuirasses; their tusks were lengthened with steel blades curved like sabres — and to make them more ferocious they had been intoxicated with a mixture of pepper, wine, and incense. They shook their necklaces of bells and shrieked; and the elephantarchs bent their heads beneath the stream of phalaricas which was beginning to fly from the tops of the towers.

In order to resist them the better the Barbarians rushed forward in a compact crowd; the elephants flung themselves impetuously upon the centre of it. The spurs on their breasts, like ships' prows, clove through the cohorts which flowed surging back. They stifled the men with their trunks, or else snatching them up from the ground delivered them over their heads to the soldiers in the towers; with their tusks they disemboweled them, and hurled them into the air, and long entrails hung from their ivory fangs like bundles of ropes from a mast. The Barbarians strove to blind them, to hamstring them; others would slip beneath their bodies, bury a sword in them up to the hilt, and perish crushed to death; the most intrepid clung to their straps; they would go on sawing the leather amid flames, bullets, and arrows, and the wicker tower would fall like a tower of stone. Fourteen of the animals on the extreme right, irritated by their wounds, turned upon the second rank; the Indians seized mallet and chisel, applied the latter to a joint in the head, and with all their might struck a great blow.

Down sank the huge beasts, falling one above another. It was like a mountain; and upon the heap of dead bodies and armor a monstrous elephant, called "The Fury of Baal," which had been caught by the leg in some chains, stood howling until the evening with an arrow in its eye.

The others, however, like conquerors delighting in extermination, overthrew, crushed, stamped, and raged against the corpses and the *débris*. To repel the maniples in serried circles around them, they turned about on their hind feet as they advanced, with a continual rotatory motion. The Carthaginians felt their energy increase, and the battle began again.

The Barbarians were growing weak; some Greek hoplites threw away their arms, and terror seized upon the rest. Spendius was seen stooping upon his dromedary, and spurring it on the shoulders with two javelins. Then they all rushed away from the wings and ran toward Utica.

The Clinabarians, whose horses were exhausted, did not try to overtake them. The Ligurians, who were weakened by thirst, cried out for an advance toward the river. But the Carthaginians, who were posted in the centre of the syntagmata, and had suffered less, stamped their feet with longing for the vengeance which was flying from them; and they were already darting forward in pursuit of the Mercenaries when Hamilcar appeared.

He held in his spotted and sweat-covered horse with silver reins. The bands fastened to the horns on his helmet flapped in the wind behind him, and he had placed his oval shield beneath his left thigh. With a motion of his triple-pointed pike he checked the army.

The Tarentines leaped quickly upon their spare horses, and set off right and left toward the river and toward the town.

The phalanx exterminated all the remaining Barbarians at leisure. When the swords appeared they would stretch out their throats and close their eyelids. Others defended themselves to the last, and were knocked down from a distance with flints like mad dogs. Hamilcar had desired the taking of prisoners, but the Carthaginians obeyed him grudgingly, so much pleasure did they derive from plunging their swords into the bodies of the Barbarians. As they were too hot they set about their work with bare arms like mowers ; and when they desisted to take breath they would follow with their eyes a horseman galloping across the country after a fleeing soldier. He would succeed in seizing him by the hair, hold him thus for a while, and then fell him with a blow of his axe.

Night fell. Carthaginians and Barbarians had disappeared. The elephants which had taken to flight roamed in the horizon with their fired towers. These burned here and there in the darkness like beacons half lost in the mist ; and no movement could be discerned in the plain save the undulation of the river, which was heaped with corpses and was drifting them away to the sea.

Two hours afterward Matho arrived. He caught sight in the starlight of long, uneven heaps lying upon the ground.

They were files of Barbarians. He stooped down ; all were dead. He called into the distance, but no voice replied.

That very morning he had left Hippo-Zarytus with his soldiers to march upon Carthage. At Utica the army under Spendius had just set out, and the inhabitants were beginning to fire the engines. All had fought desperately. But, the tumult which was going on in the direction of the bridge increasing in an incomprehensible fashion. Matho had struck across the mountain by the shortest road, and as the Barbarians were fleeing over the plain he had encountered nobody.

Facing him were little pyramidal masses rearing themselves in the shade, and on this side of the river and closer to him were motionless lights on the surface of the ground. In fact the Carthaginians had fallen back behind the bridge, and to deceive the Barbarians, the Suffet had stationed numerous posts upon the other bank.

Matho, still advancing, thought that he could distinguish Punic ensigns, for horses' heads which did not stir appeared in the air fixed upon the tops of piles of staves which could not be seen ; and further off he could hear a great clamor, a noise of songs, and clashing of cups.

Then, not knowing where he was nor how to find Spendius, assailed with anguish, scared, and lost in the darkness, he returned more impetuously by the same road. The dawn was growing gray when from the top of the mountain he perceived the town with the carcasses of the engines blackened by the flames and looking like giant skeletons leaning against the walls.

All was peaceful amid extraordinary silence and heaviness. Among his soldiers on the verge of the tents men were sleeping nearly naked, each upon his back, or with his forehead against his arm which was supported by his cuirass. Some were unwinding blood-stained bandages from their legs. Those who were going to die rolled their heads about gently ; others dragged themselves along and brought them drink. The sentries walked up and down along the narrow paths in order to warm themselves, or stood in a fierce attitude with their faces turned toward the horizon, and their pikes on their shoulders. Matho found Spendius sheltered beneath a rag of canvas, supported by two sticks set in the ground, his knee in his hands and his head cast down.

They remained for a long time without speaking.

At last Matho murmured : " Conquered ! "

Spendius rejoined in a gloomy voice : " Yes, conquered ! "

And to all questions he replied by gestures of despair.

Meanwhile sighs and death-rattles reached them. Matho partially opened the canvas. Then the sight of the soldiers reminded him of another disaster on the same spot, and he ground his teeth : " Wretch ! once already —— "

Spendius interrupted him : " You were not there either."

" It is a curse ! " exclaimed Matho. " Nevertheless, in the end I will get at him ! I will conquer him ! I will slay him ! Ah ! if I had been there —— " The thought of having missed the battle rendered him even more desperate than the defeat. He snatched up his sword and threw it upon the ground. " But how did the Carthaginians beat you ? "

The former slave began to describe the manœuvers. Matho seemed to see them, and he grew angry. The army from Utica ought to have taken Hamilcar in the rear instead of hastening to the bridge.

"Ah! I know!" said Spendius.

"You ought to have made your ranks twice as deep, avoided exposing the velites against the phalanx, and given free passage to the elephants. Everything might have been recovered at the last moment; there was no necessity to fly."

Spendius replied : —

"I saw him pass along in his large red cloak, with uplifted arms and higher than the dust, like an eagle flying upon the flank of the cohorts ; and at every nod they closed up or darted forward ; the throng carried us toward each other ; he looked at me, and I felt the cold steel, as it were, in my heart."

" He selected the day, perhaps?" whispered Matho to himself.

They questioned each other, trying to discover what it was that had brought the Suffet just when circumstances were most unfavorable. They went on to talk over the situation, and Spendius, to extenuate his fault or to revive his courage, asserted that some hope still remained.

"And if there be none, it matters not!" said Matho; "alone, I will carry on the war!"

"And I too!" exclaimed the Greek, leaping up; he strode to and fro, his eyes sparkling, and a strange smile wrinkling his jackal face.

"We will make a fresh start ; do not leave me again! I am not made for battles in the sunlight — the flashing of the swords troubles my sight; it is a disease, I lived too long in the ergastulum. But give me walls to scale at night, and I will enter the citadels, and the corpses shall be cold before cock-crow! Show me any one, anything, an enemy, a treasure, a woman — a woman, " he repeated, "were she a king's daughter, and I will quickly bring your desire to your feet. You reproach me for having lost the battle against Hanno, nevertheless I won it back again. Confess it! my herd of swine did more for us than a phalanx of Spartans."

23

And yielding to the need that he felt of exalting himself and taking his revenge, he enumerated all that he had done for the cause of the Mercenaries. " It was I who urged on the Gaul in the Suffet's gardens ! Later on, at Sicca, I maddened them all with fear of the Republic ! Gisco was sending them back, but I prevented the interpreters speaking. Ah ! how their tongues hung out of their mouths ! do you remember ? I brought you into Carthage ; I stole the zaïmph. I led you to her. I will do more yet : you shall see ! " He burst out laughing like a madman.

Matho regarded him with gaping eyes. He felt in a measure uncomfortable in the presence of this man, who was at once so cowardly and so terrible.

The Greek resumed in jovial tones and cracking his fingers : —

" Evoe ! Sun after rain ! I have worked in the quarries, and I have drunk Massic wine beneath a golden awning in a vessel of my own like a Ptolemæus. Calamity should help to make us cleverer. By dint of work we may make fortune bend. She loves politicians. She will yield ! "

He returned to Matho and took him by the arm.

" Master, at present the Carthaginians are sure of their victory. You have quite an army which has not fought, and your men obey you. Place them in the front ; mine will follow to avenge themselves. I have still three thousand Carians, twelve hundred slingers and archers, whole cohorts ! A phalanx even might be formed ; let us return ! "

Matho, who had been stunned by the disaster, had hitherto thought of no means of repairing it. He listened with open mouth, and the bronze plates which circled his sides rose with the leapings of his heart.

He picked up his sword, crying : —

" Follow me ; forward ! "

But when the scouts returned, they announced that the Carthaginian dead had been carried off, that the bridge was in ruins, and that Hamilcar had disappeared.

Hamilcar had thought that the Mercenaries would await him at Utica, or that they would return against him ; and finding his forces insufficient to make or sustain an attack, he had struck southward along the right bank of the river, thus protecting himself immediately from a surprise.

He intended first to wink at the revolt of the tribes and to detach them all from the cause of the Barbarians; then when they were quite isolated in the midst of the provinces he would fall upon them and exterminate them.

In fourteen days he pacified the region comprised between Thouccaber and Utica, with the towns of Tignicabah, Tessourah, Vacca and others further to the west. Zounghar built in the mountains, Assouras celebrated for its temple, Djeraado fertile in junipers, Thapitis, and Hagour sent embassies to him. The country people came with their hands full of provisions, implored his protection, kissed his feet and those of the soldiers, and complained of the Barbarians. Some came to offer him bags containing heads of Mercenaries slain, so they said, by themselves, but which they had cut off corpses; for many had lost themselves in their flight, and were found dead here and there beneath the olive trees and among the vines.

On the morrow of his victory, Hamilcar, to dazzle the people, had sent to Carthage the two thousand captives taken on the battlefield. They arrived in long companies of one hundred men each, all with their arms fastened behind their backs with a bar of bronze which caught them at the nape of the neck, and the wounded, bleeding as they still were, running also along; horsemen followed them, driving them on with blows of the whip.

Then there was a delirium of joy! People repeated that there were six thousand Barbarians killed; the others would not hold out, and the war was finished; they embraced one another in the streets, and rubbed the faces of the Pataec gods with butter and cinnamomum to thank them. These, with their big eyes, their big bodies, and their arms raised as high as the shoulder, seemed to live beneath their freshened paint, and to participate in the cheerfulness of the people. The Rich left their doors open; the city resounded with the noise of the timbrels; the temples were illuminated every night, and the servants of the goddess went down to Malqua and set up stages of sycamore-wood at the corners of the cross-ways, and prostituted themselves there.

Lands were voted to the conquerors, holocausts to Melkarth, three hundred gold crowns to the Suffet, and his partisans proposed to decree to him new prerogatives and honors.

He had begged the Ancients to make overtures to Autaritus for exchanging all the Barbarians, if necessary, for the aged Gisco, and the other Carthaginians detained like him. The Libyans and Nomads composing the army under Autaritus knew scarcely anything of these Mercenaries, who were men of Italiote or Greek race; and the offer by the Republic of so many Barbarians for so few Carthaginians, showed that the value of the former was nothing and that of the latter considerable. They dreaded a snare. Autaritus refused.

Then the Ancients decreed the execution of the captives, although the Suffet had written to them not to put them to death. He reckoned upon incorporating the best of them with his own troops and of thus instigating defections. But hatred swept away all circumspection.

The two thousand Barbarians were tied to the stelæ of the tombs in the Mappalian quarter; and traders, scullions, embroiderers, and even women — the widows of the dead with their children — all who would, came to kill them with arrows. They aimed slowly at them, the better to prolong their torture, lowering the weapon and then raising it in turn; and the multitude pressed forward howling. Paralytics had themselves brought thither in hand-barrows; many took the precaution of bringing their food, and remained on the spot until the evening; others passed the night there. Tents had been set up in which drinking went on. Many gained large sums by hiring out bows.

Then all these crucified corpses were left upright, looking like so many red statues on the tombs, and the excitement even spread to the people of Malqua, who were the descendants of the aboriginal families, and were usually indifferent to the affairs of their country. Out of gratitude for the pleasure it had been giving them they now interested themselves in its fortunes, and felt that they were Carthaginians, and the Ancients thought it a clever thing to have thus blended the entire people in a single act of vengeance.

The sanction of the gods was not wanting; for crows alighted from all quarters of the sky. They wheeled in the air as they flew with loud hoarse cries, and formed a huge cloud rolling continually upon itself. It was seen from Clypea, Rhades, and the promontory of Hermæum. Sometimes it would suddenly burst asunder, its black spirals extending far away, as an eagle clove the centre of it, and then departed again; here and there on the terraces, the domes, the peaks of the obelisks, and the pediments of the temples there were big birds holding human fragments in their reddened beaks.

Owing to the smell the Carthaginians resigned themselves to unbind the corpses. A few of them were burned; the rest were thrown into the sea, and the waves, driven by the north wind, deposited them on the shore at the end of the gulf before the camp of Autaritus.

This punishment had no doubt terrified the Barbarians, for from the top of Eschmoun they could be seen striking their tents, collecting their flocks, and hoisting their baggage upon asses, and on the evening of the same day the entire army withdrew.

It was to march to and fro between the mountains of the Hot Springs and Hippo-Zarytus, and so debar the Suffet from approaching the Tyrian towns, and from the possibility of a return to Carthage.

Meanwhile the two other armies were to try to overtake him in the south, Spendius in the east, and Matho in the west, in such a way that all three should unite to surprise and entangle him. Then they received a reinforcement which they had not looked for: Narr' Havas reappeared with three hundred camels laden with bitumen, twenty-five elephants, and six thousand horsemen.

To weaken the Mercenaries the Suffet had judged it prudent to occupy his attention at a distance in his own kingdom. From the heart of Carthage he had come to an understanding with Masgaba, a Gætulian brigand who was seeking to found an empire. Strengthened by Punic money, the adventurer had raised the Numidian States with promises of freedom. But Narr' Havas, warned by his nurse's son, had dropped into Cirta, poisoned the conquerors with the water of the cisterns, struck off a few heads, set all right again, and had just arrived against the Suffet more furious than the Barbarians.

The chiefs of the four armies concerted the arrangements for the war. It would be a long one, and everything must be foreseen.

It was agreed first to entreat the assistance of the Romans, and this mission was offered to Spendius, but as a fugitive he dared not undertake it. Twelve men from the Greek colonies embarked at Annaba in a sloop belonging to the Numidians. Then the chiefs exacted an oath of complete obedience from all the Barbarians. Every day the captains inspected clothes and boots; the sentries were even forbidden to use a shield, for they would often lean it against their lance and fall asleep as they stood; those who had any baggage trailing after them were obliged to get rid of it; everything was to be carried, in Roman fashion, on the back. As a precaution against the elephants Matho instituted a corps of cataphract cavalry, men and horses being hidden beneath cuirasses of hippopotamus skin bristling with nails; and to protect the horses' hoofs boots of plaited esparto grass were made for them.

It was forbidden to pillage the villages, or to tyrannize over the inhabitants who were not of Punic race. But as the country was becoming exhausted, Matho ordered the provisions to be served out to the soldiers individually, without troubling about the women. At first the men shared with them. Many grew weak for lack of food. It was the occasion of incessant quarrels and invectives, many drawing away the companions of the rest by the bait or even by the promise of their own portion. Matho commanded them all to be driven away pitilessly. They took refuge in the camp of Autaritus; but the Gaulish and Libyan women forced them by their outrageous treatment to depart.

At last they came beneath the walls of Carthage to implore the protection of Ceres and Proserpine, for in Byrsa there was a temple with priests consecrated to these goddesses in expiation of the horrors formerly committed at the siege of Syracuse. The Syssitia, alleging their right to waifs and strays, claimed the youngest in order to sell them ; and some fair Lacedæmonian women were taken by New Carthaginians in marriage.

A few persisted in following the armies. They ran on the flank of the syntagmata by the side of the captains. They called to their husbands, pulled them by the cloak, cursed them as they beat their breasts, and held out their little naked and weeping children at arm's length. The sight of them was unmanning the Barbarians ; they were an embarrassment and a peril. Several times they were repulsed, but they came back again ; Matho made the horsemen belonging to Narr' Havas charge them with the point of the lance ; and on some Balearians shouting out to him that they must have women, he replied : "*I* have none !"

Just now he was invaded by the Genius of Moloch. In spite of the rebellion of his conscience, he performed terrible deeds, imagining that he was thus obeying the voice of a god. When he could not ravage the fields, Matho would cast stones into them to render them sterile.

He urged Autaritus and Spendius with repeated messages to make haste. But the Suffet's operations were incomprehensible. He encamped at Eidous, Monchar, and Tehent successively ; some scouts believed that they saw him in the neighborhood of Ischiil, near the frontiers of Narr' Havas, and it was reported that he had crossed the river above Tebourba as though to return to Carthage. Scarcely was he in one place when he removed to another. The routes that he followed always remained unknown. The Suffet preserved his advantages without offering battle, and while pursued by the Barbarians seemed to be leading them.

These marches and counter marches were still more fatiguing to the Carthaginians ; and Hamilcar's forces, receiving no reinforcements, diminished from day to day. The country people were now more backward in bringing him in provisions. In every direction he encountered taciturn hesitation and hatred ; and in spite of his entreaties to the Great Council no succor came from Carthage.

It was said perhaps it was believed, that he had need of none. It was a trick, or his complaints were unnecessary ; and Hanno's partisans, in order to do him an ill turn, exaggerated the importance of his victory. The troops which

he commanded he was welcome to ; but they were not going
to supply all his demands continually in that way. The
war was quite burdensome enough ; it had cost too much,
and from pride the patricians belonging to his faction supported him but slackly.

Then Hamilcar, despairing of the Republic, took by force
from the tribes all that he wanted for the war — grain,
oil, wood, cattle, and men. But the inhabitants were not
long in taking to flight. The villages passed through were
empty, and the cabins were ransacked without anything
being discerned in them. The Punic army was soon encompassed by a terrible solitude.

The Carthaginians, who were furious, began to sack the
provinces ; they filled up the cisterns and fired the houses.
The sparks, being carried by the wind, were scattered far
off, and whole forests were on fire on the mountains ; they
bordered the valleys with a crown of flames, and it was
often necessary to wait in order to pass beyond them.
Then the soldiers resumed their march over the warm ashes
in the full glare of the sun.

Sometimes they would see what looked like the eyes of
a tiger cat gleaming in a bush by the side of the road.
This was a Barbarian crouching upon his heels, and
smeared with dust, that he might not be distinguished
from the color of the foliage ; or perhaps when passing
along a ravine those on the wings would suddenly hear the
rolling of stones, and raising their eyes would perceive a
bare-footed man bounding along through the opening of the
gorge.

Meanwhile, Utica and Hippo-Zarytus were free since the
Mercenaries were no longer besieging them. Hamilcar commanded them to come to his assistance. But not caring to
compromise themselves, they answered him with vague
words, with compliments, and excuses.

He went up again abruptly into the North, determined to
open up one of the Tyrian towns, though he were obliged
to lay siege to it. He required a station on the coast, so
as to be able to draw supplies and men from the islands
or from Cyrene, and he coveted the harbor of Utica as
being the nearest to Carthage.

The Suffet therefore left Zouitin and turned the lake of Hippo-Zarytus with circumspection. But he was soon obliged to lengthen out his regiments into columns in order to climb the mountain which separates the two valleys. They were descending at sunset into its hollow, funnel-shaped summit, when they perceived on the level of the ground before them bronze she-wolves which seemed to be running across the grass.

Suddenly large plumes arose and a terrible song burst forth, accompanied by the rhythm of flutes. It was the army under Spendius; for some Campanians and Greeks, in their execration of Carthage, had assumed the ensigns of Rome. At the same time long pikes, shields of leopard's skin, linen cuirasses, and naked shoulders were seen on the left. These were the Iberians under Matho, the Lusitanians, Balearians, and Gætulians; the horses of Narr' Havas were heard to neigh; they spread around the hill; then came the loose rabble commanded by Autaritus —Gauls, Libyans, and Nomads; while the Eaters of Un-cleanness might be recognized among them by the fish bones which they wore in their hair.

Thus the Barbarians, having contrived their marches with exactness, had come together again. But themselves surprised they remained motionless for some minutes in consultation.

The Suffet had collected his men into an orbicular mass, in such a way as to offer an equal resistance in every di-rection. The infantry were surrounded by their tall, pointed shields fixed close to one another in the turf. The Clina-barians were outside and the elephants at intervals further off. The Mercenaries were worn out with fatigue; it was better to wait till next day; and the Barbarians, feeling sure of their victory, occupied themselves the whole night in eating.

They had lit large bright fires, which, while dazzling themselves, left the Punic army below them in the shade. Hamilcar caused a trench fifteen feet broad and ten cubits deep to be dug in Roman fashion round his camp, and the earth thrown out to be raised on the inside into a parapet, on which sharp interlacing stakes were planted; and at sunrise the Mercenaries were amazed to perceive all the Carthaginians thus entrenched as though in a fortress.

They could recognize Hamilcar in the midst of the tents walking about and giving orders. His person was clad in a brown cuirass cut in little scales; he was followed by his horse, and stopped from time to time to point out something with his right arm outstretched.

Then more than one recalled similar mornings when, amid the din of clarions, he passed slowly before them, and his looks strengthened them like cups of wine. A kind of emotion overcame them. Those, on the contrary, who were not acquainted with Hamilcar, were mad with joy at having caught him.

Nevertheless, if all attacked at once they would do one another mutual injury in the insufficiency of space. The Numidians might dash through; but the Clinabarians, who were protected by cuirasses, would crush them. And then how were the palisades to be crossed? As to the elephants they were not sufficiently well trained.

"You are all cowards!" exclaimed Matho.

And with the best among them he rushed against the entrenchment. They were repulsed by a volley of stones; for the Suffet had taken their abandoned catapults on the bridge.

This want of success produced an abrupt change in the fickle minds of the Barbarians. Their extreme bravery disappeared; they wished to conquer, but with the smallest possible risk. According to Spendius they ought to carefully maintain the position that they held, and starve out the Punic army. But the Cathaginians began to dig wells, and as there were mountains surrounding the hill, they discovered water.

From the summit of their palisade they launched arrows, earth, dung, and pebbles which they gathered from the ground, while the six catapults rolled incessantly throughout the length of the terrace.

But the springs would dry up of themselves; the provisions would be exhausted, and the catapults worn out; the Mercenaries, who were ten times as numerous, would triumph in the end. Suffet devised negotiations so as to gain time, and one morning the Barbarians found a sheep's skin covered with writing within their lines. He justified himself for his victory : the Ancients had forced him into the war, and to show them that he was keeping his word, he offered them the pillaging of Utica or Hippo-Zarytus at their choice ; in conclusion, Hamilcar declared that he did not fear them because he had won over some traitors, and thanks to them would easily manage the rest.

The Barbarians were disturbed : this proposal of immediate booty made them consider ; they were apprehensive of treachery, not suspecting a snare in the Suffet's boasting, and they began to look upon one another with mistrust. Words and steps were watched ; terrors awaked them in the night. Many forsook their companions and chose their army as fancy dictated, and the Gauls with Autaritus went and joined themselves with the men of Cisalpine Gaul, whose language they understood.

The four chiefs met together every evening in Matho's tent, and squatting round a shield, attentively moved backward and forward the little wooden figures invented by Pyrrhus for the representation of manœuvers. Spendius would demonstrate Hamilcar's resources, and with oaths by all the gods entreat that the opportunity should not be wasted. Matho would walk about angry and gesticulating. The war against Carthage was his own personal affair ; he was indignant that the others should interfere in it without being willing to obey him. Autaritus would divine his speech from his countenance and applaud. Narr' Havas would elevate his chin to mark his disdain ; there was not a measure that he did not consider fatal ; and he had ceased to smile. Sighs would escape him as though he were thrusting back sorrow for an impossible dream, despair for an abortive enterprise.

While the Barbarians deliberated in uncertainty, the Suffet increased his defenses ; he had a second trench dug within the palisades, a second wall raised, and wooden towers constructed at the corners ; and his slaves went as far as the middle of the outposts to drive caltrops into the ground. But the elephants, whose allowances were lessened, struggled in their shackles. To economize the grass he ordered the Clinabarians to kill the least strong among the stallions. A few refused to do so and he had them decapitated. The horses were eaten. The recollection of this fresh meat was a source of great sadness to them in the days that followed.

From the bottom of the amphitheatre in which they were confined they could see the four bustling camps of the Barbarians all around them on the heights. Women moved about with leathern bottles on their heads, goats strayed bleating beneath the piles of pikes; sentries were being relieved, and eating was going on around tripods. In fact, the tribes furnished them abundantly with provisions, and they did not themselves suspect how much their inaction alarmed the Punic army.

On the second day the Carthaginians had remarked a troop of three hundred men apart from the rest in the camp of the Nomads. These were the Rich who had been kept prisoners since the beginning of the war. Some Libyans ranged them along the edge of the trench, took their station behind them, and hurled javelins, making themselves a rampart of their bodies. The wretched creatures could scarcely be recognized, so completely were their faces covered with vermin and filth. Their hair had been plucked out in places, leaving bare the ulcers on their heads, and they were so lean and hideous that they were like mummies in tattered shrouds. A few trembled and sobbed with a stupid look; the rest cried out to their friends to fire upon the Barbarians. There was one who remained quite motionless with face cast down, and without speaking; his long white beard fell to his chain-covered hands; and the Carthaginians, feeling as it were the downfall of the Republic in the bottom of their hearts, recognized Gisco. Although the place was a dangerous one they pressed forward to see him. On his head had been placed a grotesque tiara of hippopotamus leather incrusted with pebbles. It was Autaritus's idea; but it was displeasing to Matho.

Hamilcar in exasperation, and resolved to cut his way through in one way or another, had the palisades opened; and the Carthaginians went at a furious rate half way up the hill or three hundred paces. Such a flood of Barbarians descended upon them that they were driven back to their lines. One of the guards of the Legion who had remained outside was stumbling among the stones. Zarxas ran up to him, knocked him down, and plunged a dagger into his throat; he drew it out, threw himself upon the wound — and gluing his lips to it with mutterings of joy and startings which shook him to the heels, pumped up the blood by breastfuls; then he quietly sat down upon the corpse, raised his face with his neck thrown back the better to breathe in the air, like a hind that has just drunk at a mountain stream, and in a shrill voice began to sing a Balearic song, a vague melody full of prolonged modulations, with interruptions and alternations like echos answering one another in the mounains; he called upon his dead brothers and invited them to a feast —then he let his hands fall between his legs, slowly bent his head, and wept. This atrocious occurrence horrified the Barbarians, especially the Greeks.

From that time forth the Carthaginians did not attempt to make any sally; and they had no thought of surrender, certain as they were that they would perish in tortures.

Nevertheless the provisions, in spite of Hamilcar's carefulness, diminished frightfully. There was not left per man more than ten k'hommers of wheat, three hins of millet, and twelve betzas of dried fruit. No more meat, no more oil, no more salt food, and not a grain of barley for the horses, which might be seen stretching down their wasted necks seeking in the dust for blades of trampled straw. Often the sentries on vedette upon the terrace would see in the moonlight a dog belonging to the Barbarians coming to prowl beneath the entrenchment among the heaps of filth; it would be knocked down with a stone, and then, after a descent had been effected along the palisades by means of the straps of a shield, it would be eaten without a word. Sometimes horrible barkings would be heard and the man would not come up again. Three phalangites, in the fourth dilochia of the twelfth syntagma, killed one another with knives in a dispute about a rat.

All regretted their families, and their houses; the poor
their hive-shaped huts, with the shells on the threshold and
the hanging net, and the patricians their large halls filled
with bluish shadows, where at the most indolent hour of
the day, they used to rest listening to the vague noise of
the streets mingled with the rustling of the leaves as they
stirred in their gardens — to go deeper into the thought of
this, and to enjoy it more, they would half close their eyelids, only to be roused by the shock of a wound. Every
minute there was some engagement, some fresh alarm; the
towers were burning, the Eaters of Uncleanness were leaping across the palisades; their hands would be struck off
with axes; others would hasten up; an iron hail would fall
upon the tents. Galleries of rushen hurdles were raised as
a protection against the projectiles. The Carthaginians shut
themselves up within them and stirred out no more.

Every day the sun coming over the hill, used after the
early hours, to forsake the bottom of the gorge and leave
them in the shade. The gray slopes of the ground, covered with flints spotted with scanty lichen, ascended in front
and in the rear, and above their summits stretched the sky
in its perpetual purity, smoother and colder to the eye than
a metal cupola. Hamilcar was so indignant with Carthage
that he felt inclined to throw himself among the Barbarians and lead them against her. Moreover, the porters, sut-
lers, and slaves were beginning to murmur, while neither
people nor Great Council, or any one sent as much as a
hope. The situation was intolerable, especially owing to the
thought that it would become worse.

At the news of the disaster Carthage had leaped, as it
were, with anger and hate; the Suffet would have been
less execrated if he had allowed himself to be conquered
from the first.

But time and money were lacking for the hire of other
Mercenaries. As to a levy of soldiers in the town, how
were they to be equipped? Hamilcar had taken all the
arms! and then who was to command them? The best
captains were down yonder with him! Meanwhile, some
men despatched by the Suffet arrived in the streets with
shouts.

The Great Council were roused by them, and contrived to make them disappear.

It was an unnecessary precaution; every one accused Barca of having behaved with slackness. He ought to have annihilated the Mercenaries after his victory. Why had he ravaged the tribes? The sacrifices already imposed had been heavy enough! and the patricians deplored their contributions of fourteen shekels, and the Syssitia their two hundred and twenty-three thousand gold kikars; those who had given nothing lamented like the rest. The populace was jealous of the New Carthaginians, to whom he had promised full rights of citizenship; and even the Ligurians, who had fought with such intrepidity, were confounded with the Barbarians and cursed like them; their race became a crime, the proof of complicity. The traders on the threshold of their shops, the workmen passing plumb-line in hand, the vendors of pickle rinsing their baskets, the attendants in the vapor baths and the retailers of hot drinks all discussed the operations of the campaign They would trace battle-plans with their fingers in the dust, and there was not a sorry rascal to be found who could not have corrected Hamilcar's mistakes.

It was a punishment, said the priests, for his long-continued impiety. He had offered no holocausts; he had not purified his troops; he had even refused to take augurs with him; and the scandal of sacrilege strengthened the violence of restrained hate, and the rage of betrayed hopes. People recalled the Sicilian disasters, and all the burden of his pride that they had borne for so long! The colleges of the pontiffs could not forgive him for having seized their treasure, and they demanded a pledge from the Great Council to crucify him should he ever return.

The heats of the month of Eloul, which were excessive in that year, were another calamity. Sickening smells rose from the borders of the lake, and were wafted through the air together with the fumes of the aromatics that eddied at the corners of the streets. The sounds of hymns were constantly heard. Crowds of people occupied the staircases of the temples; all the walls were covered with black veils; tapers burned on the brows of the Pataec gods, and the blood of camels slain for sacrifice ran along the flights of stairs forming red cascades upon the steps. Carthage was agitated with funereal delirium. From the depths of the narrowest lanes, and the blackest dens, there issued pale faces, men with viper-like profiles and grinding their teeth. The houses were filled with the women's piercing shrieks, which, escaping through the gratings, caused those who stood talking in the squares to turn round. Sometimes it was thought that the Barbarians were arriving; they had been seen behind the mountain of the Hot Springs; they were encamped at Tunis; and the voices would multiply and swell, and be blended into one single clamor. Then universal silence would reign, some remaining where they had climbed upon the frontals of the buildings, screening their eyes with their open hand, while the rest lay flat on their faces at the foot of the ramparts straining their ears. When their terror had passed off their anger would begin again. But the conviction of their own impotence would soon sink them into the same sadness as before.

It increased every evening when all ascended the terraces, and bowing down nine times uttered a loud cry in salutation of the Sun as it sank slowly behind the Lagoon, and then suddenly disappeared among the mountains in the direction of the Barbarians.

They were waiting for the thrice holy festival when, from the summit of a funeral pile, an eagle flew heavenward as a symbol of the resurrection of the year, and a message from the people to their Baal; they regarded it as a sort of union, a method connecting themselves with the might of the Sun. Moreover, filled as they now were with hatred, they turned frankly toward Homicidal Moloch, and all forsook Tanith. In fact, Rabetna, having lost her veil, was as though she had been despoiled of part of her virtue. She denied the beneficence of her waters, she had abandoned Carthage; she was a deserter, an enemy. Some threw stones at her to insult her. But many pitied her while they inveighed against her; she was still beloved, and perhaps more deeply than she had been.

All their misfortunes came, therefore, from the loss of the zaïmph. Salammbo had indirectly participated in it;

she was included in the same ill will ; she must be punished. A vague idea of immolation spread among the people. To appease the Baalim it was without doubt necessary
to offer them something of incalculable worth, a being
handsome, young, virgin, of old family, descendant of the
gods, a human star. Every day the gardens of Megara
were invaded by strange men ; the slaves, trembling on
their own account, dared not resist them. Nevertheless,
they did not pass beyond the galley staircase. They remained below with their eyes raised to the highest terrace ;
they were waiting for Salammbo, and they would cry out
for hours against her like dogs baying at the moon.

THE SERPENT

THESE clamorings of the populace did not alarm Hamilcar's daughter.

She was disturbed by loftier anxieties : her great
serpent, the black Python, was drooping ; and, in the eyes
of the Carthaginians, the serpent was at once a national
and a private fetish. It was believed to be the offspring
of the dust of the earth, since it emerges from its depths
and has no need of feet to traverse it ; its mode of progression called to mind the undulations of rivers, its temperature the ancient viscous and fecund darkness, and the
orbit which it describes when biting its tail the harmony of
the planets, and the intelligence of Eschmoun.

Salammbo's serpent had several times already refused the
four live sparrows which were offered to it at the full
moon and at every new moon. Its handsome skin,
covered like the firmament with golden spots upon a perfectly black ground, was now yellow, relaxed, wrinkled,
and too large for its body. A cottony moldiness extended
round its head ; and in the corners of its eyelids might be
seen little red specks which appeared to move. Salammbo
would approach its silver-wire basket from time to time,
and would draw aside the purple curtains, the lotus leaves,
and the bird's down ; but it was continually rolled up

24

upon itself, more motionless than a withered bindweed; and from looking at it she at last came to feel a kind of spiral within her heart, another serpent, as it were, mounting up to her throat by degrees and strangling her.

She was in despair at having seen the zaïmph, and yet she felt a sort of joy, an intimate pride at having done so. A mystery shrank within the splendor of its folds; it was the cloud that enveloped the gods, and the secret of the universal existence, and Salammbo, horror-stricken at herself, regretted that she had not raised it.

She was almost always crouching at the back of her apartment, holding her bended left leg in her hands, her mouth half open, her chin sunk, her eye fixed. She recollected her father's face with terror; she wished to go away into the mountains of Phœnicia, on a pilgrimage to the temple of Aphaka, where Tanith descended in the form of a star; all kinds of imaginings attracted her and terrified her; moreover, a solitude which every day became greater encompassed her. She did not even know what Hamilcar was about.

Wearied at last with her thoughts she would rise, and trailing along her little sandals whose soles clacked upon her heels at every step, she would walk at random through the large silent room. The amethysts and topazes of the ceiling made luminous spots quiver here and there, and Salammbo as she walked would turn her head a little to see them. She would go and take the hanging amphoras by the neck; she would cool her bosom beneath the broad fans, or perhaps amuse herself by burning cinnamomum in hollow pearls. At sunset Taanach would draw back the black felt lozenges that closed the openings in the wall; then her doves, rubbed with musk like the doves of Tanith, suddenly entered, and their pink feet glided over the glass pavement, amid the grains of barley which she threw to them in handfuls like a sower in a field. But on a sudden she would burst into sobs and lie stretched on the large bed of ox-leather straps without moving, repeating a word that was ever the same, with open eyes, pale as one dead, insensible, cold; and yet she could hear the cries of the apes in the tufts of the palm trees, with the continuous grinding of the great wheel which brought a flow of pure water through the stories into the porphyry centre-basin.

Sometimes for several days she would refuse to eat. She could see in a dream troubled stars wandering beneath her feet. She would call Schahabarim, and when he came she had nothing to say to him.

She could not live without the relief of his presence. But she rebelled inwardly against this domination; her feeling toward the priest was at once of terror, jealousy, hatred, and a species of love, in gratitude for the singular voluptuousness which she experienced by his side.

He had recognized the influence of Rabbet, being skillful to discern the gods who sent diseases; and to cure Salammbo he had her apartment watered with lotions of vervain, and maiden hair; she ate mandrakes every morning; she slept with her head on a cushion filled with aromatics blended by the pontiffs; he had even employed baaras, a fiery-colored root which drives back fatal geniuses into the North; lastly, turning toward the polar star, he murmured thrice the mysterious name of Tanith; but Salammbo still suffered and her anguish deepened.

No one in Carthage was so learned as he. In his youth he had studied at the College of the Mogbeds, at Borsippa, near Babylon; had then visited Samothrace, Ephesus, Pessinus, Thessaly, Judæa, and the temples of the Nabathæ, which are lost in the sands; and had traveled on foot along the banks of the Nile from the cataracts to the sea. Shaking torches with veil-covered face he had cast a black cock upon a fire of sandarach before the breast of the Sphinx, the Father of Terror. He had descended into the caverns of Proserpine; he had seen the five hundred pillars of the labyrinth of Lemnos revolve, and the candelabrum of Tarentum, which bore as many sconces on its shaft as there are days in the year, shine in its splendor; at times he received Greeks by night in order to question them. The constitution of the world disquieted him no less than the nature of the gods; he had observed the equinoxes with the armils placed in the portico of Alexandria, and accompanied the bematists of Evergetes, who measure the sky by calculating the number of their steps, as far as

Cyrene; so that there was now growing in his thoughts a religion of his own, with no distinct formula, and on that very account full of infatuation and fervor. He no longer believed that the earth was formed like a fir-cone; he believed it to be round, and eternally falling through immensity with such prodigious speed that its fall was not perceived.

From the position of the sun above the moon he inferred the predominance of Baal, of whom the planet itself is but the reflection and figure; moreover, all that he saw in terrestrial things compelled him to recognize the male exterminating principle as supreme. And then [he secretly charged Rabbet with the misfortune of his life. Was it not for her that the grand-pontiff had once advanced amid the tumult of cymbals, and with a patera of boiling water, taken from him his future virility. And he followed with a melancholy gaze the men who were disappearing with the priestesses in the depths of the turpentine trees.

His days were spent in inspecting the censers, the gold vases, the tongs, the rakes for the ashes of the altar, and all the robes of the statues down to the bronze bodkin that served to curl the hair of an old Tanith in the third ædicule near the emerald vine. At the same hours he would raise the great hangings of the same swinging doors; would remain with his arms outspread in the same attitude; or prayed prostrate on the same flagstones, while around him a people of priests moved barefooted through the passages filled with an eternal twilight.

But Salammbo was in the barrenness of his life like a flower in the cleft of a sepulchre. Nevertheless he was hard upon her, and spared her neither penances nor bitter words. His condition established, as it were, the equality of a common sex between them, and he was less angry with the young girl for his inability to possess her than for finding her so beautiful, and above all so pure. Often he saw that she grew weary in following his thought. Then he would turn away sadder than before; he would feel himself more forsaken, more empty, more alone.

Strange words escaped him sometimes, which passed before Salammbo like broad lightnings illuminating the abysses. This would be at night on the terrace when, both alone, they gazed upon the stars, and Carthage spread below under their feet, with the gulf and the open sea dimly lost in the color of the darkness.

He would set forth to her the theory of the souls that descend upon the earth, following the same route as the sun through the signs of the zodiac. With outstretched arm he showed the gate of human generation in the Ram, and that of the return to the gods in Capricorn; and Salammbo strove to see them, for she took these conceptions for realities; she accepted pure symbols and even manners of speech as being true in themselves, a distinction not always very clear even to the priest.

"The souls of the dead," said he, "resolve themselves into the moon, as their bodies do into the earth. Their tears compose its humidity; 'tis a dark abode full of mire, and wreck, and tempest."

She asked what would become of her there.

"At first you will languish as light as a vapor hovering upon the waves; and after more lengthened ordeals and agonies, you will pass into the forces of the sun, the very source of Intelligence!"

He did not speak, however, of Rabbet. Salammbo imagined that it was through shame for his vanquished goddess, and calling her by a common name which designated the moon she launched into blessings upon the soft and fertile planet. At last he exclaimed: —

"No! no! she draws all her fecundity from the other! Do you not see her hovering about him like an amorous woman running after a man in a field?" And he exalted the virtue of light unceasingly.

Far from depressing her mystic desires, he sought, on the contrary, to excite them, and he even seemed to take joy in grieving her by the revelation of a pitiless doctrine. In spite of the pains of her love Salammbo threw herself upon it with transport.

But the more that Schahabarim felt himself in doubt about Tanith, the more he wished to believe in her. At the bottom of his soul he was arrested by remorse. He needed some proof, some manifestation from the gods, and

in the hope of obtaining it the priest devised an enterprise which might save at once his country and his belief.

Thenceforward he set himself to deplore before Salammbo
the sacrilege and the misfortunes which resulted from it
even in the regions of the sky. Then he suddenly announced the peril of the Suffet, who was assailed by three
armies under the command of Matho—for on account of
the veil Matho was, in the eyes of the Carthaginians, the
king as it were of the Barbarians—and he added that the
safety of the Republic and of her father depended upon her
alone.

"Upon me!" she exclaimed. "How can I—?"

But the priest with a smile of disdain:—

"You will never consent!"

She entreated him. At last Schahabarim said to her:—

"You must go to the Barbarians and recover the zaïmph!"

She sank down upon the ebony stool, and remained with
her arms stretched out between her knees and a shivering
in all her limbs, like a victim at the altar's foot awaiting
the blow of the club. Her temples were ringing, she could
see fiery circles revolving, and in her stupor she had lost
the understanding of all things save one, that she was certainly going to die soon.

But if Rabetna triumphed, if the zaïmph were restored
and Carthage delivered, what mattered a woman's life!
thought Schahabarim. Moreover, she would perhaps obtain
the veil and not perish.

He stayed away for three days; on the evening of the
fourth she sent for him.

The better to inflame her heart he reported to her all the
invectives howled against Hamilcar in open council; he told
her that she had erred, that she owed reparation for her
crime, and that Rabetna commanded the sacrifice.

A great uproar came frequently across the Mappalian district to Megara. Schahabarim and Salammbo went out
quickly, and gazed from the top of the galley staircase.

There were people in the square of Khamon shouting for
arms. The Ancients would not provide them, esteeming
such an effort useless; others who had set out without a
general had been massacred. At last they were permitted

to depart, and as a sort of homage to Moloch or from a vague need of destruction, they tore up tall cypress trees in the woods of the temples, and having kindled them at the torches of the Kabiri, were carrying them through the streets singing. These monstrous flames advanced swaying gently; they transmitted fires to the glass balls on the crests of the temples, to the ornaments of the colossuses and the beaks of the ships, passed beyond the terraces and formed suns, as it were, which rolled through the town. They descended the Acropolis. The gate of Malqua opened.

"Are you ready?" exclaimed Schahabarim, "or have you asked them to tell your father that you abandoned him?" She hid her face in her veils, and the great lights retired, sinking gradually the while to the edge of the waves.

An indeterminate dread restrained her; she was afraid of Moloch and of Matho. This man, with his giant stature who was master of the zaïmph, ruled Rabetna as much as did Baal, and seemed to her to be surrounded by the same fulgurations; and then the souls of the gods sometimes visited the bodies of men. Did not Schahabarim in speaking of him say that she was to vanquish Moloch? They were mingled with each other; she confused them together; both of them were pursuing her.

She wished to learn the future, and approached the serpent, for auguries were drawn from the attitudes of serpents. But the basket was empty; Salammbo was disturbed.

She found him with his tail rolled round one of the silver balustrades beside the hanging bed, which he was rubbing in order to free himself from his old yellowish skin, while his body stretched forth gleaming and clear like a sword half out of the sheath.

Then on the days following, in proportion as she allowed herself to be convinced, and was more disposed to succor Tanith, the python recovered and grew; he seemed to be reviving.

The certainty that Schahabarim was giving expression to the will of the gods then became established in her conscience. One morning she awoke resolved, and she asked what was necessary to make Matho restore the veil.

"To claim it," said Schahabarim.

"But if he refuses?" she rejoined.

The priest scanned her fixedly with a smile such as she had never seen.

"Yes, what is to be done?" repeated Salammbo.

He rolled between his fingers the extremities of the bands which fell from his tiara upon his shoulders, standing motionless with eyes cast down. At last seeing that she did not understand : —

"You will be alone with him."

"Well?" she said.

"Alone in his tent."

"What then?"

Schahabarim bit his lips. He sought for some phrase, some circumlocution.

"If you are to die, that will be later on," he said ; "later on! fear nothing! and whatever he may undertake to do, do not call out! do not be frightened! You will be humble, you understand, and submissive to his desire, which is ordained of heaven!"

"But the veil?"

"The gods will take thought for it," replied Schahabarim.

"Suppose you were to accompany me, O father?" she added.

"No!"

He made her kneel down, and keeping his left hand raised and his right extended, he swore on her behalf to bring back the mantle of Tanith into Carthage. With terrible imprecations she devoted herself to the gods, and each time that Schahabarim pronounced a word she falteringly repeated it.

He indicated to her all the purifications and fastings that she was to observe, and how she was to reach Matho. Moreover, a man acquainted with the routes would accompany her.

She felt as though she had been set free. She thought only of the happiness of seeing the zaïmph again, and she now blessed Schahabarim for his exhortations.

It was the period at which the doves of Carthage migrated to Sicily to the mountain of Eryx and the temple of Venus. For several days before their departure they sought out and called to one another so as to collect together; at last one evening they flew away; the wind blew them along, and the big white cloud glided across the sky high above the sea.

The horizon was filled with color of blood. They seemed to descend gradually to the waves; then they disappeared as though swallowed up, and falling of themselves into the jaws of the sun. Salammbo, who watched them retiring, bent her head, and then Taanach, believing that she guessed her sorrow, said gently to her: —

" But they will come back, Mistress. "

" Yes! I know. "

" And you will see them again. "

" Perhaps! " she said, sighing.

She had not confided her resolve to any one; in order to carry it out with the greater discretion she sent Taanach to the suburb of Kinisdo to buy all the things that she required instead of requesting them from the stewards: vermilion, aromatics, a linen girdle, and new garments. The old slave was amazed at these preparations, without daring, however, to ask any questions; and the day, which had been fixed by Schahabarim, arrived when Salammbo was to set out.

About the twelfth hour she perceived, in the depths of the sycamore trees, a blind old man with one hand resting on the shoulder of a child, who walked before him, while with the other he carried a kind of cithara of black wood against his hip. The eunuchs, slaves and women had been scrupulously sent away; no one might know the mystery that was preparing.

Taanach kindled four tripods filled with strobus and cardamomum in the corners of the apartment; then she unfolded large Babylonian hangings, and stretched them on cords all around the room, for Salammbo did not wish to be seen even by the walls. The kinnor-player squatted behind the door, and the young boy standing upright applied a reed flute to his lips. In the distance the roar of the streets was growing feebler, violent shadows were lengthening before the peristyles of the temples, and on the other side of the gulf the mountain bases, the fields of olive-trees, and the vague yellow lands undulated indefinitely, and were blended together in a bluish haze; not a sound was to be heard and an unspeakable depression weighed in the air.

Salammbo crouched down upon the onyx step on the edge of the basin; she raised her ample sleeves, fastening them behind her shoulders, and began her ablutions in methodical fashion, according to the sacred rites.

Next Taanach brought her something liquid and coagulated in an alabaster phial; it was the blood of a black dog slaughtered by barren women on a winter's night amid the rubbish of a sepulchre. She rubbed it upon her ears, her heels, and the thumb of her right hand, and even her nail remained somewhat red, as though she had crushed a fruit.

The moon rose; then the cithara and the flute both began to play together.

Salammbo unfastened her earrings, her necklace, her bracelets, and her long white simar; she unknotted the band in her hair, shaking the latter for a few minutes softly over her shoulders to cool herself by thus scattering it. The music went on outside; it consisted of three notes ever the same, hurried and frenzied; the strings grated, the flute blew; Taanach kept time by striking her hands; Salammbo, with a swaying of her whole body, chanted prayers, and her garments fell one after another around her.

The heavy tapestry trembled, and the python's head appeared above the cord that supported it. The serpent descended slowly like a drop of water flowing along a wall, crawled among the scattered stuffs, and then glueing its tail to the ground, rose perfectly erect; and his eyes more brilliant than carbuncles, darted upon Salammbo.

A horror of cold, or perhaps a feeling of shame, at first made her hesitate. But she recalled Schahabarim's orders and advanced; the python turned downward, and resting the centre of its body upon the nape of her neck, allowed its head and tail to hang like a broken necklace with both ends trailing to the ground. Salammbo rolled it around her

sides, under her arms, and between her knees; then taking
it by the jaw she brought the little triangular mouth to the
edge of her teeth, and half shutting her eyes, threw herself back beneath the rays of the moon. The white light
seemed to envelop her in a silver mist, the prints of her
humid steps shone upon the flag-stones, stars quivered in
the depth of the water; it tightened upon her its black
rings that were spotted with scales of gold. Salammbo
panted beneath the excessive weight, her loins yielded, she
felt herself dying, and with the tips of its tail the serpent
gently beat her thigh; then the music becoming still it fell
off again.

Taanach came back to her; and after arranging two candelabra, the lights of which burned in crystal balls filled
with water, she tinged the inside of her hands with Law-
sonia, spread vermilion upon her cheeks, and antimony
along the edge of her eyelids, and lengthened her eyebrows
with a mixture of gum, musk, ebony, and crushed legs of
flies.

Salammbo, seated on a chair with ivory uprights, gave
herself up to the attentions of the slave. But the touch-
ings, the odor of the aromatics, and the fasts that she had
undergone, were enervating her. She became so pale that
Taanach stopped.

"Go on!" said Salammbo and bearing up against herself, she suddenly revived. Then she was seized with impatience; she urged the Taanach to make haste, and the old
slave grumbled: —

"Well! well! Mistress! Besides, you have no one waiting for you!"

"Yes!" said Salammbo, "some one is waiting for me."

Taanach drew back in surprise, and in order to learn
more about it, said: —

"What orders do you give me, Mistress? for if you are
to remain away —— "

But Salammbo was sobbing; the slave exclaimed: —

"You are suffering! what is the matter? Do not go
away! take me! When you were quite little and used to
cry, I took you to my heart and made you laugh with the
points of my breasts; you have drained them, Mistress!"

She struck herself upon her dried-up bosom. " Now I am old ! I can do nothing for you ! you no longer love me ! you hide your griefs from me, you despise the nurse ! " And tears of tenderness and vexation flowed down her cheeks in the gashes of her tatooing.

" No," said Salammbo, " no, I love you ! be comforted ! "

With a smile like the grimace of an old ape, Taanach resumed her task. In accordance with Schahabarim's recommendations Salammbo had ordered the slave to make her magnificent ; and she was obeying her mistress with barbaric taste full at once of refinement and ingenuity.

Over a first delicate and vinous-colored tunic she passed a second embroidered with birds' feathers. Golden scales clung to her hips, and from this broad girdle descended her blue flowing silver-starred drawers. Next Taanach put upon her a long robe made of the cloth of the country of Seres, white and streaked with green lines. On the edge of her shoulders she fastened a square of purple weighted at the hem with grains of sandrastum ; and above all these garments she placed a black mantle with a flowing train ; then she gazed at her, and proud of her work could not help saying : —

" You will not be more beautiful on the day of your bridal ! "

" My bridal ! " repeated Salammbo ; she was musing with her elbow resting upon the ivory chair.

But Taanach set up before her a copper mirror, which was so broad and high that she could see herself completely in it. Then she rose, and with a light touch of her finger raised a lock of her hair which was falling too low.

Her hair was covered with gold dust, was crisped in front, and hung down behind over her back in long twists ending in pearls. The brightness of the candelabra heightened the paint on her cheeks, the gold on her garments, and the whiteness of her skin ; around her waist, and on her arms, hands, and toes, she had such a wealth of gems that the mirror sent back rays upon her like a sun — and Salammbo, standing by the side of Taanach, who leaned over to see her, smiled amid this dazzling display.

Then she walked to and fro embarrassed by the time that was still left.

Suddenly the crow of a cock resounded. She quickly pinned a long yellow veil upon her hair, passed a scarf around her neck, thrust her feet into blue leather boots, and said to Taanach : —

"Go and see whether there is not a man with two horses beneath the myrtles."

Taanach had scarcely re-entered when she was descending the galley staircase.

"Mistress!" cried the nurse.

Salammbo turned round with one finger on her mouth as a sign for discretion and immobility.

Taanach stole softly along the prows to the foot of the terrace, and from a distance she could distinguish by the light of the moon a gigantic shadow walking obliquely in the cypress avenue to the left of Salammbo, a sign which presaged death.

Taanach went up again into the chamber. She threw herself upon the ground tearing her face with her nails; she plucked out her hair, and uttered piercing shrieks with all her might.

It occurred to her that they might be heard; then she became silent, sobbing quite softly with her head in her hands and her face on the pavement.

MOLOCH

THE Barbarians had no need of a circumvallation on the side of Africa, for it was theirs. But to faciltate the approach to the walls, the entrenchments bordering the ditch were thrown down. Matho next divided the army into great semi-circles so as to encompass Carthage the better. The hoplites of the Mercenaries were placed in the first rank, and behind them the slingers and horsemen; quite at the back were the baggage, chariots, and horses; and the engines bristled in front of this throng at a distance of three hundred paces from the towers.

Amid the infinite variety of their nomenclature (which changed several times in the course of the centuries) these machines might be reduced to two systems : some acted like slings, and the rest like bows.

The first, which were the catapults, were composed of a square frame with two vertical uprights and a horizontal bar. In its anterior portion was a cylinder, furnished with cables, which held back a great beam bearing a spoon for the reception of projectiles ; its base was caught in a skein of twisted thread, and when the ropes were let go it sprang up and struck against the bar, which, checking it with a shock, multiplied its power.

The second presented a more complicated mechanism. A cross-bar had its centre fixed on a little pillar, and from this point of junction there branched off at right angles a sort of channel ; two caps containing twists of horse-hair stood at the extremities of the cross-bar ; two small beams were fastened to them to hold the extremities of a rope which was brought to the bottom of the channel upon a tablet of bronze. This metal plate was released by a spring, and sliding in grooves impelled the arrows.

The catapults were likewise called onagers, after the wild asses which fling up stones with their feet, and the ballistas scorpions, on account of a hook which stood upon the tablet, and being lowered by a blow of the fist, released the spring.

Their construction required learned calculations ; the wood selected had to be of the hardest substance, and their gearing all of brass ; they were stretched with levers, tackle-blocks, capstans or tympanums ; the direction of the shooting was changed by means of strong pivots ; they were moved forward on cylinders, and the most considerable of them, which were brought piece by piece, were set up in front of the enemy.

Spendius arranged three catapults opposite the three principal angles ; he placed a ram before every gate, a ballista before every tower, while carroballistas were to move about in the rear. But it was necessary to protect them against the fire thrown by the besieged, and first of all to fill up the trench which separated them from the walls.

They pushed forward galleries formed of hurdles of green reeds, and oaken semi-circles like enormous shields gliding on three wheels; the workers were sheltered in little huts covered with raw hides and stuffed with wrack; the catapults and ballistas were protected by rope curtains which had been steeped in vinegar to render them incombustible. The women and children went to procure stones on the strand, and gathered earth with their hands and brought it to the soldiers.

The Carthaginians also made preparations.

Hamilcar had speedily reassured them by declaring that there was enough water left in the cisterns for one hundred and twenty-three days. This assertion, together with his presence, and above all that of the zaïmph in their midst, gave them good hopes. Carthage recovered from its dejection; those who were not of Chanaanitish origin were carried away by the passion of the rest.

The slaves were armed, the arsenals were emptied, and every citizen had his own post and his own employment. Twelve hundred of the fugitives had survived, and the Suffet made them all captains; and carpenters, armorers, blacksmiths, and goldsmiths were intrusted with the engines. The Carthaginians had kept a few in spite of the conditions of the peace with Rome. These were repaired. They understood such work.

The two northern and eastern sides, being protected by the sea and the gulf, remained inaccessible. On the wall fronting the Barbarians they collected tree-trunks, millstones, vases filled with sulphur, and vats filled with oil, and built furnaces. Stones were heaped up on the platforms of the towers, and the houses bordering immediately on the rampart were crammed with sand in order to strengthen it and increase its thickness.

The Barbarians grew angry at the sight of these preparations. They wished to fight at once. The weights which they put into the catapults were so extravagantly heavy that the beams broke, and the attack was delayed.

At last on the thirteenth day of the month of Schabar —at sunrise—a great blow was heard at the gate of Khamon.

Seventy-five soldiers were pulling at ropes arranged at the base of a gigantic beam which was suspended horizontally by chains hanging from a framework, and which terminated in a ram's head of pure brass. It had been swathed in ox-hides; it was bound at intervals with iron bracelets; it was thrice as thick as a man's body, one hundred and twenty cubits long, and under the crowd of naked arms pushing it forward and drawing it back, it moved to and fro with a regular oscillation.

The other rams before the other gates began to be in motion. Men might be seen mounting from step to step in the hollow wheels of the tympanums. The pulleys and caps grated, the rope curtains were lowered, and showers of stones and showers of arrows burst forth simultaneously; all the scattered slingers ran up. Some approached the ramparts hiding pots of resin under their shields; then they would hurl these with all their might. This hail of bullets, darts, and flames passed above the first ranks in the form of a curve which fell behind the walls. But long cranes, used for masting vessels, were reared on the summit of the ramparts; and from them there descended some of those enormous pincers which terminated in two semi-circles toothed on the inside. They bit the rams. The soldiers clung to the beam and drew it back. The Carthaginians hauled in order to pull it up; and the action was prolonged until the evening.

When the Mercenaries resumed their task on the following day, the tops of the walls were completely carpeted with bales of cotton, sails, and cushions; the battlements were stopped up with mats; and a line of forks and blades, fixed upon sticks, might be distinguished among the cranes on the rampart. A furious resistance immediately began.

Trunks of trees fastened to cables fell and rose alternately and battered the rams; cramps hurled by the ballistas tore away the roofs of the huts; and streams of flints and pebbles poured from the platforms of the towers.

At last the rams broke the gates of Khamon and Tagaste. But the Carthaginians had piled up such an abundance of materials on the inside that the leaves did not open. They remained standing.

Then they drove augers against the walls; these were applied to the joints of the blocks, so as to detach the latter. The engines were better managed, the men serving them were divided into squads, they were worked from morning till evening without interruption, and with the monotonous precision of a weaver's loom.

Spendius attended to them untiringly. It was he who stretched the skins of the ballistas. In order that the twin tensions might completely correspond, the ropes as they were tightened were struck on the right and left alternately until both sides gave out an equal sound. Spendius would mount upon the timbers. He would strike the ropes softly with the extremity of his foot, and strain his ears like a musician tuning a lyre. Then when the beam of the catapult rose, when the pillar of the ballista trembled with the shock of the spring, when the stones were shooting in rays, and the darts pouring in streams, he would incline his whole body and fling his arms into the air as though to follow them.

The soldiers admired his skill and executed his commands. In the gayety of their work they gave utterances to jests on the names of their machines. Thus the plyers for seizing the rams were called "wolves," and the galleries were covered with "vines;" they were lambs, or they were going to gather the grapes; and as they loaded their pieces they would say to the onagers: "Come, pick well!" and to the scorpions: "Pierce them to the heart!" These jokes, which were ever the same, kept up their courage.

Nevertheless the machines did not demolish the rampart. It was formed of two walls and was completely filled with earth. The upper portions were beaten down, but each time the besieged raised them again. Matho ordered the construction of wooden towers which should be as high as the towers of stone. They cast turf, stakes, pebbles, and chariots with their wheels into the trench so as to fill it up the more quickly; but before this was accomplished the immense throng of Barbarians undulated over the plain with a single movement and came beating against the foot of the walls like an overflowing sea.

They moved forward the rope ladders, straight ladders, and sambucas, the latter consisting of two poles from which a series of bamboos terminating in a movable bridge were lowered by means of tackling. They formed numerous straight lines resting against the wall, and the Mercenaries mounted them in files, holding their weapons in their hands. Not a Carthaginian showed himself; already two-thirds of the rampart had been covered. Then the battlements opened, vomiting flames and smoke like dragon jaws; the sand scattered and entered the joints of their armor; the petroleum fastened on their garments; the liquid lead hopped on their helmets and made holes in their flesh; a rain of sparks splashed against their faces, and eyeless orbits seemed to weep tears as big as almonds. There were men all yellow with oil, with their hair in flames. They began to run and set fire to the rest. They were extinguished with mantles steeped in blood, which were thrown from a distance over their faces. Some who had no wounds remained motionless, stiffer than stakes, their mouths open and their arms outspread.

The assault was renewed for several days in succession, the Mercenaries hoping to triumph by extraordinary energy and audacity.

Sometimes a man raised on the shoulders of another would drive a pin between the stones, and then making use of it as a step to reach further, would place a second and a third; and, protected by the edge of the battlements, which stood out from the wall, they would gradually raise themselves in this way; but on reaching a certain height they always fell back again. The great trench was full to overflowing; the wounded were massed pell-mell with the dead and dying beneath the footsteps of the living. Calcined trunks formed black spots amid opened entrails, scattered brains, and pools of blood; and arms and legs projecting half way out of a heap, would stand straight up like props in a burning vineyard.

The ladders proving insufficient the tollenos were brought into requisition — instruments consisting of a long beam set transversely upon another, and bearing at its extremity a quadrangular basket which would hold thirty foot-soldiers with their weapons.

Matho wished to ascend in the first that was ready. Spendius stopped him.

Some men bent over a capstan; the great beam rose, became horizontal, reared itself almost vertically, and being overweighted at the end, bent like a huge reed. The soldiers, who were crowded together, were hidden up to their chins; only their helmet-plumes could be seen. At last when it was twenty cubits high in the air it turned several times to the right and to the left, and then was depressed; and like a giant arm holding a cohort of pigmies in its hand, it laid the basketful of men upon the edge of the wall. They leaped into the crowd and never returned.

All the other tollenos were speedily made ready. But a hundred times as many would have been needed for the capture of the town. They were utilized in a murderous fashion: Ethiopian archers were placed in the baskets; then, the cables having been fastened, they remained suspended and shot poisoned arrows. The fifty tollenos commanding the battlements thus surrounded Carthage like monstrous vultures; and the Negroes laughed to see the guards on the rampart dying in grievous convulsions.

Hamilcar sent hoplites to these posts, and every morning made them drink the juice of certain herbs which protected them against the poison.

One evening when it was dark he embarked the best of his soldiers on lighters and planks, and turning to the right of the harbor, disembarked on the Taenia. Then he advanced to the first lines of the Barbarians, and taking them in flank, made a great slaughter. Men hanging to ropes would descend from the top of the wall with torches in their hands, burn the works of the Mercenaries, and then mount up again.

Matho was exasperated; every obstacle strengthened his wrath, which led him into terrible extravagances. He mentally summoned Salammbo to an interview; then he waited. She did not come; this seemed to him a fresh piece of treachery — and henceforth he execrated her. If he had seen her corpse he would perhaps have gone away. He doubled the outposts, he planted forks at the foot of the rampart, he drove caltrops into the ground, and he commanded the Libyans to bring him a whole forest that he might set it on fire and burn Carthage like a den of foxes.

Spendius went on obstinately with the siege. He sought
to invent terrible machines such as had never before been
constructed.

The other Barbarians, encamped at a distance on the
isthmus, were amazed at these delays; they murmured, and
they were let loose.

Then they rushed with their cutlasses and javelins, and
beat against the gates with them. But the nakedness of
their bodies facilitating the infliction of wounds, the Carthaginians massacred them freely; and the Mercenaries rejoiced at it, no doubt through jealousy about the plunder.
Hence there resulted quarrels and combats between them.
Then, the country having been ravaged, provisions were
soon scarce. They grew disheartened. Numerous hordes
went away, but the crowd was so great that the loss was
not apparent.

The best of them tried to dig mines, but the earth, being badly supported, fell in. They began again in other
places, but Hamilcar always guessed the direction that they
were taking by holding his ear against a bronze shield.
He bored counter-mines beneath the path along which the
wooden towers were to move, and when they were pushed
forward they sank into the holes.

At last all recognized that the town was impregnable, unless a long terrace were raised to the same height as the
walls, so as to enable them to fight on the same level.
The top of it should be paved so that the machines might
be rolled along. Then Carthage would find it quite impossible to resist.

The town was beginning to suffer from thirst. The
water which was worth two kesitahs the bath at the opening of the siege was now sold for a shekel of silver; the
stores of meat and corn were also becoming exhausted;
there was a dread of famine, and some even began to speak
of useless mouths, which terrified every one.

From the square of Khamon to the temple of Melkarth
the streets were cumbered with corpses; and, as it was the
end of the summer, the combatants were annoyed by great
black flies. Old men carried off the wounded, and the devout continued the fictitious funerals of their relatives and

friends who had died far away during the war. Waxen statues with clothes and hair were displayed across the gates. They melted in the heat of the tapers burning beside them; the paint flowed down upon their shoulders, and tears streamed over the faces of the living, as they chanted mournful songs beside them. The crowd meanwhile ran to and fro; armed bands passed; captains shouted orders, while the shock of the rams beating against the rampart was constantly heard.

The temperature became so heavy that the bodies swelled and would no longer fit into the coffins. They were burned in the centre of the courts. But the fires, being too much confined, kindled the neighboring walls, and long flames suddenly burst from the houses like blood spurting from an artery. Thus, Moloch was in possession of Carthage; he clasped the ramparts, he rolled through the streets, he devoured the very corpses.

Men wearing cloaks made of collected rags in token of despair, stationed themselves at the corners of the crossways. They declaimed against the Ancients and against Hamilcar, predicted complete ruin to the people, and invited them to universal destruction and license. The most dangerous were the henbane-drinkers; in their crisis they believed themselves wild beasts, and leaped upon the passers-by to rend them. Mobs formed around them, and the defense of Carthage was forgotten. The Suffet devised the payment of others to support his policy.

In order to retain the Genius of the gods within the town their images had been covered with chains. Black veils were placed upon the Pataec gods, and hair cloths around the altars; and attempts were made to excite the pride and jealousy of the Baals by singing in their ears: "Thou art about to suffer thyself to be vanquished! Are the others perchance more strong? Show thyself! aid us! that the people may not say: 'Where are now their gods?'"

The colleges of the pontiffs were agitated by unceasing anxiety. Those of Rabetna were especially afraid—the restoration of the zaïmph having been of no avail. They kept themselves shut up in the third inclosure which was as impregnable as a fortress. Only one among them, the high priest Schahabarim, ventured to go out.

He used to visit Salammbo. But he would either remain perfectly silent, gazing at her with fixed eyeballs, or else would be lavish of words, and the reproaches that he uttered were harder than ever.

With inconceivable inconsistency he could not forgive the young girl for having followed his commands; Schahabarim had guessed all, and this haunting thought revived the jealousies of his impotence. He accused her of being the cause of the war. Matho, according to him, was besieging Carthage to recover the zaïmph; and he poured out imprecations and sarcasms upon this Barbarian who pretended to the possession of holy things. Yet it was not this that the priest wished to say.

But just now Salammbo felt no terror of him. The anguish which she used formerly to suffer had left her. A strange peacefulness possessed her. Her gaze was less wandering, and shone with limpid fire.

Meanwhile the Python had become ill again; and as Salammbo, on the contrary, appeared to be recovering, old Taanach rejoiced in the conviction that by its decline it was taking away the languor of her mistress.

One morning she found it coiled up behind the bed of ox-hides, colder than marble, and with its head hidden by a heap of worms. Her cries brought Salammbo to the spot. She turned it over for awhile with the tip of her sandal, and the slave was amazed at her insensibility.

Hamilcar's daughter no longer prolonged her fasts with so much fervor. She passed whole days on the top of her terrace, leaning her elbows against the balustrade, and amusing herself by looking out before her. The summits of the walls at the end of the town cut uneven zigzags upon the sky, and the lances of the sentries formed what was like a border of corn-ears throughout their length. Further away she could see the manœuvres of the Barbarians between the towers; on days when the siege was interrupted she could even distinguish their occupations. They mended their weapons, greased their hair, and washed their blood-stained arms in the sea; the tents were closed; the beasts of burden were feeding; and in the distance the scythes of the chariots which were all ranged in a semi-circle, looked like a silver scimitar lying at the base of the mountains. She was waiting for Narr' Havas, her betrothed. In spite of her hatred she would have liked to have seen Matho again. Of all the Carthaginians she was perhaps the only one who would have spoken to him without fear.

Her father often came into her room. He would sit down panting on the cushions, and gaze at her with an almost tender look, as though he found rest from his fatigues in the sight of her. He sometimes questioned her about her journey to the camp of the Mercenaries. He even asked her whether any one had urged her to it; and with a shake of the head she answered, No — so proud was Salammbo of having saved the zaïmph.

But the Suffet always came back to Matho under pretense of making military inquiries. He could not understand how the hours which she had spent in the tent had been employed. Salammbo, in fact, said nothing about Gisco; for as words had an effective power in themselves, curses, if reported to any one, might be turned against him; and she was silent about her wish to assassinate, lest she should be blamed for not having yielded to it. She said that the schalischim appeared furious, that he had shouted a great deal, and that he had then fallen asleep. Salammbo told no more, through shame perhaps, or else because she was led by her extreme ingenuousness to attach but little importance to the soldier's kisses. Moreover, it all floated through her head in a melancholy and misty fashion, like the recollection of a depressing dream; and she would not have known in what way or in what words to express it.

One evening when they were thus face to face with each other, Taanach came in looking quite scared. An old man with a child was yonder in the courts, and wished to see the Suffet.

Hamilcar turned pale, and then quickly replied: —

"Let him come up!"

Iddibal entered without prostrating himself. He held a young boy, covered with a goat's hair cloak, by the hand, and at once raised the hood which screened his face.

"Here he is, Master! Take him!"

The Suffet and the slave went into a corner of the room.

The child remained in the centre standing upright, and with a gaze of attention rather than of astonishment he surveyed the ceiling, the furniture, the pearl necklaces trailing on the purple draperies, and the majestic maiden who was bending over toward him.

He was perhaps ten years old, and was not taller than a Roman sword. His curly hair shaded his swelling forehead. His eyeballs looked as though they were seeking for space. The nostrils of his delicate nose were broad and palpitating, and upon his whole person was displayed the indefinable splendor of those who are destined to great enterprises. When he had cast aside his extremely heavy cloak, he remained clad in a lynx skin, which was fastened about his waist, and he rested his little naked feet, which were all white with dust, resolutely upon the pavement. But he no doubt divined that important matters were under discussion, for he stood motionless, with one hand behind his back, his chin lowered, and a finger in his mouth.

At last Hamilcar attracted Salammbo with a sign and said to her in a low voice: —

"You will keep him with you, you understand! No one, even though belonging to the house, must know of his existence!"

Then, behind the door, he again asked Iddibal whether he was quite sure that they had not been noticed.

"No!" said the slave, "the streets were empty."

As the war filled all the provinces he had feared for his master's son. Then, not knowing where to hide him, he had come along the coasts in a sloop, and for three days Iddibal had been tacking about in the gulf and watching the ramparts. At last, that evening, as the environs of Khamon seemed to be deserted, he had passed briskly through the channel and landed near the arsenal, the entrance to the harbor being free.

But soon the Barbarians posted an immense raft in front
of it in order to prevent the Carthaginians from coming
out. They were again rearing the wooden towers, and the
terrace was rising at the same time.

Outside communications were cut off and an intolerable
famine set in.

The besieged killed all the dogs, all the mules, all the
asses, and then the fifteen elephants which the Suffet had
brought back. The lions of the temple of Moloch had become ferocious, and the hierodules no longer durst approach
them. They were fed at first with the wounded Barbarians;
then they were thrown corpses that were still warm; they
refused them, and they all died. People wandered in the
twilight along the old enclosures, and gathered grass and
flowers among the stones to boil them in wine, wine being
cheaper than water. Others crept as far as the enemy's
outposts, and entered the tents to steal food, and the stupefied Barbarians sometimes allowed them to return. At last
a day arrived when the Ancients resolved to slaughter the
horses of Eschmoun privately. They were holy animals whose
manes were plaited by the pontiffs with gold ribbons, and
whose existence denoted the motion of the sun — the idea
of fire in its most exalted form. Their flesh was cut into
equal portions and buried behind the altar. Then every
evening the Ancients, alleging some act of devotion, would
go up to the temple and regale themselves in secret, and
each would take away a piece beneath his tunic for his
children. In the deserted quarters remote from the walls,
the inhabitants, whose misery was not so great, had barri-
caded themselves through fear of the rest.

The stones from the catapults, and the demolitions commanded for purposes of defense, had accumulated heaps of
ruins in the middle of the streets. At the quietest times
masses of people would suddenly rush along with shouts;
and from the top of the Acropolis the conflagrations were
like purple rags scattered upon the terraces and twisted by
the wind.

The three great catapults did not stop in spite of all
these works. Their ravages were extraordinary: thus a
man's head rebounded from the pediment of the Syssitia; a

woman who was being confined in the street of Kinisdo was crushed by a block of marble, and her child was carried with the bed as far as the crossways of Cinasyn, where the coverlet was found.

The most annoying were the bullets of the slingers. They fell upon the roofs, and in the gardens, and in the middle of the courts, while people were at table before a slender meal with their hearts big with sighs. These cruel projectiles bore engraved letters which stamped themselves upon the flesh — and insults might be read on corpses such as "pig," "jackal," "vermin," and sometimes jests: "catch it !" or "I have well deserved it !"

The portion of the rampart which extended from the corners of the harbors to the height of the cisterns was broken down. Then the people of Malqua found themselves caught between the old inclosure of Byrsa behind, and the Barbarians in front. But there was enough to be done in thickening the wall and making it as high as possible without troubling about them; they were abandoned; all perished; and although they were generally hated, Hamilcar came to be greatly abhorred.

On the morrow he opened the pits in which he kept stores of corn, and his stewards gave it to the people. For three days they gorged themselves.

Their thirst, however, only became the more intolerable, and they could constantly see before them the long cascade formed by the clear falling water of the aqueduct. A thin vapor, with a rainbow beside it, went up from its base, beneath the rays of the sun, and a stream curving through the plain fell into the gulf.

Hamilcar did not give way. He was reckoning upon an event, upon something decisive and extraordinary.

His own slaves tore off the silver plates from the temple of Melkarth; four long boats were drawn out of the harbor, they were brought by means of capstans to the foot of the Mappalian quarter, the wall facing the shore was bored, and they set out for the Gauls to buy Mercenaries there at no matter what price. Nevertheless, Hamilcar was distressed at his inability to communicate with the king of the Numidians, for he knew that he was behind the Barbarians, and ready to fall upon them. But Narr' Havas, being too weak, was not going to make any venture alone; and the Suffet had the rampart raised twelve palms higher, all the material in the arsenals piled up in the Acropolis, and the machines repaired once more.

Sinews taken from bulls' necks, or else stags' hamstrings, were commonly employed for the twists of the catapults. However, neither stags nor bulls were in existence in Carthage. Hamilcar asked the Ancients for the hair of their wives; all sacrificed it, but the quantity was not sufficient. In the buildings of the Syssitia there were twelve hundred marriageable slaves destined for prostitution in Greece and Italy, and their hair, having been rendered elastic by the use of unguents, was wonderfully well adapted for engines of war. But the subsequent loss would be too great. Accordingly it was decided that a choice should be made of the finest heads of hair among the wives of the plebeians. Careless of their country's needs they shrieked in despair when the servants of the Hundred came with scissors to lay hands upon them.

The Barbarians were animated with increased fury. They could be seen in the distance taking fat from the dead to grease their machines, while others pulled out the nails and stitched them end to end to make cuirasses. They devised a plan of putting into the catapults vessels filled with serpents which had been brought by the Negroes; the clay pots broke on the flagstones, the serpents ran about, seemed to multiply, and, so numerous were they, to issue naturally from the walls. Then the Barbarians, not satisfied with their invention, improved upon it; they hurled all kinds of filth, human excrements, pieces of carrion, corpses. The plague reappeared. The teeth of the Carthaginians fell out of their mouths, and their gums were discolored like those of camels after too long a journey.

The machines were set up on the terrace, although the latter did not yet reach everywhere to the height of the rampart. Before the twenty-three towers on the fortifications stood twenty-three others of wood. All the tollenos were mounted again, and in the centre, a little further back, appeared the formidable helepolis of Demetrius Poli-

orcetes, which Spendius had at last reconstructed. Of
pyramidal shape, like the pharos of Alexandria, it was one
hundred and thirty cubits high and twenty-three wide, with
nine stories, diminishing as they approached the summit,
and protected by scales of brass; they were pierced with
numerous doors and were filled with soldiers, and on the
upper platform there stood a catapult flanked by two ballistas.

Then Hamilcar planted crosses for those who should
speak of surrender, and even the women were brigaded.
The people lay in the streets, and waited full of distress.

Then one morning before sunrise (it was the seventh day
of the month of Nyssan) they heard a great shout uttered
by all the Barbarians simultaneously; the leaden-tubed
trumpets pealed, and the great Paphlagonian horns bellowed
like bulls. All rose and ran to the rampart.

A forest of lances, pikes and swords bristled at its base.
It leaped against the walls, the ladders grappled them;
and Barbarians' heads appeared in the intervals of the
battlements.

Beams supported by long files of men were battering at
the gates; and, in order to demolish the wall at places
where the terrace was wanting, the Mercenaries came up in
serried cohorts, the first line crawling, the second bending
their hams, and the others rising in succession to the last
who stood upright; while elsewhere, in order to climb up,
the tallest advanced in front and the lowest in the rear,
and all rested their shields upon their helmets with their
left arms, joining them together at the edges so tightly
that they might have been taken for an assemblage of
large tortoises. The projectiles slid over these oblique
masses.

The Carthaginians threw down mill-stones, pestles, vats,
casks, beds, everything that could serve as a weight and
could knock down. Some watched at the embrasures with
fishermen's nets, and when the Barbarian arrived he found
himself caught in the meshes, and struggled like a fish.
They demolished their own battlements; portions of wall
fell down raising a great dust; and as the catapults on the
terrace were shooting over against one another, the stones

would strike together and shiver into a thousand pieces, making a copious shower upon the combatants.

Soon the two crowds formed but one great chain of human bodies ; it overflowed into the intervals in the terrace, and, somewhat looser at the two extremities, swayed perpetually without advancing. They clasped one another, lying flat on the ground like wrestlers. They crushed one another. The women leaned over the battlements and shrieked. They were dragged away by their veils, and the whiteness of their suddenly uncovered sides shone in the arms of the Negroes as the latter buried their daggers in them. Some corpses did not fall, being too much pressed by the crowd, and, supported by the shoulders of their companions, advanced for some minutes quite upright and with staring eyes. Some who had both temples pierced by a javelin swayed their heads about like bears. Mouths, opened to shout, remained gaping ; several hands flew through the air. Mighty blows were dealt, which were long talked of by the survivors.

Meanwhile arrows darted from the towers of wood and stone. The tollenos moved their long yards rapidly ; and as the Barbarians had sacked the old cemetery of the aborigines beneath the catacombs, they hurled the tombstones against the Carthaginians. Sometimes the cables broke under the weight of too heavy baskets, and masses of men, all with uplifted arms, would fall from the sky.

Up to the middle of the day the veterans had attacked the Taenia fiercely in order to penetrate into the harbor and destroy the fleet. Hamilcar had a fire of damp straw lit upon the roofing of Khamon, and as the smoke blinded them they fell back to the left, and came to swell the horrible rout which was pressing forward in Malqua. Some syntagmata composed of sturdy men, chosen expressly for the purpose, had broken in three gates. They were checked by lofty barriers made of planks studded with nails, but a fourth yielded easily ; they dashed over it at a run and rolled into a pit in which there were hidden snares. At the south-west angle Autaritus and his men broke down the rampart, the fissure in which had been stopped up with bricks. The ground behind rose, and they climbed it nimbly. But on the top they found a second wall composed of stones and long beams lying quite flat and alternating like the squares on a chess board. It was a Gaulish fashion, and had been adapted by the Suffet to the requirements of the situation ; the Gauls imagined themselves before a town in their own country. Their attack was weak, and they were repulsed.

All the roundway, from the street of Khamon as far as the Green Market, now belonged to the Barbarians, and the Samnites were finishing off the dying with blows of stakes ; or else with one foot on the wall were gazing down at the smoking ruins beneath them, and the battle which was beginning again in the distance.

The slingers, who were distributed through the rear, were still shooting. But the springs of the Acarnanian slings had broken from use, and many were throwing stones with the hand like shepherds ; the rest hurled leaden bullets with the handle of a whip. Zarxas, his shoulders covered with his long, black hair, went about everywhere, and led on the Barbarians. Two pouches hung at his hips ; he thrust his left hand into them continually, while his right arm whirled round like a chariot-wheel.

Matho had at first refrained from fighting, the better to command all the Barbarians at once. He had been seen along the gulf with the Mercenaries, near the lagoon with the Numidians, and on the shores of the lake among the Negroes, and from the back part of the plain he urged forward masses of soldiers who came ceaselessly against the ramparts. By degrees he had drawn near ; the smell of blood, the sight of carnage, and the tumult of clarions had at last made his heart leap. Then he had gone back into his tent, and throwing off his cuirass had taken his lion's skin as being more convenient for battle. The snout fitted upon his head, bordering his face with a circle of fangs ; the two fore-paws were crossed upon his breast, and the claws of the hinder ones fell beneath his knees.

He had kept on his strong waist-belt, wherein gleamed a two-edged axe, and with his great sword in both hands he had dashed impetuously through the breach. Like a pruner cutting willow-branches and trying to strike off as much as

possible so as to make the more money, he marched along
mowing down the Carthaginians around him. Those who
tried to seize him in flank he knocked down with blows of
the pommel ; when they attacked him in front he ran them
through ; if they fled he clove them. Two men leaped together upon his back ; he bounded backward against a gate
and crushed them. His sword fell and rose. It shivered
on the angle of a wall. Then he took his heavy axe, and
front and rear he ripped up the Carthaginians like a flock
of sheep. They scattered more and more, and he was
quite alone when he reached the second inclosure at the
foot of the Acropolis. The materials which had been flung
from the summit cumbered the steps and were heaped up
higher than the wall. Matho turned back amid the ruins
to summon his companions.

He perceived their crests scattered over the multitude ;
they were sinking and their wearers were about to perish ;
he dashed toward them ; then the vast wreath of red
plumes closed in, and they soon rejoined him and surrounded
him. But an enormous crowd was discharging from the
side streets. He was caught by the hips, lifted up and
carried away outside the rampart to a spot where the terrace was high.

Matho shouted a command and all the shields sank upon
the helmets ; he leaped upon them in order to catch hold
somewhere so as to re-enter Carthage ; and, flourishing his
terrible axe, ran over the shields, which resembled waves
of bronze, like a marine god, with brandished trident, over
his billows.

However, a man in a white robe was walking along the
edge of the rampart, impassible, and indifferent to the death
which surrounded him. Sometimes he would spread out
his right hand above his eyes in order to find out some one.
Matho happened to pass beneath him. Suddenly his eyeballs flamed, his livid face contracted ; and raising both his
lean arms he shouted out abuse at him.

Matho did not hear it ; but he felt so furious and cruel a
look entering his heart that he uttered a roar. He hurled his
long axe at him ; some people threw themselves upon Schahabarim ; and Matho seeing him no more fell back exhausted.

A terrible creaking drew near, mingled with the rhythm of hoarse voices singing together.

It was the great helepolis surrounded by a crowd of soldiers. They were dragging it with both hands, hauling it with ropes, and pushing it with their shoulders — for the slope rising from the plain to the terrace, though extremely gentle, was found impracticable for machines of such prodigious weight. However, it had eight wheels banded with iron, and it had been advancing slowly in this way since the morning, like a mountain raised upon another. Then there appeared an immense ram issuing from its base. The doors along the three fronts which faced the town fell down, and cuirassed soldiers appeared in the interior like pillars of iron. Some might be seen climbing and descending the two staircases which crossed the stories. Some were waiting to dart out as soon as the cramps of the doors touched the walls; in the middle of the upper platform the skeins of the ballistas were turning, and the great beam of the catapult was being lowered.

Hamilcar was at that moment standing upright on the roof of Melkarth. He had calculated that it would come directly toward him, against what was the most invulnerable place in the wall, and was for that very reason denuded of sentries. His slaves had for a long time been bringing leathern bottles along the roundway, where they had raised with clay two transverse partitions forming a sort of basin. The water was flowing insensibly along the terrace, and strange to say, it seemed to cause Hamilcar no anxiety.

But when the helepolis was thirty paces off, he commanded planks to be placed over the streets between the houses from the cisterns to the rampart; and a file of people passed from hand to hand helmets and amphoras, which were emptied continually. The Carthaginians, however, grew indignant at this waste of water. The ram was demolishing the wall, when suddenly a fountain sprang forth from the disjointed stones. Then the lofty brazen mass, nine stories high, which contained and engaged more than three thousand soldiers, began to rock gently like a ship. In fact, the water, which had penetrated the terrace, had broken up the path before it ; its wheels stuck in the mire ; the head of Spendius, with distended cheeks blowing an ivory cornet, appeared between leathern curtains on the first story. The great machine, as though convulsively upheaved, advanced perhaps ten paces ; but the ground softened more and more, the mire reached to the axles, and the helepolis stopped, leaning over frightfully to one side. The catapult rolled to the edge of the platform, and carried away by the weight of its beam, fell, shattering the lower stories beneath it. The soldiers who were standing on the doors slipped into the abyss, or else held on to the extremities of the long beams, and by their weight increased the inclination of the helepolis, which was going to pieces with creakings in all its joints.

The other Barbarians rushed up to help them, massing themselves into a compact crowd. The Carthaginians descended from the rampart, and, assailing them in the rear, killed them at leisure. But the chariots furnished with the sickles hastened up, and galloped round the outskirts of the multitude. The latter ascended the wall again ; night came on ; and the Barbarians gradually retired.

Nothing could now be seen on the plain but a sort of perfectly black, swarming mass, which extended from the bluish gulf to the purely white lagoon ; and the lake, which had received streams of blood, stretched further away like a great purple pool.

The terrace was now so laden with corpses that it looked as though it had been constructed of human bodies. In the centre stood the helepolis covered with armor ; and from time to time huge fragments broke off from it, like stones from a crumbling pyramid. Broad tracks made by the streams of lead might be distinguished on the walls. A broken-down wooden tower burned here and there, and the houses showed dimly like the stages of a ruined amphitheatre. Heavy fumes of smoke were rising, and rolling with them sparks which were lost in the dark sky.

The Carthaginians however, who were consumed by thirst, had rushed to the cisterns. They broke open the doors. A miry swamp stretched at the bottom.

26

What was to be done now? Moreover, the Barbarians were countless, and when their fatigue was over they would begin again.

The people deliberated all night in groups at the corners of the streets. Some said that they ought to send away the women, the sick and the old men; others proposed to abandon the town, and found a colony far away. But vessels were lacking, and when the sun appeared no decision had been made.

There was no fighting that day, all being too much exhausted. The sleepers looked like corpses.

Then the Carthaginians, reflecting upon the cause of their disasters, remembered that they had not dispatched to Phœnicia the annual offering due to Tyrian Melkarth, and a great terror came upon them. The gods were indignant with the Republic, and were, no doubt, going to prosecute their vengeance.

They were considered as cruel masters, who were appeased with supplications and allowed themselves to be bribed with presents. All were feeble in comparison with Moloch the Devourer. The existence, the very flesh of men, belonged to him; and hence, in order to preserve it, the Carthaginians used to offer up a portion of it to him, which calmed his fury. Children were burned on the forehead, or on the nape of the neck, with woolen wicks; and as this mode of satisfying Baal brought in much money to the priests, they failed not to recommend it as being easier and more pleasant.

This time, however, the Republic itself was at stake. But as every profit must be purchased by some loss, and as every transaction was regulated according to the needs of the weaker and the demands of the stronger, there was no pain great enough for the god, since he delighted in such as was of the most horrible description, and all were now at his mercy. He must accordingly be fully gratified. Precedents showed that in this way the scourge would be made to disappear. Moreover, it was believed that an immolation by fire would purify Carthage. The ferocity of the people was predisposed toward it. The choice, too, must fall exclusively upon the families of the great.

The Ancients assembled. The sitting was a long one. Hanno had come to it. As he was now unable to sit he remained lying down near the door, half hidden among the fringes of the lofty tapestry; and when the pontiff of Moloch asked them whether they would consent to surrender their children, his voice suddenly broke forth from the shadow like the roaring of a Genius in the depths of a cavern. He regretted, he said, that he had none of his own blood to give; and he gazed at Hamilcar, who faced him at the other end of the hall. The Suffet was so much disconcerted by this look that it made him lower his eyes. All successively bent their heads in approval; and in accordance with the rites he had to reply to the high priest: "Yes; be it so." Then the Ancients decreed the sacrifice in traditional circumlocution — because there are things more troublesome to say than to perform.

The decision was almost immediately known in Carthage, and lamentations resounded. The cries of women might everywhere be heard; their husbands consoled them, or railed at them with remonstrances.

But three hours afterward extraordinary tidings were spread abroad: the Suffet had discovered springs at the foot of the cliff. There was a rush to the place. Water might be seen in holes dug in the sand, and some were already lying flat on the ground and drinking.

Hamilcar did not himself know whether it was by the determination of the gods or through the vague recollection of a revelation which his father had once made to him; but on leaving the Ancients he had gone down to the shore and had begun to dig the gravel with his slaves.

He gave clothing, boots, and wine. He gave all the rest of the corn that he was keeping by him. He even let the crowd enter his palace, and he opened kitchens, stores and all the rooms — Salammbo's alone excepted. He announced that six thousand Gaulish Mercenaries were coming, and that the king of Macedonia was sending soldiers.

But on the second day the springs diminished, and on the evening of the third they were completely dried up.

Then the decree of the Ancients passed everywhere from lip to lip, and the priests of Moloch commenced their task.

Men in black robes presented themselves in the houses. In many instances the owners had deserted them under pretense of some business, or of some dainty that they were going to buy; and the servants of Moloch came and took the children away. Others themselves surrendered them stupidly. Then they were brought to the temple of Tanith, where the priestesses were charged with their amusement and support until the solemn day.

They visited Hamilcar suddenly and found him in his gardens.

" Barca ! we come for that that you know of — your son ! " They added that some people had met him one evening during the previous moon in the centre of the Mappalian district being led by an old man.

He was as though suffocated at first. But speedily understanding that any denial would be vain, Hamilcar bowed ; and he brought them into the commercial house. Some slaves who had run up at a sign kept watch round about it.

He entered Salammbo's room in a state of distraction. He seized Hannibal with one hand, snatched up the cord of a trailing garment with the other, tied his feet and hands with it, thrust the end into his mouth to form a gag, and hid him under the bed of ox-hides by letting an ample drapery fall to the ground.

Afterward he walked about from right to left, raised his arms, wheeled round, bit his lips. Then he stood still with staring eyeballs, and panted as though he were about to die.

But he clapped his hands three times. Giddenem appeared.

" Listen ! " he said, " go and take from among the slaves a male child from eight to nine years of age, with black hair and swelling forehead ! Bring him here ! make haste ! "

Giddenem soon entered again, bringing forward a young boy.

He was a miserable child, at once lean and bloated ; his skin looked grayish, like the infected rag hanging to his sides ; his head was sunk between his shoulders, and with the back of his hand he was rubbing his eyes, which were filled with flies.

How could he ever be confounded with Hannibal ! and there was no time to choose another. Hamilcar looked at Giddenem ; he felt inclined to strangle him.

" Begone ! " he cried ; and the master of the slaves fled.

The misfortune which he had so long dreaded was therefore come, and with extravagant efforts he strove to discover whether there was not some mode, some means to escape it.

Abdalonim suddenly spoke from behind the door. The Suffet was being asked for. The servants of Moloch were growing impatient.

Hamilcar repressed a cry as though a red hot iron had burned him ; and he began anew to pace the room like one distraught. Then he sank down beside the balustrade and, with his elbows on his knees, pressed his forehead into his shut fists.

The porphyry basin still contained a little clear water for Salammbo's ablutions. In spite of his repugnance and all his pride, the Suffet dipped the child into it, and, like a slave merchant, began to wash him and rub him with strigils and red earth. Then he took two purple squares from the receptacles round the wall, placed one on his breast and the other on his back, and joined them together on the collar bones with two diamond clasps. He poured perfume upon his head, passed an electrum necklace around his neck, and put on him sandals with heels of pearls — sandals belonging to his own daughter ! But he stamped with shame and vexation ; Salammbo, who busied herself in helping him, was as pale as he. The child, dazzled by such splendor, smiled, and, growing bold even, was beginning to clap his hands and jump, when Hamilcar took him away.

He held him firmly by the arm as though he were afraid of losing him, and the child, who was hurt, wept a little as he ran beside him.

When on a level with the ergastulum, under a palm tree, a voice was raised, a mournful and supplicant voice. It murmured : " Master ! oh ! master ! "

Hamilcar turned and beside him perceived a man of abject appearance, one of the wretches who led a haphazard existence in the household.

" What do you want? " said the Suffet.

The slave, who trembled horribly, stammered : —

" I am his father ! "

Hamilcar walked on ; the other followed him with stooping loins, bent hams, and head thrust forward. His face was convulsed with unspeakable anguish, and he was choking with suppressed sobs, so eager was he at once to question him, and to cry " Mercy ! "

At last he ventured to touch him lightly with one finger on the elbow.

" Are you going to ——? " He had not strength to finish, and Hamilcar stopped quite amazed at such grief.

He had never thought — so immense was the abyss separating them from each other — that there could be anything in common between them. It even appeared to him a sort of outrage, an encroachment upon his own privileges. He replied with a look colder and heavier than an executioner's axe ; the slave swooned and fell in the dust at his feet. Hamilcar strode across him.

The three black-robed men were waiting in the great hall, and standing against the stone disc. Immediately he tore his garments, and rolled upon the pavement uttering piercing cries.

" Ah ! poor little Hannibal ! Oh ! my son ! my consolation ! my hope ! my life ! Kill me also ! take me away ! Woe ! Woe ! " He plowed his face with his nails, tore out his hair, and shrieked like the women who lament at funerals. " Take him away then ! my suffering is too great ! begone ! kill me like him ! " The servants of Moloch were astonished that the great Hamilcar was so weakspirited. They were almost moved by it.

A noise of naked feet became audible, with a broken throat-rattling like the breathing of a wild beast speeding along, and a man, pale, terrible, and with outspread arms appeared on the threshold of the third gallery, between the ivory posts; he exclaimed: —

"My child!"

Hamilcar threw himself with a bound upon the slave, and covering the man's mouth with his hand exclaimed still more loudly: —

"It is the old man who reared him! he calls him 'my child!' it will make him mad! enough! enough!" And hustling away the three priests and their victim he went out with them and with a great kick shut the door behind him.

Hamilcar strained his ears for some minutes in constant fear of seeing them return. He then thought of getting rid of the slave in order to be quite sure that he would see nothing; but the peril had not wholly disappeared, and, if the gods were provoked at the man's death, it might be turned against his son. Then, changing his intention, he sent him by Taanach the best from his kitchens — a quarter of a goat, beans, and preserved pomegranates. The slave, who had eaten nothing for a long time, rushed upon them; his tears fell into the dishes.

Hamilcar at last returned to Salammbo, and unfastened Hannibal's cords. The child in exasperation bit his hand until the blood came. He repelled him with a caress.

To make him remain quiet, Salammbo tried to frighten him with Lamia, a Cyrenian ogress.

"But where is she?" he asked.

He was told that brigands were coming to put him into prison. "Let them come," he rejoined, "and I will kill them!"

Then Hamilcar told him the frightful truth. But he fell into a passion with his father, contending that he was quite able to annihilate the whole people since he was the master of Carthage.

At last, exhausted by his exertions and anger, he fell into a wild sleep. He spoke in his dreams, his back leaning against a scarlet cushion; his head was thrown back somewhat, and his little arm, outstretched from his body, lay quite straight in an attitude of command.

When the night had grown dark Hamilcar lifted him up gently, and, without a torch, went down the galley staircase. As he passed through the mercantile house he took up a basket of grapes and a flagon of pure water; the child awoke before the statue of Aletes in the vault of gems, and he smiled — like the other — on his father's arm at the brilliant lights which surrounded him.

Hamilcar felt quite sure that his son could not be taken from him. It was an impenetrable spot communicating with the beach by a subterranean passage which he alone knew, and casting his eyes around he inhaled a great draught of air. Then he set him down upon a stool beside some golden shields.

No one at present could see him; he had no further need for watching; and he relieved his feelings. Like a mother finding again her first-born that was lost, he threw himself upon his son; he clasped him to his breast, he laughed and wept at the same time, he called him by the fondest names and covered him with kisses; little Hannibal was frightened by this terrible tenderness and was silent now.

Hamilcar returned with silent steps, feeling the walls around him, and came into the great hall where the moonlight entered through one of the apertures in the dome; in the centre the slave lay sleeping after his repast, stretched at full length upon the marble pavement. He looked at him and was moved with a sort of pity. With the tip of his cothurn he pushed forward a carpet beneath his head. Then he raised his eyes and gazed at Tanith, whose slender crescent was shining in the sky, and felt himself stronger than the Baals and full of contempt for them.

The arrangements for the sacrifice were already begun.

Part of a wall in the temple of Moloch was thrown down in order to draw out the brazen god without touching the ashes of the altar. Then as soon as the sun appeared the hierodules pushed it toward the square of Khamon.

It moved backward sliding upon cylinders; its shoulders overlapped the walls. No sooner did the Carthaginians perceive it in the distance than they speedily took to flight, for the Baal could be looked upon with impunity only when exercising his wrath.

A smell of aromatics spread through the streets. All the temples had just been opened simultaneously and from them there came forth tabernacles borne upon chariots, or upon litters carried by the pontiffs. Great plumes swayed at the corners of them, and rays were emitted from their slender pinnacles which terminated in balls of crystal, gold, silver, or copper.

These were the Chanaanitish Baalim, offshoots of the supreme Baal, who were returning to their first cause to humble themselves before his might and annihilate themselves in his splendor.

Melkarth's pavilion, which was of fine purple, sheltered a petroleum flame; on Khamon's, which was of hyacinth color, there rose an ivory phallus bordered with a circle of gems; between Eschmoun's curtains, which were blue as the ether, a sleeping python formed a circle with his tail, and the Pataec gods, held in the arms of their priests, looked like great infants in swaddling clothes with their heels touching the ground.

Then came all the inferior forms of the Divinity: Baal-Samin, god of celestial space; Baal-Peor, god of the sacred mountains; Baal-Zeboub, god of corruption, with those of the neighboring countries and congenerous races: the Irabal of Libya, the Adrammelech of Chaldæa, the Kijun of the Syrians; Derceto, with her virgin's face, crept on her fins and the corpse of Tammouz was drawn along in the midst of a catafalque among torches and heads of hair. In order to subdue the kings of the firmament to the Sun, and prevent their particular influences from disturbing his, diversely colored metal stars were brandished at the end of long poles; and all were there, from the dark Nebo, the Genius of Mercury, to the hideous Rahab, which is the constellation of the Crocodile. The Abaddirs, stones which had fallen from the moon, were whirling in slings of silver thread; little loaves, representing a woman's sex, were borne on baskets by the priests of Ceres; others brought their fetishes and amulets; forgotten idols reappeared, while the mystic symbols had been taken from the very ships as though Carthage wished to concentrate herself wholly upon a single thought of death and desolation.

Before each tabernacle a man balanced a large vase of smoking incense on his head. Clouds hovered here and there, and the hangings, pendants, and embroideries of the sacred pavilions might be distinguished amid the thick vapors. These advanced slowly owing to their enormous weight. Sometimes the axles became fast in the streets; then the pious took advantage of the opportunity to touch the Baalim with their garments which they preserved afterward as holy things.

The brazen statue continued to advance toward the square of Khamon. The Rich, carrying sceptres with emerald balls, set out from the bottom of Megara; the Ancients, with diadems on their heads, had assembled in Kinisdo, and masters of the finances, governors of provinces, sailors, and the numerous horde employed at funerals, all with the insignia of their magistracies or the instruments of their calling, were making their way toward the tabernacles which were descending from the Acropolis between the colleges of the pontiffs.

Out of deference to Moloch they had adorned themselves with the most splendid jewels. Diamonds sparkled on their black garments; but their rings were too large and fell from their wasted hands — nor could there have been anything so mournful as this silent crowd where earrings tapped against pale faces, and gold tiaras clasped brows contracted with stern despair.

At last the Baal arrived exactly in the centre of the square. His pontiffs arranged an enclosure with trellis-work to keep off the multitude, and remained around him at his feet.

The priests of Khamon, in tawny woolen robes, formed a line before their temple beneath the columns of the portico; those of Eschmoun, in linen mantles with necklaces of koukouphas' heads and pointed tiaras, posted themselves on the steps of the Acropolis; the priests of Melkarth, in violet tunics, took the western side; the priests of the Abaddirs, clasped with bands of Phrygian stuffs, placed themselves on the east, while toward the south, with the necromancers all covered with tatooings and the shriekers in patched cloaks, were ranged the curates of the Pataec gods, and the Yidonim, who put the bone of a dead man into their mouths to learn the future. The priests Ceres, who were dressed in blue robes, had prudently stopped in the

street of Satheb, and in low tones were chanting a thesmo-
phorion in the Megarian dialect.

From time to time files of men arrived, completely naked,
their arms outstretched, and all holding one another by the
shoulders. From the depths of their breasts they drew
forth a hoarse and cavernous intonation ; their eyes, which
were fastened upon the colossus, shone through the
dust, and they swayed their bodies simultaneously, and
at equal distances, as though they were all affected by a
single movement. They were so frenzied that to restore
order the hierodules compelled them, with blows of the
stick, to lie flat upon the ground, with their faces resting
against the brass trellis-work.

Then it was that a man in a white robe advanced from
the back of the square. He penetrated the crowd slowly,
and people recognized a priest of Tanith — the high-priest
Schahabarim. Hootings were raised, for the tyranny of
the male principle prevailed that day in all consciences,
and the goddess was actually so completely forgotten that
the absence of her pontiffs had not been noticed. But the
amazement increased when he was seen to open one of the
doors in the trellis-work intended for those who entered to
offer up victims. It was an outrage to their god, thought
the priests of Moloch, that he had just committed, and
they sought with eager gestures to repel him. Fed on the
meat of the holocausts, clad in purple like kings, and
wearing triple-storied crowns, they despised the pale eunuch,
weakened with his macerations, and angry laughter shook
their black beards, which were displayed on their breasts in
the sun.

Schahabarim walked on, giving no reply, and, traversing
the whole enclosure with deliberation, reached the legs of
the colossus ; then, spreading out both arms, he touched it
on both sides, which was a solemn form of adoration. For
a long time Rabbet had been torturing him, and in despair,
or perhaps for lack of a god that completely satisfied his
ideas, he had at last decided for this one.

The crowd, terrified by this act of apostasy, uttered a
lengthened murmur. It was felt that the last tie which
bound their souls to a merciful divinity was breaking.

But owing to his mutilation Schahabarim could take no part in the cult of the Baal. The men in the red cloaks shut him out from the enclosure; then, when he was outside, he went round all the colleges in succession, and the priest, henceforth without a god, disappeared in the crowd. It scattered at his approach.

Meanwhile a fire of aloes, cedar, and laurel was burning between the legs of the colossus. The tips of its long wings dipped into the flame; the unguents with which it had been rubbed flowed like sweat over its brazen limbs. Around the circular flagstone on which its feet rested, the children, wrapped in black veils, formed a motionless circle; and its extravagantly long arms reached down their palms to them as though to seize the crown that they formed and carry it to the sky.

The Rich, the Ancients, the women, the whole multitude thronged behind the priests and on the terraces of the houses. The large painted stars revolved no longer; the tabernacles were set upon the ground; and the fumes from the censers ascended perpendicularly, spreading their bluish branches through the azure like gigantic trees.

Many fainted; others became inert and petrified in their ecstasy. Infinite anguish weighed upon the breasts of the beholders. The last shouts died out one by one — and the people of Carthage stood breathless, and absorbed in the longing of their terror.

At last the high priest of Moloch passed his left hand beneath the children's veils, plucked a lock of hair from their foreheads, and threw it upon the flames. Then the men in the red cloaks chanted the sacred hymn: —

"Homage to thee, Sun! king of the two zones, self-generating Creator, Father and Mother, Father and Son, God and Goddess, Goddess and God!" And their voices were lost in the outburst of instruments sounding simultaneously to drown the cries of the victims. The eight-stringed scheminiths, the kinnors which had ten strings, and the nebals which had twelve, grated, whistled, and thundered. Enormous leathern bags, bristling with pipes, made a shrill clashing noise; the tabourines, beaten with all the players' might, resounded with heavy, rapid blows;

and, in spite of the fury of the clarions, the salsalim snapped like grasshoppers' wings.

The hierodules, with a long hook, opened the seven-storied compartments on the body of the Baal. They put meal into the highest, two turtle-doves into the second, an ape into the third, a ram into the fourth, a sheep into the fifth, and as no ox was to be had for the sixth, a tawny hide taken from the sanctuary was thrown into it. The seventh compartment yawned empty still.

Before undertaking anything it was well to make trial of the arms of the god. Slender chainlets stretched from his fingers up to his shoulders and fell behind, where men by pulling them made the two hands rise to a level with the elbows, and come close together against the belly; they were moved several times in succession with little abrupt jerks. Then the instruments were still. The fire roared.

The pontiffs of Moloch walked about on the great flag-stones scanning the multitude.

An individual sacrifice was necessary, a perfectly voluntary oblation; which was considered as carrying the others along with it. But no one had appeared up to the present, and the seven passages leading from the barriers to the colossus were completely empty. Then the priests, to encourage the people, drew bodkins from their girdles and gashed their faces. The Devotees, who were stretched on the ground outside, were brought within the enclosure. They were thrown a bundle of horrible irons, and each chose his own torture. They drove in spits between their breasts; they split their cheeks; they put crowns of thorns upon their heads; then they twined their arms together, and surrounded the children in another large circle which widened and contracted in turns. They reached to the balustrade. They threw themselves back again, and then began once more, attracting the crowd to them by the dizziness of their motion with its accompanying blood and shrieks.

By degrees people came into the end of the passages; they flung into the flames pearls, gold vases, cups, torches, all their wealth; the offerings became constantly more numerous and more splendid. At last a man who tottered, a man pale and hideous with terror, thrust forward a child;

then a little black mass was seen between the hands of the colossus, and sank into the dark opening. The priests bent over the edge of the great flagstone — and a new song burst forth celebrating the joys of death and of new birth into eternity.

The children ascended slowly, and as the smoke formed lofty eddies as it escaped, they seemed at a distance to disappear in a cloud. Not one stirred. Their wrists and ankles were tied, and the dark drapery prevented them from seeing anything and from being recognized.

Hamilcar, in a red cloak, like the priests of Moloch, was beside the Baal, standing upright in front of the great toe of its right foot. When the fourteenth child was brought every one could see him make a great gesture of horror. But he soon resumed his former attitude, folded his arms, and looked upon the ground. The high pontiff stood on the other side of the statue as motionless as he. His head, laden with an Assyrian mitre, was bent, and he was watching the gold plate on his breast; it was covered with fatidical stones, and the flames mirrored in it formed irisated lights. He grew pale and dismayed. Hamilcar bent his brow; and they were both so near the funeral-pile that the hems of their cloaks brushed it as they rose from time to time.

The brazen arms were working more quickly. They paused no longer. Every time that a child was placed in them the priests of Moloch spread out their hands upon him to burden him with the crimes of the people, vociferating: "They are not men, but oxen!" and the multitude round about repeated: "Oxen! oxen!" The devout exclaimed: "Lord! eat!" and the priests of Proserpine, complying through terror with the needs of Carthage, muttered the Eleusinian formula: "Pour out rain! bring forth!"

The victims, when scarcely at the edge of the opening, disappeared like a drop of water on a red-hot plate, and white smoke rose amid the great scarlet color.

Nevertheless the appetite of the god was not appeased. He ever wished for more. In order to furnish him with a larger supply, the victims were piled up on his hands with a big chain above them which kept them in their place.

Some devout persons had at the beginning wished to count them, to see whether their number corresponded with the days of the solar year; but others were brought, and it was impossible to distinguish them in the giddy motion of the horrible arms. This lasted for a long, indefinite time until the evening. Then the partitions inside assumed a darker glow, and burning flesh might be seen. Some even believed that they could descry hair, limbs, and whole bodies.

Night fell; clouds accumulated above the Baal. The funeral-pile, which was flameless now, formed a pyramid of coals up to his knees; completely red like a giant covered with blood, he looked, with his head thrown back, as though he were staggering beneath the weight of his intoxication.

In proportion as the priests made haste, the frenzy of the people increased; as the number of the victims was diminishing, some cried out to spare them, others that still more were needful. The walls, with their burden of people, seemed to be giving way beneath the howlings of terror and mystic voluptuousness. Then the faithful came into the passages, dragging their children, who clung to them; and they beat them in order to make them let go, and handed them over to the men in red. The instrument-players sometimes stopped through exhaustion; then the cries of the mothers might be heard, and the frizzling of the fat as it fell upon the coals. The henbane-drinkers crawled on all fours around the colossus, roaring like tigers; the Yidonim vaticinated, the Devotees sang with their cloven lips; the trellis-work had been broken through, all wished for a share in the sacrifice — and fathers, whose children had died previously, cast their effigies, their playthings, their preserved bones into the fire. Some who had knives rushed upon the rest. They slaughtered one another. The hierodules took the fallen ashes at the edge of the flagstone in bronze fans, and cast them into the air that the sacrifice might be scattered over the town and even to the region of the stars.

The loud noise and great light had attracted the Barbarians to the foot of the walls; they clung to the wreck of the helepolis to have a better view, and gazed open-mouthed in horror.